THE

RAY SOCIETY

Instituted 1844

This volume (No. 135 of the series) is issued to members of the Ray Society for the Year 1949, and is sold at a price of 27/6d.

LONDON
1951

The frontispiece is reproduced from one of a collection of illustrations made by A. T. Hollick about 1870 for a Ray Society volume planned but never published, by the Rev. O. Pickard-Cambridge to supplement J. Blackwall's " Spiders of Great Britain and Ireland " (Ray Society, 1861–1864). Published by permission of the Hope Professor, Dept. of Entomology, University Museum, Oxford.

PRINTED BY
METCHIM & SON LTD.
AT THEIR PRESS AT WESTMINSTER

26.5.51

2

2

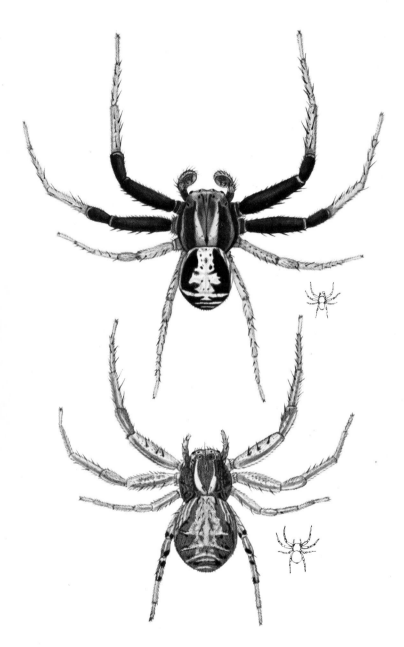

XYSTICUS ULMI (Hahn)
(Male above ; female below)

BRITISH SPIDERS

by

G. H. LOCKET, M.A. (Oxon.), M.Sc. (Lond.), F.Z.S.
& A. F. MILLIDGE, Ph.D., B.Sc. (Lond.)

VOL. I

with a frontispiece and 142 figures in the text

Dedicated to the Memory of Dr. A. Randall Jackson, whose teaching, help and encouragement in past years has enabled us to write this book.

PREFACE

JOHN BLACKWALL'S splendid book, "The Spiders of Great Britain and Ireland," was published by the Ray Society in two volumes with numerous coloured plates in 1861 and 1864. Since that time no comprehensive work has appeared dealing with the identification of the British spider fauna, with the exception of the Rev. O. Pickard-Cambridge's "Spiders of Dorset" (1879–1881) which lacks adequate illustrations. The remaining information on British spiders is often incomplete and lies scattered in the literature. Since the publication of Blackwall's volumes the number of species recorded as British has been practically doubled, and the nomenclature has in many cases undergone considerable revision. The most important modern works useful for the identification of the British spider fauna have been foreign, the most noteworthy being Simon's "Arachnides de France" (Vol. VI, revised by Berland and Fage), "Tierwelt Deutschlands" of which only a few of the parts relevant to spiders had been published by the end of 1939 and "Svensk Spindelfauna" by A. Tullgren and A. Holm (1944, 1946, 1947). These books (except the last) are now difficult to obtain. For a long time the need for an illustrated and accurate account of all the British species has hindered and discouraged much systematic work and regular collecting by naturalists. The late Dr. A. R. Jackson had always intended to write such a book, and his untimely death in March, 1944, deprived naturalists of the most authoritative work which could have been produced. For many years, right up to the beginning of 1944, he had freely given his expert assistance in the matter of identification of spiders, and indeed he was responsible for the examination and naming of the majority of the rarer spiders captured in Britain during the previous twenty-five years. With his death the need became all the more pressing for an effort to be made to provide the necessary information in an accessible form for British naturalists without further avoidable delay. The present work, though it cannot pretend to take the place of the book which Jackson could have written, is an attempt to fulfil that need.

The material studied in the compilation of this book was drawn largely from Dr. Jackson's collection (which he bequeathed to the British Museum (Natural History)), from the Pickard-Cambridge collection (in the University Museum, Oxford), from Mr. A. A. D. La Touche's collection, and from our own collections. It is hoped to describe and illustrate all the British species in this volume and one subsequent volume.

In the past the study of spiders has been for beginners one of the most difficult of all branches of natural history, because of the scarcity of books and of the difficulties of interpreting unambiguously some of the keys in the books available. We have ourselves been through all the difficulties of the " beginner stage," and have tried to make the present work really trustworthy for its prime purpose, viz., the identification of the species of British spiders.

The authors wish to acknowledge with deep gratitude the help received from many quarters, especially the following : Mr. A. A. D. La Touche for the loan from time to time of fresh specimens of rare species drawn from his fine collection, and help in other ways ; Prof. G. Hale Carpenter, Prof. G. C. Varley and those workers of the Hope Department of the University Museum, Oxford, who rendered much help in making readily available specimens from the Pickard-Cambridge collection ; the authorities of the Muséum d'Histoire Naturelle of Paris for the loan of occasional specimens from the Simon Collection ; the British Museum (Natural History), and in particular to Mr. E. Browning, to whom we owe an especial debt of thanks for the extremely helpful and co-operative spirit shown in making readily available for study the specimens from the Jackson and other collections of the Museum.

To Dr. W. S. Bristowe we owe a special and more personal debt of gratitude for his constant help and encouragement. Although he was unable to take (as originally planned) a full part in the preparation of this book, he was able to carry out most of the work associated with the spiders of the Families ATYPIDÆ, OONOPIDÆ, DYSDERIDÆ, and SCYTODIDÆ and for his permission to use this work we are very grateful. He has also written the introductory chapter, which is a valuable survey of the historical side of British arachnology, and provided a great number of the synonyms and principal references. For his permission to use this material we are very grateful.

We also wish to express our indebtedness to Dr. Errol White for his helpful criticism and advice during the preparation of the manuscript.

CONTENTS: VOLUME 1

CONTENTS (*cont.*)

CONTENTS (*cont.*)

I. AN INTRODUCTORY CHAPTER ON BRITISH ARANEOLOGISTS AND THEIR WORK

by W. S. Bristowe, M.A., Sc.D.(Cantab.), F.Z.S.

" I do not want anyone to think that I have described absolutely all the species," wrote Martin Lister in 1678, " but I make bold to say that no one can find casually in this country any new species [of spider] not described by me." The moral to be drawn from Lister's claim is obvious when it is pointed out that his list comprised 34 species and that more than 560 species are now known to inhabit the British Isles ! The total is still incomplete. Luck, skill and diligence will reveal species as yet unrecognised.

We can, however, "make bold to say " that, in all probability, knowledge of the British spider fauna compares favourably with that of any other country in the world. This is a remarkable achievement when it is realised that we owe our present knowledge almost entirely to the spare-time enthusiasm of a series of clergymen, doctors, schoolmasters and business men, a tradition in which the authors of this book and the writer of this chapter are proud to follow.

The history of araneology in the British Isles can be traced by speaking of the men who have contributed most to the knowledge of our spider fauna. In this way tribute is paid to those earlier pioneers on whose labours of love the present authors depend so greatly. The important influence of researches abroad ought not to be overlooked but in this chapter attention is confined to works dealing with the spiders of the British Isles.

Periods in history are seldom sharply defined, but three main phases can roughly be recognised in the history of British araneology. These overlap to some extent and are capable of sub-division.

The first phase covers the mediæval period and a period of gradual escape from the spell of ancient authority. During this phase original research and careful observations were rare. Attempts to classify or describe spiders were primitive in nature.

The gateway to the second phase was opened by Clerck (1757) and Linnaeus (1758) but we in England barely started to pass through it until the second quarter of the nineteenth century. Then, for the first time, the binomial system of nomenclature was adopted and species were described with care and scientific precision. Immense advances were made in the knowledge of our fauna and during the second half of the phase, which lasted until about 1925, the publication of county lists became a major object of collector and expert alike.

In the third phase, from say 1925 onwards, the direct and indirect influence of Darwin is more apparent. The importance of wide and detailed studies of the living spider and the relations on which it lives with other animals is now recognised. Experiments are made in order to test theories and to reach conclusions. Distribution by environments, and the reasons for such distribution, is receiving greater attention than distribution by artificial geographical areas. Biology and taxonomy are now complementary to one another. Studies of internal anatomy, physiology, biochemistry and palæontology may be expected to play a more important part in the study of the Order.

Since the beginning of the second phase we have been fortunate in having an uninterrupted sequence of enthusiasts, each personally acquainted with his successors in the next generation. Thus the Rev. O. Pickard-Cambridge, who had gained help and knowledge from John Blackwall, in his turn passed both on to A. R. Jackson and several other disciples. We ourselves sat at the feet of Jackson. If the present book should help to keep the torch aflame during the fifth generation the authors' principal object will have been achieved.

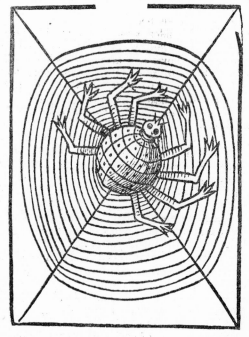

TEXT-FIG. 1.—" An orb-weaver " (from Hortus Sanitatis, 1491).

Little need be said of the mediæval period. The most entertaining accounts of spiders are to be found in " The History of Four-footed Beasts and Serpents " (1658). This work contains the writings of the Rev. E. TOPSEL (1607) and DR. T. MUFFET, alias Mouffet (1634). To the modern reader Topsel and Muffet are remarkable for their credulity, exaggerations, and subservience to ancient authority, but they were typical of their times.

The first araneologist to break with mediæval tradition was DR. MARTIN LISTER (1638–1712). Lister's father was a Yorkshire squire who sent him to Cambridge and afterwards to France to study medicine. Whilst in France Lister met John Ray. This was the start of a long friendship to which Lister, in all probability, owed much of his subsequent interest in natural history. After he returned to practise medicine in York a long correspondence ensued on the subject of spiders (despite Ray's professed horror of them) and the careful observations of these two naturalists were the earliest to be recorded in this country. Some of Lister's early observations were on gossamer and aeronautic spiders, but his most important work was his " Historiae Animalium Angliae " (1678) which contained an illustrated tract on the spiders of England. He was the first naturalist to draw attention to the part played by the male palps during copulation, and he distinguished between 34 species of which he gave brief descriptions. These were numbered but not named.

Lister was elected to the Royal Society in 1671 and moved to London in 1683, where he became a fashionable physician and did little more work of importance on natural history. He attended Charles II and served as second physician to Queen Anne.

One forms the impression that Lister had a somewhat jealous eye to his own interests and that he gained excessive satisfaction from his own achievements, but nevertheless he was undoubtedly a skilful observer and a pioneer of considerable importance.

After Lister we come to ELEAZAR ALBIN (circa 1713–1759). Albin was primarily a teacher of water colour painting, but he wrote an interesting book on spiders in 1736 entitled " A Natural History of Spiders and Other Curious Insects." In this book he delineated in colour about 150 English spiders. These are numbered but not named or adequately described in the text. A substantial proportion are colour variations of the same species or else unrecognisable, but nevertheless he undoubtedly distinguished more species than Lister. Apart from the historical interest of his book, it helps us to see how greatly the fauna of London and its northern outskirts has changed since his day as a result of town development.

THOMAS MARTYN (circa 1760–1816), a natural history draughtsman and pamphleteer from Coventry, published a book on similar lines in 1793, but with finer illustrations. It was little more than a revision of Albin's work combined with a translation of Clerck's book on Swedish Spiders (see below). To the extent that Clerck used the binominal system of nomenclature, it could be claimed that Martyn's book was the first in English to recognise it. The book was entitled " Aranei, or a Natural History of Spiders."

Before we reach the beginning of the second phase in British araneological history, several works of importance had been published on the Continent. Notable amongst these were the writings of C. Clerck (1757), C. Linnaeus (1758), P. A. Latreille (1802 onwards) and C. A. Walckenaer (1802 onwards). We were slow to enter the second phase in the British Isles, but when we did so three workers arose at about the same time in London, Belfast and Manchester. These were Leach, Templeton and Blackwall respectively.

DR. W. E. LEACH (1790–1836) was a remarkable man whose brilliant career was brought to a tragic end by mental disorder, whilst he was still young. After qualifying in medicine he accepted a post at the British Museum in 1813. Crustacea were his particular subject but his interests were wide and his brilliance was recognised in 1817 by election to the Royal Society at the early age of 27. His article on Annulosa in the supplement to the 4th, 5th and 6th editions of the Encyclopædia Britannica in 1816 does not appear to set out a list of all British species known to him, but he mentions about 30 species as examples in the scheme of classification he adopts. The binominal system of nomenclature is used and his list is remarkable for containing several rarities which were not rediscovered in Britain for many years, species such as *Atypus affinis* Eich., *Segestria florentina* (Ross.), *Scytodes thoracica* (Latr.), *Eresus niger* (Pet.), and *Myrmarachne formicaria* (Degeer). It was a tragedy for British zoology that in 1821 when he was still only 31 his brain became affected and he had to relinquish his post. Fifteen years later he died of cholera in Italy where he had gone to live with his sister.

DR. R. T. TEMPLETON (circa 1805–1894) of Belfast began to make a study of spiders a few years later than Leach. Like his father before him, Templeton had a wide and expert knowledge of natural history. Unfortunately he only published one brief paper on spiders in 1834. In this paper he founded a genus *Oonops*, the type species *pulcher*, and the genus *Harpactes* (changed to *Harpactea* by Bristowe in 1939 because *Harpactes* had been preoccupied for birds in 1833). Templeton also wrote a History of Irish Spiders containing a list of 43 species with descriptions of several new genera and species, but this was never published. Blackwall used the descriptions of the new species in his book in 1864, but these were too indefinite to make subsequent identification certain so they have now all been abandoned. Templeton's MS. genera were not adopted by Blackwall.

Now we come to the great JOHN BLACKWALL (1788-1881). He was born near Manchester and entered his father's business concerned with the merchanting of Irish linen. He was able to retire when he was 44 and for the rest of his long life he devoted himself to natural history. He had an expert knowledge of ornithology, botany, astronomy and meteorology in addition to spiders.

Problems connected with gossamer and web-spinning had first attracted Blackwall's attention to spiders shortly after 1820 and his study of the Order never flagged until failing sight and health made further work impossible at about the age of 86. His publications on British spiders spanned nearly half a century, 1827 to 1875.

Blackwall paid some attention to the habits of spiders, but he concerned himself chiefly with the structure and description both of British and foreign species. His descriptions were detailed and excellent, indeed they were marvellous when it is realised that he had to rely almost entirely on a strong pocket lens. Despite this handicap he made use of the male palps as a means of distinguishing species, and he was the first araneologist to call attention to their value for this purpose.

Blackwall led a secluded life at Llanrwst. There were no experts in Britain with whom to compare notes until Pickard-Cambridge, towards the end of Blackwall's career. Abroad he had too little contact with contemporary experts such as Sundevall, Hahn, Keyserling, Westring, Menge, C. L. and L. Koch, Thorell and Canestrini, whose work was of great importance. Blackwall's famous book " A History of the Spiders of Great Britain and Ireland " (Ray Society, 1861–4), is still invaluable for its illustrations, but his lack of contact with current work led to his describing as new species many which had already been described on the Continent. It was also unfortunate that at a period when so much work was in progress on the Continent the publication of his book was delayed about 10 years through the illness of his artist. Of the total British list today, 67 of his species were new to science at the time he described them.

The magnitude of Blackwall's contributions becomes apparent when we realise that at the start of his work no British spiders had been adequately described and that less than 50 were fully recognised in Britain by their Latin names. By 1852, Blackwall had described 210 species. By 1864 this number had been increased to 304 and after this date he added several more to the total before he finally retired in 1874.

A number of naturalists used to send Blackwall spiders for identification, and a few of these, such as F. Walker, J. Hardy, the Rev. Hamlet Clarke and R. H. Meade, published notes or lists. Hamlet Clarke, a relation of Blackwall, described a species in 1855 which he called *Salticus blackwalli* but this later proved to be a synonym of *Marpissa pomatia* (Walck.). Meade was the most important of these correspondents and is deserving of special mention.

R. H. MEADE (1814–1899) was a surgeon with a practice in Bradford. He was a skilful naturalist with a considerable knowledge of Diptera and a keen interest in Arachnida. He wrote the first monograph on British Phalangidea and published several short notes on spiders. He was the first araneologist to advocate the keeping of spiders in small corked glass tubes containing alcohol—one species to each tube (1852, 1860). This advice came too late to be of service to Blackwall, some of whose new species have had to be abandoned because the types were mixed or lost and the descriptions inadequate. As recently as 1930 Monsieur P. Bonnet has recorded *Dolomedes plantarius* (Clerck) as British on the evidence of a specimen in one of Blackwall's bottles mixed with British specimens of *D. fimbriatus* (Clerck). Knowing how little importance Blackwall placed on keeping English and foreign specimens apart, or of segregating different species, we do not accept Bonnet's discovery as valid evidence that *D. plantarius* (Clerck) is found in Britain.

Meade was a keen collector and he also helped others by identifying the commoner species. The more critical species he always sent to Blackwall for examination. In 1853 he published for private circulation a list of 231 British species. Meade described *Epeira bella* as new to science in 1861, but this was a synonym of *Cercidia prominens* (Westr). He also recorded *Xysticus sabulosus* (Hahn), *Philodromus levipes* (Linn.), *Araneus angulatus* Clerck and *Mangora acalypha* (Walck.), as new to Britain in 1857 after consulting Blackwall (who also listed them in the same year). Two of these species had been sent to him by the Rev. O. Pickard-Cambridge and it is to Meade that we must offer thanks for stimulating Pickard-Cambridge's interest in spiders and for introducing him to Blackwall.

The REV. O. PICKARD-CAMBRIDGE (1828–1917) was the fifth son of the Rev. George Pickard, Rector and Squire of Bloxworth, Dorset, who, with his family, took the additional name of Cambridge on succeeding to the property of a cousin of that name in 1848.

After reading law for two years in London, Pickard-Cambridge decided to take Holy Orders. He entered Durham University and was ordained in 1858. Before settling down at Bloxworth, first as curate to his father and later as rector, he had two years as curate at Scarisbrook, near Southport and made two extended tours of Europe, Egypt, Palestine and Syria.

Pickard-Cambridge's life at Bloxworth was one of varied interests. Not only did he have a deep interest in his parish, but he gained an expert knowledge of music, poetry, gardening and antiquities, apart from natural history, in which he became an eminent authority. Spiders, phalangids and chelonethids were his principal subjects, but he also published numerous papers on birds, mammals, reptiles and Lepidoptera. His work on Arachnida, much of which related to foreign species, led to his election to the Royal Society in 1887.

Pickard-Cambridge took little interest in the habits of spiders except in so far as these helped him to find the specimens he needed. He was himself an expert collector but when, according to his own phrase, he began to lose " the eye of faith and the finger of instinct " he relied on his family and on the band of enthusiasts he had helped to inspire to send him specimens from various parts of Britain.

His first paper was published in 1852. His last, in 1914, was beautifully illustrated with drawings he had made at the age of 85. Indeed, it is a remarkable phenomenon, not solely explained by the acquisition of a good microscope in 1882, that the older he got the better became his drawings.

Pickard-Cambridge only wrote one book on British spiders, modestly called " The Spiders of Dorset " (1879–1881), but he published a large number of valuable papers both on British and foreign species. His chief interest was in the description of spiders. Some idea of the magnitude of his contribution to the knowledge of our fauna is gained by the increase in the British list. Blackwall's 304 species in 1864 rose in successive lists published by Pickard-Cambridge to 457 species in

1874, to 518 in 1881 and to 532 in 1900. Several more species were added before Pickard-Cambridge finally retired 14 years later. The British list today contains 116 species described by Pickard-Cambridge as new to science and he must be regarded as our greatest British arachnologist of all time.

Pickard-Cambridge's warm-hearted kindness and keen sense of humour endeared him to young and old alike. As a young man he gave unstinted help to the ageing Blackwall. As an old man his kindness and enthusiasm inspired numerous young collectors. Several of these became experts capable of supplementing and carrying on his work, but between 1864 and 1914 hardly a paper was published on spiders in the preparation of which he had provided no help.

Two of his earlier correspondents whose contributions to our knowledge of spiders were somewhat different from those of later writers were F. ENOCK (1846–1916) and F. MAULE CAMPBELL (1843–1920).

ENOCK turned aside from the engineering profession for which he had been intended to devote himself to the study of natural history. The life histories of insects were his speciality but he also made the first detailed study in this country of the life history of a spider, *Atypus affinis* Eich.

CAMPBELL had a wide interest in nature and published papers on plants, mammals, insects and spiders whilst he was President of the Hertfordshire Natural History Society. His interest in spiders was fleeting, but the papers he published between 1880 and 1883 showed such originality and promise that it was disappointing he did not pursue his researches further. His papers included studies of stridulating organs, glands, sexual organs, and a suspected case of parthenogenesis (subsequently shown by P. Bonnet (1927, 1935) to be unfounded).

The writings of Enock and Campbell attracted considerable attention, although they did not influence contemporary naturalists to pay more attention to the biology or physiology of spiders.

An attractive little book called " Spiders " was published by C. WARBURTON (1854—) in 1912, but Warburton's period of enthusiasm really belonged to the last 15 years of the nineteenth century. His interest had been aroused early in the '80s by seeing a list of Southport spiders compiled by O. Pickard-Cambridge. At this time Warburton was living in Southport and teaching at a school in Manchester, the place of his birth, but later he graduated in science at Cambridge and remained there as a lecturer and coach for the rest of his career.

Warburton became an ardent collector of spiders and started sending his specimens to Pickard-Cambridge for identification about the year 1885. His best captures included *Mengea warburtoni* (Camb.) (new to science), *Agroeca pullata* Thor., *Thanatus formicinus* (Clerck) and *Singa heri* (Hahn), all of which were new to Britain. He also paid some attention to the spider's spinning organs. By 1900, however, his interest was concentrated on arachnids and other invertebrates of economic importance and he became Zoologist to the Royal Agricultural Society of England, a post which he continued to hold until after he was 93.

B

The first five years of the 1860's were remarkable " vintage " years. During this brief period no less than six British araneologists of importance were born—F. O. Pickard-Cambridge, W. Falconer, J. E. Hull, R. I. Pocock, D. Pack-Beresford and G. H. Carpenter.

F. O. PICKARD-CAMBRIDGE (1860–1905) was a nephew of the Rev. O. Pickard-Cambridge. His father was Rector of Warmwell, Dorset, and he himself was a curate in Carlisle for a few years after being educated at Sherborne and Oxford. As a young man he was overflowing with fun and energy, with a keen interest in cricket, shooting, drawing and natural history. Whilst he was still in the 30's, however, a marked change occurred in him which led to misfortune. Strong views on religion forced him to resign his Holy Orders. Extreme political views estranged him from most of his relations and friends. Fierce arguments over questions of nomenclature led to quarrels with other naturalists. When his life ended in tragedy in 1905 araneology lost one of its most brilliant devotees, at a time when he should have been doing his best work had circumstances worked out differently.

F. O. Pickard-Cambridge was a brilliant all-round naturalist whose talents as an observer were enhanced by his lively imagination and skill as an artist. His enthusiasm sometimes made him hasty in reaching conclusions on matters of classification and nomenclature, but his papers, more of which dealt with foreign than with British spiders, were of great value. At the time he appeared on the scene, about 1890, a need existed for the re-examination and re-grouping of the numerous British species which had been described during the previous half century, often without the aid of a microscope. This he started to do, making discoveries in the process. Genera were examined one by one—*Tetragnatha, Lepthyphantes, Porrhomma, Lycosa,* etc. In some cases he found the same species had been described more than once under different names. In other cases, *Tetragnatha* for instance, several species were found to be lying hid under one name. His new genera included *Hillhousia* and *Mengea* ; his British species new to science comprised *Lycosa purbeckensis, Trochosa spinipalpis, Lepthyphantes whymperi,* and *Bathyphantes setiger.* In addition to these, he added more than twelve species to the British list including four Tetragnathids which had previously been confused under the single species *Tetragnatha extensa.* County lists and rules of nomenclature also engaged his attention to a considerable extent.

During his later years, when the need to earn a living became a pressing necessity, F. O. Pickard-Cambridge made use of his skill at drawing to illustrate books and papers on natural history and other subjects. In this manner it came about that he illustrated many of the papers published by R. I. POCOCK (1863–1947) who was in charge of Arachnida and Myriopoda at the British Museum (Natural History) between 1885 and 1903. Pocock's valuable work on Arachnida was confined almost entirely to the anatomy, classification and palæontology of the larger foreign species. His successors, S. Hirst, S. Finnegan and R. J. Whittick, each in turn found it necessary to devote the bulk of their time to mites and other forms of greater economic importance than spiders, a state of affairs that is bound to continue so long as the British Museum can arrange to have at their disposal only one expert to cover the Arachnida and Myriopoda of the world.

G. H. CARPENTER and W. EVANS are the next two writers to be mentioned. Both covered a wide field of natural history but in other respects they have little resemblance to one another. Carpenter was essentially an indoor man who attempted to gain an expert knowledge of too many Orders with the result that his diagnoses were sometimes unreliable. Evans was an outdoor naturalist with an extremely wide knowledge of natural history but with no pretentions to being an authority on any single Order. Together (with O. Pickard-Cambridge helping in the background) these two did much to advance the knowledge of Scottish spiders. Carpenter also made important contributions to our knowledge of the Irish fauna.

The REV. DR. G. H. CARPENTER (1865–1938) was a Londoner by birth who completed his education at the Royal College of Science in Dublin. From an engineer's office he moved to the British Museum as a clerk and thence to Dublin Museum as assistant naturalist in 1888. From 1904 to 1922 he was Professor of Zoology at the Royal College of Science, Dublin, and then Keeper of the Manchester Museum until 1934. On retirement he completed a varied career by becoming a curate at Broxbourne, Herts., following ordination eight years previously at the age of 61.

Before Carpenter started examining collections of Irish spiders, T. WORKMAN (1844–1900), a widely travelled naturalist who was also interested in religious and philanthropic work, had brought the list to 125 species in 1881 with specimens he had sent to O. Pickard-Cambridge for identification. In 1895 Carpenter increased this list to 225 and added much to the known distribution of the species within the island.

Carpenter's work on Scottish spiders depended entirely on collections sent to him by W. EVANS (1851–1922). Evans was perhaps the most competent Scottish field naturalist of his day. When ill-health forced him to retire in 1892 from the post of actuary to the Scottish Widows' Fund he devoted himself to natural history. In the years which followed, he published papers on animals and plants belonging to most Orders. Seven of his eleven notes and papers on spiders were published jointly with G. H. Carpenter to whom he sent most of his captures. Some were sent direct to O. Pickard-Cambridge.

The chief value of these papers lies in the substantial increase in the knowledge of Scottish fauna which they provided. Species new to science included *Evansia merens* Camb., *Caledonia evansi* Camb., *Silometopus ambiguus* (Camb.), *Rhœbothorax faustus* (Camb.) and *Macrargus carpenteri* Camb. (perhaps an abnormal specimen of *M. rufus* (Wid.). Additions to the British list included *Dictyna major* Menge, *Zelotes electus* (C.L.K.), *Typhocrestus digitatus* (Camb.), and *Cornicularia karpinskii* Camb.

Carpenter invariably sent critical species to O. Pickard-Cambridge or his nephew, so he himself only described three species as new to Britain : *Agelena longipes* Carp. (undoubtedly an imported specimen), *Cnephalocotes silus* Camb. (later found to be a synonym of two other species), both from Southport, and *Porrhomma myops* Sim. (now regarded as a form of *P. convexum Westr.* (=*P. proserpina* Sim.)) from the Mitchelstown cave in Tipperary.

Carpenter's work on Irish spiders was soon continued by D. R. PACK-BERESFORD (1864–1942). Pack-Beresford was a man who excelled in all the country pursuits to which he devoted himself after leaving Rugby and Oxford. He was a keen hunting man, a good shot, and an expert fisherman. On his estate in Carlow he kept pedigree herds of cattle and pigs. Here and at his smaller house near Dublin he showed great skill as a gardener. In the field of natural history he paid at first considerable attention to wasps and woodlice, but his interest in spiders continued for the rest of his life, although failing eyesight prevented active work during the last few years.

Pack-Beresford knew all the commoner spiders but submitted the more critical specimens to O. Pickard-Cambridge and later, to A. R. Jackson for determination. A few were new to Britain at the time of their capture and *Erigone welchi* Jacks. was new to science. Apart from a few species added to the Irish list by H. Wallis Kew (1910) and W. S. Bristowe (1931), Pack-Beresford was responsible for Carpenter's list of 225 being increased to the present total of 318 species. His papers also added much to our knowledge of the distribution of the Irish species.

F. P. SMITH (1880–1946) was a stimulating enthusiast from London, a Cockney from Islington, who flashed into prominence in 1899 as a writer on spiders and then vanished ten years later as suddenly as he had appeared. He had had no educational or monetary advantages and yet somehow he managed to acquire a substantial knowledge and to start writing about spiders with an air of authority by the time he was nineteen. He was then a junior clerk at the Board of Education earning about a pound a week.

As a youth he joined a number of Field Clubs. Finding that none of the members could tell him anything about spiders, he decided to specialise. For literature, he went to the British Museum. For equipment he depended on improvisation. Thus a microscope was made from the tube of a garden syringe fitted with an eye piece and an objective. A broom handle sawn into three pieces served as a tripod.

In 1899, the year in which he started to write, he began to send the species which puzzled him to the Rev. O. Pickard-Cambridge for determination. He also received help from F. O. Pickard-Cambridge, but in large measure he had overcome all handicaps and taught himself most of what he knew about spiders. When still in the early twenties he was elected Honorary Secretary of the Quekett Microscopical Club and enlarged his horizon by making a close study of Foraminifera.

Smith's work shows originality and courage. He made mistakes but he also made discoveries. He was the first araneologist to consider on a statistical basis which species were the principal aeronauts (1904). He recognised that *Drassodes macer* (Thor.) and *D. cupreus* (Bl.) were forms of *lapidosus* (Walck.) rather than distinct species (1907) and that the *opisthographus* Kulcz. form of *Araneus cucurbitinus* Clk. was found in Britain (1908). He contributed to the grouping of Linyphiid species and three of his own genera have survived (*Erigonidium* 1904, *Monocephalus* 1906, and *Lessertia* 1908). His best paper, illustrated with his own excellent drawings made with ink of his own invention, dealt with the family Lycosidæ (1906) ; in this family he was the first to collect *Xerolycosa nemoralis* (Westr.) in Britain and to give a name (*intermedia* Smith) to a form of *Lycosa herbigrada* Bl.

Smith was an ingenious photographer and the Film Industry claimed him before he was 30. Soon after marriage he left the Board of Education and devoted all his time and enthusiasm to the production of nature films of which he was a free-lance pioneer. Spiders were abandoned. His collection was acquired by his friend, R. Hancock of Birmingham, after whom Smith (1905) had once named a spider *Anglia hancocki*, which subsequently proved to be *Tmeticus affinis* (Bl.).

Our extensive knowledge of the spiders of the northern counties of England is due mainly to the work of three men—W. Falconer, J. E. Hull and A. R. Jackson.

W. FALCONER (1862–1943) was one of our most reliable experts and also one of our most prolific writers on the subject.

Born in Northumberland and educated in Durham at St. Bede's College, he became headmaster of Slaithwaite Council School after a few years' teaching in Leeds. On his retirement in 1923 he went to live in Liverpool.

As a young man he was a keen and expert botanist. So, too, was his college friend, the Rev. J. E. Hull, and both owed their interest in spiders to a spark kindled by Canon Norman, himself an expert on Crustacea. Their serious work on spiders started towards the end of the century and spanned the next 40 years. Both were also interested in other arachnid Orders.

Falconer was an untiring collector who was seldom parted from an old umbrella which was his principal collecting instrument used as a beating tray. His greatest triumph was achieved in a series of visits to Wicken Fen from 1912 onwards. Here he found and described four species new to science and one new to Britain. In the course of his career he described seven species new to Britain from various localities of which five were new to science : *Neon valentulus* Falc., *Zora armillata* Sim., *Centromerus incultus* Falc., *Maro sublestus* Falc., *Troglohyphantes margerisoni* Falc., *Eboria caliginosa* Falc. (new genus), and *Maso gallica* Sim. In addition to this the Rev. O. Pickard-Cambridge, from whom he received much help in his early years, described two of his discoveries as new to science and one new to Britain : *Maro minutus* Camb., *Meioneta beata* (Camb.) and *Asthenargus paganus* (Sim.). Jackson described *Hahnia pusilla* L.K. as new to Britain which he and Falconer jointly found at Delamere.

Ill health and failing sight prevented extensive work after the age of 75, but up to within a few weeks of his death in his eighty-first year, he took pleasure in identifying individual specimens sent to him by correspondents.

The REV. DR. J. E. HULL (1862—), as we have mentioned, was a friend and contemporary of W. Falconer with whom he shared an interest in botany, spiders and mites. Hull has done more work on mites and less on spiders than Falconer, but he has been nevertheless one of our leading experts on the latter.

After leaving St. Bede's College he took a degree in mathematics at Durham University before returning to St. Bede's as Vice-Principal in 1890. While occupying this post his study of spiders began with the assistance of O. Pickard-Cambridge and his nephew. After publishing his first paper in 1896, his work as a clergyman in Northumberland parishes prevented further studies until 1905 when he was transferred to a less exacting parish at Ninebanks, near Whitfield. From this date he has never lost interest in spiders although mites became his principal study from 1912 onwards.

Hull's sorting of Linyphiid species into groups led to his proposing a number of new genera, several of which have been accepted by other araneologists—*Halorates, Diplocentria, Ostearius, Agyneta* and *Rhabdoria* in 1910 ; *Meioneta* in 1920. He described six species as new to science. Three of these were subsequently found to be synonyms. *Hilaira pervicax* Hull and *H. nubigena* Hull have been re-discovered by Mr. A. A. D. La Touche. Further examination of *Lepthyphantes moratus* Hull and *Oxyptila maculosa* Hull is desirable.

In his later years Hull has been apt to record the discovery of rarities or even species new to Britain after what appears to have been too casual examination. The rarities so recorded included *Araneus bituberculatus* (Walck.). from Essex and *Tegenaria larva* Sim. from Suffolk. The species new to Britain *Episinus maculipes* Cav. from Essex (1934), *Chalcoscirtus infimus* (Sim.) from Dartmoor (in litteris, 1934), *Thanatus arenarius* Thor., and *Echemus rhenanus* Bertk, etc., from Essex (1947). Further descriptions and facilities to re-examine the specimens are desirable before we feel persuaded to accept these additions.

Many of Hull's papers and notes were published in " The Vasculum," a journal not readily accessible to other workers, so his valuable contributions and his sometimes controversial views have often escaped attention. His choice of cheliceral teeth as a principal character for defining Linyphiid genera and his attempted resurrection of Black-wall's doubtful species, abandoned by all other araneologists, were further examples of his independent nature.

Greatest of this northern trio was DR. A. R. JACKSON (1877–1944). He was born in Southport and spent most of his adult life as a busy medical practitioner in Chester. It was whilst studying zoology under

Professor Herdman in 1897 that his interest in spiders was aroused. G. H. Carpenter gave him some preliminary assistance but by 1901 he was corresponding with O. Pickard-Cambridge whom he visited in Dorset a few years later. This was a momentous visit which was followed by others. Pickard-Cambridge became a hero, a model for Jackson's own treatment of young naturalists who sought his aid in later years. The kindness and generous help he had received from Pickard-Cambridge was invariably extended to his own numerous correspondents who sent or brought him collections of spiders to identify.

Jackson was not interested in the habits of spiders except in so far as this helped him to find them. His great skill as a collector was best shown by his two carefully planned expeditions to Scotland in 1913 and 1914 when he discovered ten species new to Britain (of which one was new to science) in the course of four weeks. After his return from the war in 1917 conscientious attention to his medical practice prevented him going on many collecting holidays.

For brilliance in diagnosis and detailed care in identification Jackson has never been surpassed. His re-examination of British species and comparisons he carried out with foreign specimens enabled him both to clear up many synonymic muddles and to detect a number of new species. His flair for this kind of work amounted almost to genius, but throughout his life the extent of his success was always limited by the amount of time he had available.

Jackson's work led to many species being relegated to the rank of synonyms, but his additions to the list exceeded these reductions. Forty-seven species were added to the British list of which the following nine were new to science ; *Ischnothyreus velox*, *Robertus scoticus*, *Erigone welchi*, *Maro falconeri*, *Perimones britteni*, *Agyneta ramosa*, *Porrhomma pallidum*, *P. montanum*, and *Lepthyphantes carri*.

The Linyphiidae were Jackson's pet family and this helps to explain the special interest he showed from 1922 onwards in arctic species. Between 1922 and 1938 he published nine important papers on arctic spiders.

Jackson had a considerable knowledge of birds, bees, dragonflies and myriapods. His other interests included water colours and etchings, good literature and his garden.

His last work, which he never saw in print, was an obituary notice of his friend, W. Falconer.

At the close of the second phase let us look back for a moment at the men responsible for the vast increase in our knowledge during the hundred years from 1825 to 1925. Clergymen, doctors and teachers (at schools or universities) have predominated, all of whom pursued their studies with microscope and lens for their own pleasure. They have set a fine example of co-operation with one another and of kindness to all who needed help in the identification of their captures. Though they sprang from many walks of life they have usually been men with wide interests whose longevity may be partially explained by the mental activity and contentment of their lives.*

One striking coincidence has been the association of araneologists with a small area in Lancashire. Blackwall and Warburton were born in Manchester where Carpenter worked for eleven years. Jackson was born in Southport where O. Pickard-Cambridge and Warburton both lived for a time. Falconer spent the last 20 years of his life in Liverpool.

Apart from Miss E. F. Staveley, whose book (1866) was little more than an abbreviated version of Blackwall's two volumes, women in England have left spiders severely alone after the example of Miss Muffet. Patience Muffet, if my surmise is correct, was the daughter of Dr. T. Muffet whose name I have mentioned earlier in the present chapter.

" We want now badly a new work on British spiders up to date " wrote the Rev. O. Pickard-Cambridge to F. Maule Campbell on March 24th, 1896. " It is only a question of finances," he continued. " My nephew will do it if we can get a guarantee of costs beyond what the book will pay of itself. Have you no ' millionaires' who could be squeezed in so good a cause ? "

Thirty years earlier he had planned to do this himself and had had a number of coloured plates prepared. Twenty years later, in 1917, Dr. A. R. Jackson started to plan such a book but, strangely enough, it was the absence of a book which prevented him from writing one ! His time was too fully occupied in identifying specimens which a book would have enabled their collectors to distinguish for themselves.

Now, at last, a book is published by the Ray Society which will fill the longfelt need. The absence of such a work has hampered ecologists for many years and, to my knowledge, has diverted the attention of several spider enthusiasts to the study of other Orders. The authors are to be congratulated both on the excellence of their work and on the resolution they have shown in undertaking such a task in the limited spare time available to a schoolmaster and an industrial research chemist respectively.

---

* Note also the ages of some eminent foreign naturalists who studied spiders : H. Lucas 84, C. L. Koch 79, L. Koch 83, J. H. Fabre 92, E. Simon 76, H. McCook 74, J. H. Emerton 83, J. H. Comstock 82, van Hasselt 88, E. L. Homberg 85, N. Westring 85, W. A. Wagner 85, L. Dufour 85, L. Becker 83, F. Karsch 83, C. A. Walckenaer 80. O. Herman 79.

II. THE COLLECTION, PRESERVATION AND EXAMINATION OF SPIDERS

Although certain of our spiders can be identified with tolerable certainty in the field with the aid of characteristic shapes, colours or patterns, it is necessary in the majority of cases to capture the specimens for subsequent examination at leisure ; and it is usual to make a collection for reference when studying the group systematically. The following notes indicate the procedures most usually adopted as the result of the experience of several generations of arachnologists.

Spiders are among the most widespread of living creatures, and there are few situations in this country from the sea-shore to the summits of our highest mountains where they do not occur. They are usually to be found in dwelling houses (on the walls, ceilings, etc., especially after dark), in outhouses and cellars, in hothouses, under logs and stones, under loose bark on trees and posts, amongst dead leaves and detritus (particularly in woods), in moss and sphagnum in swampy areas, amongst hay and straw, in grass and other low-growing vegetation, on bushes and trees, and in almost every conceivable type of surrounding.

Methods of collection are similar to those used for other wingless arthropods. Dead leaves and other loose material should be shaken over newspaper ; low trees, bushes, etc., should be beaten with a stick into an inverted umbrella ; low herbage, such as heather, rushes, long grass, etc., should be swept with a strong canvas net. Searching around the roots of grass and other plants, and under dead grass and heather, etc. (usually termed " grubbing in the undergrowth ") is frequently profitable. When searching under stones (e.g., on mountains, in quarries, in woods or by the sea-shore) the under-surface of the stone should be examined as well as the ground which it covered. Many web-building species can be located readily, as can a number of active species which run in the open in the sunshine ; a quick eye is a great asset in this as in other pursuits.

The rarer and more interesting species are likely to be found in areas which have not been too disturbed by agriculture, though there are exceptions to this. Woodlands of long standing (e.g., the older State Forests), particularly if there be clearings, open moorland, heath and mountain, swamps, sand-dunes and undisturbed fenland are likely to provide an interesting variety of species ; for example, the New Forest area, and Wicken Fen are both most profitable hunting-grounds. For an account of the spiders of some specialised localities, see W. S. Bristowe, " Comity of Spiders," Vol. I (1939).

In the systematic descriptions of the species given later in this book, the most likely habitat for each species is mentioned where possible. Often, however, there are insufficient data on the normal type of habitat, and it must be remembered that some spiders seem to be very local and restricted in their occurrence.

Spiders are killed and preserved in alcohol of about 70–75 per cent. strength. Being rather soft-bodied creatures they cannot be preserved satisfactorily in the dry state, for they shrink badly and usually become mere unidentifiable husks. They are caught in small corked glass tubes (specimen tubes) of suitable size ; it is inadvisable to capture the specimens with the fingers as rough handling may result in the loss of legs or other damage. In these tubes they may be examined with a hand-lens, and then transferred at once to spirit or kept alive as desired. Spiders are by nature cannibals, and it is desirable to have no more than one live specimen per tube. The smaller species may also be picked up with the moistened finger, or by means of a small camel hair brush dipped in spirit, and then dropped at once into the spirit. Besides having a number of empty tubes available, sufficient tubes or bottles of spirit must also be carried, so that one spirit receptacle shall contain the species from one locality only.

The collection of spiders is kept in a number of glass tubes, with at least one tube for each species ; often there are several tubes for one species, examples from different localities being kept separate. The tubes are then filled with spirit, plugged with cotton wool and inverted in spirit in a larger wide-mouthed bottle or jar which is closed with a stopper, cork or rubber bung. In this way, loss of the specimens through evaporation of the alcohol is rendered less likely, the bottles being filled up periodically. The annoyance of losing specimens through desiccation as a result of evaporation of the spirit can be avoided altogether by adding 5–10 per cent. of glycerol (or other high-boiling liquid miscible with water and alcohol, e.g., ethylene glycol) to the spirit used for preservation. If sufficient wide-mouthed bottles are available it is convenient to allocate one bottle to each species, but tubes containing several species can in fact be stored in one jar. A slip of paper giving the name, the locality and date of capture should be placed in each tube ; these labels are preferably written in indian ink, but lead pencil will also serve as a temporary measure. A similar label can be placed in the jar if desired. Specimens can also be stored in separate glass tubes which are closed with rubber bungs to prevent evaporation, and under these circumstances the tubes are not inverted in alcohol in a jar.

Spiders frequently contract their legs and palps up to the body after being killed in spirit, and become hardened and set in this position. This may render the examination of the epigyne, palps, sternum, etc. (definitions of these terms will be found under " External Anatomy of Spiders," p. 19) more difficult, and, if desired, specimens (particularly of the larger species) may be set out in spirit immediately after death and before full hardening has occurred, so that the legs are extended and all the parts are fully visible. Hardening is not so rapid or pronounced and setting is carried out more easily if specimens selected for this purpose are killed with ethyl acetate vapour, by placing a piece of cotton wool soaked in ethyl acetate in the tube (private communication from Mr. E. Browning, British Museum (Natural

History)), setting being carried out as soon as the specimen is dead and limp.

For the examination and identification of most species a microscope is necessary ; usually 2-inch and 1-inch objectives, with a suitable eyepiece, are all that are required. The specimens are examined in spirit in shallow vessels of glass or china, being held in the required position by small pieces of cotton wool or paper, etc., if necessary, and illuminated by a powerful top light.

When interpreting the descriptions given in this book it must be borne in mind that specimens of any species may vary appreciably both in colour and size. When the colouration varies regularly or frequently this fact will be noted in the descriptions but depth of colour may vary in nature and different parts of a pattern may be accentuated or obliterated in specimens from different or even the same locality. Immediately following the final moult the spider is normally very pale in colour, and if captured in this condition the pattern is often very indistinct. Colour and size are not always reliable characters for use in identification ; for this reason the identity of immature spiders has always a certain degree of uncertainty, and should be included in any list of captures only with extreme caution. The descriptions given apply to adult spiders, and may not be true for immature specimens.

The appearance of the epigynes of female spiders, so universally important for identification, may vary appreciably, depending on the transparency of the integuments, and newly moulted specimens for example may appear somewhat different in colour and detail from older specimens. Reliance must therefore be placed more in the form and outline of the constituent parts than in the relative colouration of these. Fresh specimens may appear at first sight to differ a good deal from older specimens, such as reference specimens from museum collections with which comparison must sometimes be made. Owing to the fact that an increased transparency of the outer integument of the epigyne enables more internal detail to be observed, it follows that the refractive index of the fluid in which the specimen is immersed during examination has a marked effect on the appearance of the epigyne. At a refractive index of 1.50–1.55 the chitinous integument becomes more or less transparent (" cleared "), and outlines of the internal parts of the genitalia can be viewed quite clearly while the outer chitinous shield becomes much less visible. All the drawings given in this book were made on specimens immersed in 75 per cent. alcohol, the epigyne being viewed from a position vertically above it, unless a statement is made to the contrary.

The palps of the mature male spider, which are used almost invariably for the final identification of a species, usually vary less in general appearance as a result of storing or a recent moult, though the depth of colour may vary appreciably. Owing to the complexity of these organs, however, they may appear very different when viewed from slightly different positions. It is impossible to define exactly this viewpoint, which may be from the outside, from the inside, from below, from above, etc., these terms being defined on the assumption that the palp is fully extended forwards. Even a slight twist of the organ may, in some cases, make all the difference to its appearance. Enough detail has been included in the drawings to enable the positions of the parts figured to be found, and it is clearly essential that examinations be made with the specimen and the drawing in comparable positions.

The identification of species of spiders is based ultimately, with few exceptions, on the sexual organs ; nevertheless, other characters, such as positions of the eyes, the spines on the legs, the general pattern, etc., are frequently typical of families or genera and are of considerable importance in placing a specimen in its family or genus. Such characters may occasionally fail, e.g., spines may have become detached or may be abnormal in number or position ; such latter occurrences where known have been allowed for in the descriptions.

III. EXTERNAL ANATOMY

The form and disposition of the different parts of spiders

Although the classification of spiders is based upon their external and internal anatomy, the British species at least can be identified with the help of characters normally visible without dissection. We shall therefore confine our attention to the external characters, which are used in identification of the species. The names assigned to the various parts are not altogether consistent among different writers and objections have been raised against several of those in common use on the grounds of the lack of homology with similarly named parts in the INSECTA. The names used in the present work are mostly anglicised forms of those given by Simon in the "Histoire Naturelle des Araignées" (Paris 1892) and which have been largely employed in the British literature in recent years. Where other names are likely to be found in the literature at all commonly, they are given in brackets. Neither fine points of structure and anatomy, nor the functions of the different organs, will be discussed unless they have a bearing upon identification. (For a more complete account of anatomy and functions see, for instance, J. H. Comstock, "The Spider Book," 2nd edition, New York, 1940 ; The Cambridge Natural History, Vol. IV (Crustacea and Arachnida) London 1923 ; E. Simon, "Histoire Naturelle des Araignées," Paris 1892, and P. P. Grassé, "Traité de Zoologie", Tome VI, Paris 1949).

The body of a spider consists of two main parts, the *cephalothorax* (=prosoma) and the *abdomen* (=opisthosoma) joined by a narrow stalk called the *pedicel* (Text-figs. 2 ; 3 ; 7,C.). Both of these regions are without visible external segmentation in all the British species.

The *cephalothorax* is covered above by a hard chitinous shield called the *carapace* and below by a heart-shaped or oval plate, the *sternum*, to the anterior edge of which is attached a sclerite called the *labium* (Text-fig. 3). With few exceptions, there is a deep groove, forming a kind of hinge, between the sternum and the labium. The sternum is usually indented opposite the coxa of each leg (Text-fig. 3) and the limbs are attached between the edges of the carapace and the sternum. The cephalothorax is regarded as consisting of the *head* (sometimes called the "cephalic region" or the "caput") which bears the eyes, and the *thoracic region* ; these two regions are, in many cases, separated by a more or less distinct groove, the *cephalic groove*. In the centre of the thoracic region may often be found a narrow dark median indentation, called the *fovea*, from which there radiate, as a rule, a number of paired striae or furrows indicating the attachment of the muscles inside the carapace wall. The *facies* is a term applied to the view obtained of the carapace when it is looked at from in front of the spider (Text-

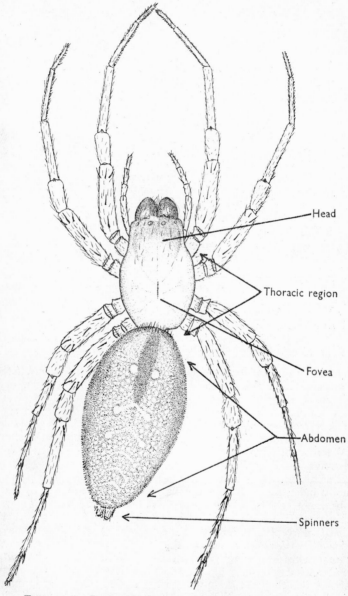

Head

Thoracic region

Fovea

Abdomen

Spinners

TEXT-FIG. 2.—Parts of the body of a spider (*Clubiona*) from above.

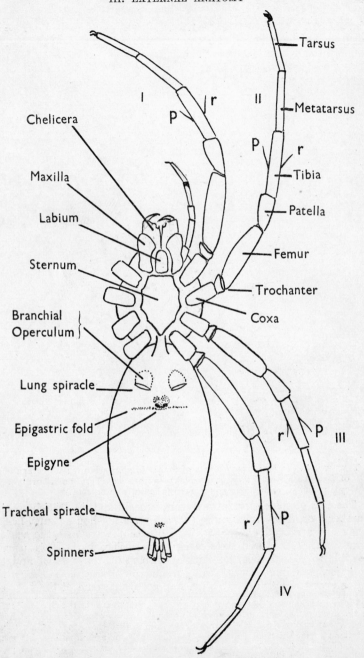

TEXT-FIG. 3.—Diagram of the ventral side of the body of a spider, showing the different parts. (*p*=prolateral, *r*=retrolateral spines).

fig. 5,A.). The *facies* is occupied partly by the eyes and partly by the
clypeus, which is the region between the anterior eyes and the anterior
edge of the carapace (where the cheliceræ are inserted).*

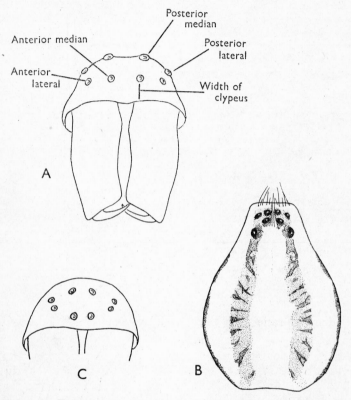

Text-fig. 4.—Various arrangements of eyes : A, nomenclature ; B, carapace
  of *Zora;* both rows of eyes recurved (as seen from above). C, anterior row of
  eyes recurved, posterior row procurved (as seen from in front.)

The eyes of spiders are always simple ocelli and, in British species,
number 6 or, more usually, 8. (*Diblemma*, a hot-house genus, has 2.)
They are arranged on the head in different ways and the various
arrangements are used extensively in classification. It is usually
possible to regard them as being in two rows, the *anterior* and the
posterior, the inner two eyes of each row being the *medians*, the
outer eyes the *laterals*. It often happens that some of the eyes are

---

* It should be noted that, in descriptions, the term " *width* of the clypeus " refers
to the distance between the eyes and the anterior margin of the carapace. Thus if
the clypeus be described as " narrow," this means that the eyes are close to the
anterior margin, but it does *not* mean that the head is narrow from one side to the
other (Text-fig. 4, A). New recruits to the ranks of araneologists should guard
themselves against this error.

raised upon tubercles (Text-figs. 87, A ; 89, A), as in some of the
THOMISIDAE. In most cases each row of eyes is not straight but is
curved in one direction or another. In specifying the curvature of the
eyes it will be assumed that they are viewed from vertically above,
unless a statement is made to the contrary. In Text-fig. 4, B, each row
of eyes is *recurved*, the posterior row strongly. In Text-fig. 4, C the
anterior row, as seen from in front, is *recurved*, while the posterior row
is *procurved*. (It should be noted that the two descriptions could well
be contradictory, in the sense that the apparent curvature could be
altered by a change of view-point.) Two types of eyes have been
recognised, according to where the nerve-fibres join the visual cells,
the anterior medians being different from the others in eight-eyed
spiders. Some authors speak of "diurnal" and "nocturnal" eyes,
the latter showing a pearly lustre by reflected light. To refer to eyes
as nocturnal or diurnal, according to whether they possess this white
appearance or not, is misleading (Comstock, J. H., " The Spider Book,"
New York, 1940, p. 161 and J. Millot in P. P. Grassé " Traité de
Zoologie " Tome VI, Paris (1949) pp. 596 and 627) and we shall refer
to the eyes, where necessary, as having a pearly lustre or not. If both
types of eyes are present they may be referred to collectively as
heterogeneous and, if they all *appear* alike, as *homogeneous*.

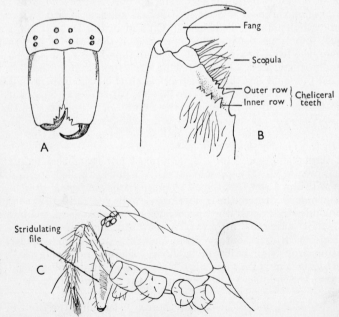

TEXT-FIG. 5.—A, facies and cheliceræ of *Araneus;* B, apical portion of a
    chelicera (seen from behind) ; C, cephalothorax with cheliceræ (*Linyphiidæ*),
    showing stridulating file.

C

The abdomen, as viewed from above, varies very much in appearance and in many species bears a characteristic colour or pattern. There is very frequently a longitudinal lanceolate stripe situated in the fore half, which is followed by a series of light or dark chevrons ($\wedge$). In some species the abdomen bears a wide marking, somewhat like a leaf, called by some writers the *folium* (Text-fig. 85). There will also be seen sometimes on the dorsal side a series of depressed spots of varying size, indicating the points of attachment of muscles to the body wall. The *spinners* (which extrude the spider's silk and which will be referred to again) may or may not be visible from above. They are attached to the posterior end, and on the dorsal side of them is the *anus,* which may be associated with a small tubercle called the *anal tubercle* (Text-fig. 15, C.). On the ventral side of the abdomen will be found the entrances to the respiratory organs. In the fore part lie a pair of plates, often light coloured, called the *branchial opercula* (Text-fig. 3) and at the posterior margin of each of these is a slit-like opening called the *lung-spiracle,* leading to the " lung books " (for the structure of these reference must be made to the standard works on the internal anatomy). *Atypus* is exceptional among the British species in possessing two pairs of lung spiracles (Text-fig. 18, C.). The *tracheal spiracle,* leading to tracheæ, is usually situated immediately in front of the spinners and is often very hard to see. The species *Anyphaena accentuata* (Walck.) is exceptional in that its tracheal spiracle is situated a long way from the spinners (Text-fig. 83, C.) and in the DYSDERIDÆ there are four, sometimes conspicuous, spiracles on the anterior part of the abdomen, the front pair mark entrances to lung books, the second pair are tracheal spiracles (Text-fig. 41, A.). Immediately behind the branchial opercula lies the *epigastric fold,* within which in the mature spider is the genital opening (Text-fig. 3). In the great majority of mature female spiders there is in the middle of this fold a chitinous plate or process, the *epigyne,* covering the genital opening. This process is very variable in form and structure and is of the utmost value in the identification of female spiders.

The term " epigyne " (or " epigynum ") has been used in slightly different ways. In the present work it will be applied to, and the figures will illustrate, the *general appearance of the female genital area from the outside,* when the spider is viewed ventrally (Text-fig. 3). As it includes frequently the appearance of certain pigmented internal organs, the " epigyne " may vary somewhat depending on the degree of transparency of the outer chitinous shield. In the male spider, the genital opening is generally invisible and there is no " epigyne."

The appendages (Text-fig. 3). There are six pairs of appendages (excluding the spinners) : the *chelicerœ,* the *pedipalpi* (which will be referred to as the *palps*) and *four pairs of legs.* The *chelicerœ* are attached to the front of the cephalothorax just behind the front of the carapace. They may project forwards (e.g. in *Segestria* (Text-fig. 39)), when they are largely visible from above, or they may be placed vertically (Text-fig. 5, A.). In the sub-order MYGALOMORPHÆ (of which *Atypus affinis* is the only British representative) the chelicerae move up and down in a plane parallel to the major axis of the body (Text-fig. 8, A.). In the sub-order ARANEOMORPHÆ, which includes all the other British species, they move in and out sideways, as it might be a pair of pincers. The chelicerae consist of two segments, the basal, called the *paturon* and an apical one called the *fang* (=the " unguis " (Text-fig. 5, A, B.)). The fang is articulated in a small membranous cavity to the basal segment and folds on to the inner side of the latter along a groove, whose edges are frequently provided with rows of teeth, the *cheliceral teeth*, often useful characters in identification. We shall refer in descriptions to the outer and inner cheliceral teeth. The *outer* row is anterior, often visible from in front (Text-figs. 5, A ; 14, A.) ; the *inner* row is posterior to these and can be seen when the spider is lying on its back and the chelicerae, if necessary, forced forwards (Text-fig. 5, B.). There is often a scopula of hairs at the apical end of the basal segment, on the outside (Text-fig. 5, B.). The fang is pierced not far from its tip, with a small hole and this is connected to a poison sac lying in the basal segment or partly in the head. At the base of the paturon on the outer side there is to be found in many spiders a smooth area which may be prominent, called the *lateral condyle* (Text-fig. 7, C.). It is not always present and is thus of some use in classification. In many spiders (LINYPHIIDÆ), the outside of the basal segment of the chelicerae may bear a number of horizontal ridges forming the *stridulating file* (Text-fig. 5, C.).

Immediately behind the chelicerae are the *palps* (pedipalps) (Text-figs. 3 ; 6, A.) consisting of six segments : *coxa* (basal), *trochanter* (a narrow ring), *femur, patella, tibia* and *tarsus.* The coxæ are greatly enlarged on their inner sides to form the *maxillæ* (" endites ") (Text-fig. 6, A.) which are used for crushing food. They usually bear a scopula of hairs on their inner margins and sometimes there is a fine ridge of minute teeth (the *serrula*) running along part of their outer edges (Text-fig. 6, A.). There is always a deep stria running across the base of each maxilla from the point of insertion of the trochanter to the inner side. The shape of the maxillæ is often a point of taxonomic importance. The tarsus of the female palp may bear a claw at its extremity. In male spiders the palpal tarsi are greatly modified into secondary sexual organs and contain an apparatus used for taking up sperm (exuded from the genital orifice in the epigastric fold on to a thread or small web) and transferring it to the female. That part of the palpal tarsus, which is hollowed to receive the sexual organs, is called the *cymbium* ; an accessory branch of the cymbium arising from its basal end, and present in many web-spinning spiders, is known as the *paracymbium* (Text-fig. 13, E.). The *alveolus* is the cavity in the cymbium in which the palpal organs lie. These organs are referred to as the *palpal organs*, and when one speaks of the " sexual organs " of a male spider reference is made usually to these. In the mature male spider the palp is the most important character on which final identification is based ; it is figured for each species discussed in this book.

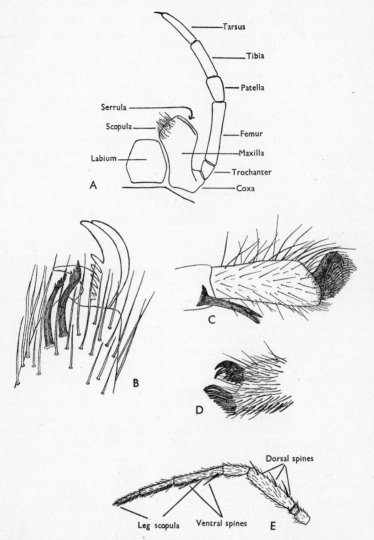

TEXT-FIG. 6.—A, Labium, maxilla and palp of a female spider (from below); B, foot claw of *Araneus;* C, tarsus of *Marpissa*, showing claw tufts; D, do. of *Clubiona;* E, leg, with spines and scopula.

It is extremely variable from species to species and often very complex; a discussion of its structure is beyond the scope of the present book. (Reference may be made to J. H. Comstock's "The Spider Book," 2nd edition New York, 1940, p. 106. If and where special terms are required for descriptive purposes they will be made clear in the appropriate places.)

The tibia of the male palp may be enlarged or modified and may bear one or more projections or *tibial apophyses*. The patella and femur also may be modified, either by carrying apophyses, extra spines or hairs or in their shape.

The legs, eight in number, are arranged in four pairs and are numbered conventionally from the front : I, II, III, and IV (see Text-fig. 3). Each leg has seven segments : *coxa, trochanter, femur, patella, tibia, metatarsus* and *tarsus*. In addition, there is sometimes a small extension of the tarsus, to which the foot claws are attached, called the *onychium* by Simon (="prætarsus") (Text-figs. 33, G. ; 41, E.). In the family PHOLCIDÆ (two species are found in Britain) the tarsus is sub-divided in a curious manner by a number of so-called "false joints" (Text-fig. 12, D.). When referring to a particular segment of the leg one speaks of, say, "metatarsus I," or "femur IV," meaning the metatarsus of the first pair of legs and the femur of the fourth pair respectively. The tarsus of each leg bears normally at least two *foot claws*, or *tarsal claws*, which are frequently toothed (pectinate). In addition there may be a third median claw, smaller than the other two (Text-fig. 10, F, G.). Some spiders, notably among the ARGIOPIDÆ, possess hairs at the end of the tarsus so modified that they have a claw-like structure (Text-fig. 6, B.). Bundles of strong hairs beneath the claws called *claw tufts* (Text-fig. 6, C, D.) are found in other families (*e.g.*, CLUBIONIDÆ and SALTICIDÆ). The ends of these hairs are frequently modified and enable the spider to obtain a grip on a vertical or overhanging surface.

Scopula (meaning literally a little brush) is a word applied to rows or groups of thick-set hairs (frequently blunt hairs) such as are found along the ventral sides of the tarsi, and sometimes the metatarsi and tibiæ of the legs (Text-fig. 6, E.). The *calamistrum* (Text-fig. 8, D.) is a comb-like series of little curved spines set along the upper margins of the metatarsi of the legs IV in the cribellate spiders, so-called because they have an additional spinning organ termed the cribellum (see under *Spinners*). The calamistrum frequently disappears in the male spider as it reaches maturity.

The *spinnerets* or *spinners* (the latter term will be used in the present work) are arranged in three pairs at the posterior end of the abdomen. It is necessary to be clear about their nomenclature in descriptions. In Text-fig. 7, A, the spinners are seen from below (*i.e.*, with the spider lying on its back) ; in Text-fig. 7, B, they are seen from the side. If it be remembered that the spinners are modified abdominal appendages, which must have been placed on the ventral surface of the abdomen (and indeed the spinners are still in this position in primitive foreign spiders such as *Liphistius* and *Myandra*) it will be seen at once why the superior spinners are called *posterior* and the inferior called *anterior*. In the present work we shall speak of *posterior, anterior* and *median* spinners. The latter are always the smallest, are close together and consist of a single segment ; the remaining four are larger and consist of two segments (the posterior spinners of *Atypus* have three segments). Their disposition is variable but usually approaches a square or a trapezium ; in *Hahnia* and *Antistea* the spinners are ranged in a single line (Text-fig. 11, H.). The *fusules* from which the silk is produced are situated on the tips or on the apical segments of the spinners. In some spiders an additional spinning organ is present immediately in front of the anterior spinners. It consists of a sieve-like plate, sometimes divided and is called the *cribellum* (Text-fig. 8, C.). It is associated with the presence of a *calamistrum* on metatarsus IV (see above) and spiders possessing this organ can spin a peculiar type of web in which single threads are surrounded by fine flocculent silk. The presence of the cribellum is of importance in classification and the whole group is

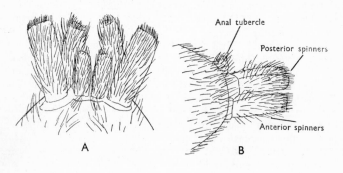

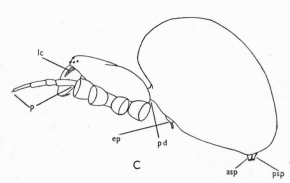

TEXT-FIG. 7.—A, spinners of *Drassodes lapidosus* (below) ; B, do. (side) ; C, body of a spider (*Araneus*). (*lc*=lateral condyle, *p*=palp, *ep*=epigyne, *pd*= pedicel, *asp*=anterior spinners, *psp*=posterior spinners.)

usefully divided into the *cribellate* and *ecribellate* spiders. The cribellum frequently degenerates or disappears in the male spider as the latter reaches maturity, but the wide spacing of the anterior spinners usually indicates clearly the space which it would occupy (see Text-fig. 16, A, B.). The *colulus* is a small tubercle set just in front of the anterior pair of spinners in certain spiders. It has no known function and may represent degenerate spinning organs.

The *hairs*, with which the body and limbs are usually clothed, are various in structure and have been classified in different ways according to their form and supposed functions. They may be more or less erect or lie prone. If coloured they may form patterns or reinforce an existing pattern due to pigmentation of the integument. For purposes of description reference may be made to the following types apart from the usual aculeate hairs of varying fineness.

Squamiform : glistening and scale-like ; *Clavate* : club-shaped, *i.e.*, broader at the apex than at the base (Text-fig. 89, B.) ; *Spatulate* similar to clavate, but flattened ; *Plumose* : having a feathery serrated structure ; *Serrated* : having a saw-like edge (usually applied to larger hairs or bristles, as on the tarsi IV of the THERIDIIDÆ (Text-fig. 13, A.). *Trichobothria* are very fine, often long, erect hairs (sometimes called " acoustic setæ," since they have been supposed to have some auditory functions) set, sometimes singly, sometimes in a series, at various points of the legs (Text-figs. 11, E, F, G ; 14, B.). Each one has its origin in a tiny circle on the surface of the limb. They are of considerable value in identification. The legs and palps frequently bear *spines*, in addition to the normal clothing of hairs. The difference between these spines and the hairs is generally quite distinct, the spines being thicker and longer, but in a few cases the difference is not marked. *Bristles* are intermediate in size between spines and hairs : obviously the term is only useful when all three are clearly differentiated on a particular spider.

Dorsal and *ventral* spines are those situated on the upper and lower sides of a limb respectively when the latter is extended straight out from the point of attachment (Text-fig. 6, E.). Spines attached to the sides of a limb are said to be *prolateral* or *retrolateral* (for the positions see Text-fig. 3).

IV. NOTE ON NOMENCLATURE

The scheme of classification and the nomenclature which we have used in this book follows closely that adopted by W. S. Bristowe (1939). The only major changes introduced are the substitution of the family name GNAPHOSIDÆ for DRASSIDÆ, and the removal of the genus *Nesticus* from the family THERIDIIDÆ to the family NESTICIDÆ. The reasons for the change to GNAPHOSIDÆ are briefly as follows : C. J. Sundevall proposed the name DRASSIDÆ in 1833. Its retention is contrary to Article (4) of the Rules of Nomenclature, if the genus *Drassus* has been correctly abandoned. The case for DRASSODIDÆ, proposed by L. Berland in 1932, does not seem to be so strong as for GNAPHOSIDÆ, proposed by R. I. Pocock in 1898, although B. J. Kaston (1948) oversimplifies the complicated situation by claiming that *Drassus* is a synonym of *Gnaphosa* (see F. O. Pickard-Cambridge, 1901 and 1903). If F. O. Pickard-Cambridge's facts and arguments are sound, the species at present in the genus *Drassodes* should displace those in the genus *Gnaphosa*, a situation which we hope the obscurity of the early literature will make unnecessary. The substitution of GNAPHOSIDÆ for DRASSIDÆ brings us into line with most arachnologists in other countries. As to *Nesticus*, this genus sits uneasily with the THERIDIIDÆ, and we have followed recent authors in assigning it to the separate family NESTICIDÆ.

Certain minor errors in the list of British spiders given by W. S. Bristowe in 1939, have been corrected.

Very recently the International Commission of Zoological Nomenclature has revised its previous ruling and has now decided to admit the specific names proposed by C. Clerck in 1757 for a number of species. We are therefore reintroducing the Clerckian names, excluded from Bristowe's list of 1939. To avoid further confusion in these cases however, we are inserting, after the Clerckian name, that name next in priority, since this alternative has been used by some continental arachnologists (particularly of the German school) for a number of years.

The list of synonyms of British spiders given by Bristowe in the second volume of his " Comity of Spiders " (1941), is almost essential when consulting the literature.

V. KEY TO THE FAMILIES.

Note on the use of the Family and Generic Keys

The experience of many arachnologists has shown that a strictly dichotomous key can be misleading as a guide to the families and genera of this Order, especially for those unfamiliar with the group. It has often appeared that so much attention has been devoted to preserving the strict form of the key that the main object, to provide a guide to enable one to steer one's way amongst groups of unfamiliar animals, has been neglected. Anyone with experience of spiders will rarely use a key to the families ; nevertheless some such guide is essential to begin with, and we believe that the present family key, which does not always follow the strictly dichotomous form, will not at any rate mislead (and this also applies to generic and other keys given in the text). Figures are given of characters included which are not perfectly obvious and it should be mentioned that those selected for inclusion in the keys have been chosen because they are the most easy to see and recognise, rather than for their (necessarily) taxonomic significance. In order that a key of this kind shall not be unduly cumbrous or that characters which are generally helpful shall not be left out on account of a few exceptions, it was considered better to refer to such exceptions at once in the family key, wherever they occur, and this has been done in a series of notes following the key itself. These notes sometimes include additional information on exactly what characters to look for in special cases. It should be emphasised that the key is meant as a guide only, and reference to the illustrations of the species within a family will soon decide whether the diagnosis is correct up to the point reached. The key has been drawn up for use with the British species only and is not intended to apply necessarily to the continental or world fauna.

The British spiders are divided into the following 24 Families :—

    1. ATYPIDÆ (1 species)
    2. ERESIDÆ (1 species)
    3. DICTYNIDÆ (16 species)
    4. ULOBORIDÆ (2 species)
    5. OONOPIDÆ (5 species)
    6. DYSDERIDÆ (6 species)
    7. SCYTODIDÆ (1 species)
    8. PHOLCIDÆ (2 species)
    9. GNAPHOSIDÆ (25 species)
  10. CLUBIONIDÆ (35 species)
  11. ANYPHÆNIDÆ (1 species)
  12. SPARASSIDÆ (1 species)
  13. THOMISIDÆ (37 species)
  14. SALTICIDÆ (32 species)

15. OXYOPIDÆ (1 species)
16. LYCOSIDÆ (37 species)
17. PISAURIDÆ (2 species)
18. AGELENIDÆ (24 species)
19. MIMETIDÆ (3 species)
20. THERIDIIDÆ (46 species)
21. NESTICIDÆ (1 species)
22. TETRAGNATHIDÆ (9 species)
23. ARGIOPIDÆ (38 species)
24. LINYPHIIDÆ (241 species)

Families 1 to 17 are dealt with in Vol. I of this work.

KEY TO THE FAMILIES

1. Cheliceræ very massive, articulated vertically ; the fangs when folded and at rest lie in a plane parallel to the axis of the body (Text-fig. 8, A.). Posterior spinners long, with three segments (Text-fig. 8, B.) (Note (1)) **ATYPIDÆ** p. 46

——Cheliceræ articulated horizontally, projecting downwards, or obliquely forwards, and moving laterally (Text-fig. 5, A.). Spinners never with more than two segments **2**

2. Cribellum present (Text-fig. 8, C.) with a calamistrum on metatarsus IV (Text-fig. 8, D.) (Note (2)) **14**

——Cribellum and calamistrum absent **3**

3. Spiders with two eyes   genus : **Diblemma** (Fam. :
OONOPIDÆ (in part)) p. 79
Spiders with eight eyes **6**
Spiders with six eyes **4**

4. *Spiders with six eyes* (all readily seen in a small group). Carapace unusually high behind (Text-fig. 9, A.). Legs slender. Labium fused to sternum (Text-fig. 46, A.). The single species, *Scytodes thoracica* has the appearance shown in Text-fig. 45 . . . . . **SCYTODIDÆ** p. 89

——Carapace of normal height behind (v. however *Oonops*, Text-fig. 33, F.). Legs relatively shorter and always more robust. Labium hinged to sternum **5**

5. Eyes as in Text-fig. 40, A, B, C. Maxillæ straight, not markedly inclined inwards (Text-fig. 40, D, E, F.) Female palpal tarsus with a claw. No distinct onychium on leg tarsi (except on IV in *Harpactea*). Length of adults : 6·5 to ca. 19 mm. . . **DYSDERIDÆ** p. 81

——Eyes as in Text-fig. 33, A, B, C. Maxillæ inclined definitely inwards (Text-fig. 34). Female palpal tarsus without a claw. Foot claws on a distinct onychium (Text-

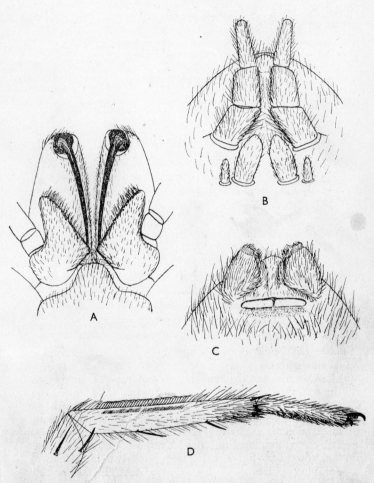

TEXT-FIG. 8.—*Atypus affinis:* A, cheliceræ and fangs; B, spinners. *Ciniflo similis:* C, spinners, with cribellum (below); D, metatarsus and tarsus IV, showing calamistrum.

fig. 33, G.). Small spiders, length of adults : up to about
3 mm. .... **OONOPIDÆ** (excluding genus *Diblemma*) p. **73.**

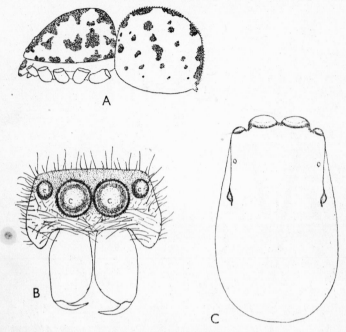

TEXT-FIG. 9.—A, *Scytodes thoracica:* body from side. B, *Marpissa* (SALTICIDÆ:)
carapace and eyes (from in front) ; C, do. (above).

6. *Spiders with eight eyes* (but possessing no cribellum nor
   calamistrum).

   (*a*) Carapace square-fronted ; eyes very unequal in size, in
   three rows—1st row : four large eyes on the front of the
   carapace directed forwards (Text-fig. 9, B.) the medians
   much larger than the laterals.   2nd row : two small
   inconspicuous eyes situated behind the anterior laterals.
   3rd row : two medium sized eyes behind those in the
   2nd row (Text-fig. 9, C.).   Legs with two tarsal claws.
   Jumping spiders .   .   .   .   .   .   **SALTICIDÆ** p. 206

   (*b*) Eyes in three rows, unequal in size (Text-fig. 10, A,
   B, C, D.).   Apical edges of trochanters all deeply
   notched below (Text-fig. 10, E.) (NOTE (3)).   Legs with
   three tarsal claws (Text-fig. 10, F, G.).

   (i) Second row of eyes not much shorter than the third
   row (Text-fig. 10, A, B.).   The distance between the
   posterior eyes not double the distance of each from the
   corresponding eye in the 2nd row.   The larger, paired,
   foot claws with few teeth (Text-fig. 10, F.).   Abdomen

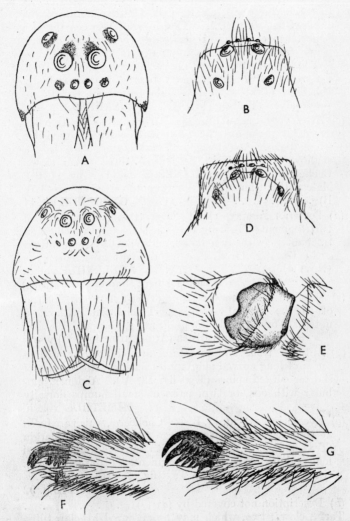

TEXT-FIG. 10.—LYCOSIDÆ: A, eyes (from in front); B, eyes (above); E, notched trochanter; F, foot claws.
PISAURIDÆ: C, eyes (from in front); D, eyes (above); G, foot claws.

rather obtuse behind (Text-fig. 121). Male palpal
tibia with no apophysis . . . **LYCOSIDÆ** p. 247

(ii) Second row of eyes much shorter than the third row
(Text-fig. 10, C, D.). The distance between the two
posterior eyes more than double the distance of each
eye from the corresponding eye in the second row.
The larger, paired, foot claws with many teeth (Text-
fig. 10, G.). Abdomen tapering more gradually
behind (Text-fig. 141). Male palpal tibia with an
apophysis (Text-fig. 142, A) . . **PISAURIDÆ** p. 292

(c) Eyes very unequal in size, arranged as in Text-fig.
11, A, B. ; the anterior medians frequently not visible
from above. Apical edges of trochanters with only a
shallow notch below. Legs with three tarsal claws.
Cheliceræ appearing weak and tapering (Text-fig. 11, B.).
Male palpal tibia with a large apophysis (Text-fig. 120,
B) . . . . **OXYOPIDÆ** p. 244

(d) Posterior spinners clearly larger than anterior and of
two segments (Text-fig. 11, C, D.). Apical edges of
trochanters without a notch. Tarsi with trichobothria
as in Text-fig. 11, E, F, G, and with three foot claws
(NOTE 4) . . . . **AGELENIDÆ** vol. ii.
(excluding genera *Hahnia* and *Antistea*)

(e) Spinners in a transverse row (Text-fig. 11, H.) instead
of in the normal grouping. Trochanters without a
notch. Three tarsal claws. Small spiders
Hahnia and **Antistea** (AGELENIDÆ in part) vol. ii

(f) Anterior tibiæ and metatarsi armed dorsally with a
series of long curved spines, alternating with a series of
shorter curved spines (Text-fig. 12, A.). Abdomen globular with one, or two, pairs of small humps dorsally
MIMETIDÆ vol. ii.

(g) Eyes as in Text-fig. 12, B, C. Cheliceræ, which are fused
at the base, each with a large tooth on inner margin
(Text-fig. 48, B.). Spiders with long thin legs ; tarsi
long and flexible with " false segments " (Text-fig. 12, D.).
General appearance as in Text-fig. 47. (NOTE (5))
PHOLCIDÆ p. 92

(h) Description not covered by (a)–(g) 7

7. Tarsal claws: two, which may be obscured by claw tufts,
scopulæ, etc. (If three claws are not fairly readily
visible, then it may be decided safely that only two are
present) 8

——Tarsal claws : three, not hidden by scopulæ, claw tufts, etc. 11

8. (i) Legs laterigrade, with second pair the longest usually.
Typical members crab-like (Text-figs. 85, 86). Inner

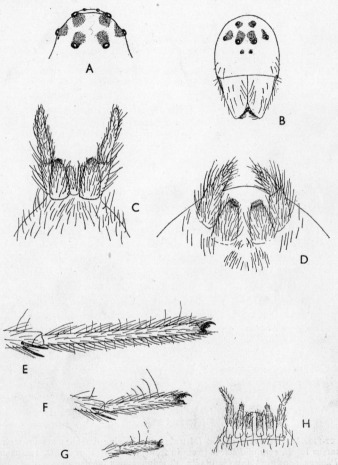

TEXT-FIG. 11.—A, B, Eyes of *Oxyopes*.
Spinners: C, *Agelena*; D, *Tegenaria*; H, *Hahnia*.
Tarsi, showing trichobothria: E, *Tegenaria*; F, *Cicurina*; G, *Cryphoeca*.

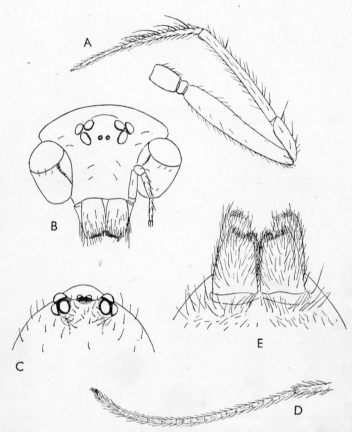

TEXT-FIG. 12.—A, leg I of *Ero* (MIMETIDÆ), showing dorsal spines on metatarsus I.   B, eyes of *Pholcus* (from in front); C, do. (above); D, tarsus of
Pholcus, showing "false joints"; E, spinners of *Clubiona*.

margin of the cheliceræ without teeth. Both rows of
eyes recurved. The posterior eyes, especially, dark and
ringed with black, small and widely separated (Text-fig.
89) (particularly in *Thanatus* and *Tibellus* (Text-fig. 101,
C.), in which the second pair of legs is exceptional, and
not the longest). (NOTE (6)) . .**THOMISIDÆ** p. 168

(ii) Legs normal (Text-figs. 2, 49, 82).   Inner margin of the
cheliceræ with a tooth or teeth **9**

9. Anterior spinners cylindrical and distinctly separated,
slightly longer than the posteriors (Text-fig. 7, A.)
(NOTE (7)). Eyes heterogeneous, only the anterior
medians dark. (In some species the posterior medians
oval or of other shapes, not circular) **GNAPHOSIDÆ** p. 95

——Anterior spinners conical, shorter generally, close together
(Text-fig. 12, E.). Eyes generally homogeneous (NOTE
(8)) the posterior medians regular **10**

10. Tracheal spiracle far removed from the spinners and easily
seen (Text-fig. 83, C.). Abdomen with a distinctive
mark (Text-fig. 82) peculiar to the only British species
ANYPHÆNIDÆ p. 163

——Tracheal spiracle close to the spinners and difficult to see.
Abdominal markings, when present, never in the form of
species of the last family . . . **CLUBIONIDÆ** p. 124
and **SPARASSIDÆ** p. 166
(This single species of the latter family (*Micrommata
virescens* Cl.) is very striking, the female being bright
green all over ; the abdomen of the male has a yellow
and roseate marking dorsally). (NOTE (9)).

11. Tarsi IV, with a series of ventral bristles, serrated along
their dorsal edges (Text-fig. 13, A.) (NOTE (10)). Labium
flat, not rebordered (Text-fig. 13, B.) (NOTE (11)).
Inner margin of the cheliceræ without teeth. ♂ palp
without a paracymbium (Text-fig. 13, D.). Builders of
webs with an irregular criss-cross structure with no
clearly developed sheet (NOTE (12)) **THERIDIIDÆ** vol. ii.

——The same, but with labium rebordered and ♂ palp bearing
a paracymbium (Text-fig. 13, E.) **NESTICIDÆ** vol. ii.

——Tarsi IV, without the characteristic series of serrated
bristles. Labium rebordered (Text-fig. 13, C.)
(NOTE (11)). The inner margin of the cheliceræ with a
tooth or teeth. Builders of sheet webs or orb webs.
(NOTE (13)) **12**

12. Spiders having long cheliceræ of the type shown in Text-
fig. 14, A. With no lateral condyle. The femora with
a series of trichobothria near the base (Text-fig 14, B)
(NOTE (14)) Females with no epigyne ; male palpal

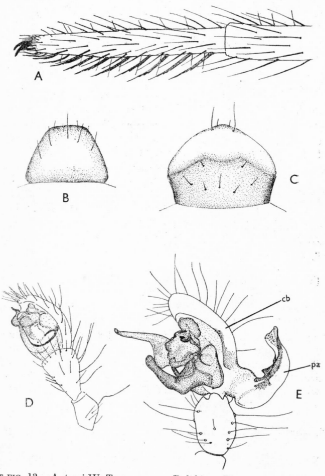

TEXT-FIG. 13.—A, tarsi IV, THERIDIIDÆ; B, labium, THERIDIIDÆ; C, labium of *Araneus* (ARGIOPIDÆ); D, male palp of *Theridion lineatum* (THERIDIIDÆ); E, do. *Nesticus cellulanus* (NESTICIDÆ). (*cb*=cymbium, *pa*=paracymbium.)

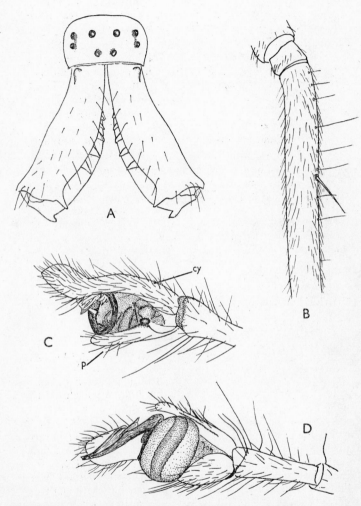

TEXT-FIG. 14.—*Tetragnatha montana* (♀) (TETRAGNATHIDÆ): A, head
and cheliceræ; B, trichobothria on femora; C, D, male palpal organs.
(*cb*=cymbium *p*=paracymbium.)

organs simple, of the type shown in Text-fig. 14, C, D. Some species build orb webs **TETRAGNATHIDÆ** vol. ii.

——Spiders without a regular series of trichobothria at the base of the femora, the females having epigynes and the male palpal organs other than in the last family **13**

13. Chelicerae with stridulating ridges (Text-fig. 5, C.) (less developed in some males) and without a lateral condyle. Clypeus wider than the diameter of the anterior median eyes (except in *Tapinopa longidens*), builders of sheet webs . . . . **LINYPHIIDÆ** vol. ii.

——Chelicerae without stridulating ridges, usually with a lateral condyle (Text-fig. 7, C.). Clypeus rarely much wider than the diameter of the anterior median eyes. Builders of orb webs . . . . . . **ARGIOPIDÆ** vol. ii.

14. *Spiders possessing a cribellum and calamistrum*—
Eyes dark, arranged as shown in Text-fig. 15, A. Cribellum divided (Text-fig. 19, C.) Anal tubercle short
ERESIDÆ p. 49

Eyes dark, arranged as in Text-fig. 15, B. Cribellum not divided (Text-fig. 15, D.). Tarsi IV very short. Anal tubercle long (Text-fig. 15, C.) (NOTE (15))
ULOBORIDÆ p. 70

Eyes not as above ; usually all pearly white ; grouped more closely in two rows (Text-fig. 21). Cribellum divided or entire . . . . . . **DICTYNIDÆ** p. 51

Notes on the Family Key

NOTE (1). The appearance of the single species, *Atypus affinis*, is so striking (Text-fig. 17) that no confusion could possibly exist. The chelicerae of some species of the SALTICIDÆ (e.g. *Myrmarachne formicaria* and *Salticus*) are enlarged, and the fang, when closed up, may appear to be parallel to the axis of the body.

NOTE (2). The calamistrum and cribellum are reduced and may be absent in some mature males. The anterior spinners, widely separated, still present however a characteristic appearance. Text-fig. 16, A represents those of *Ciniflo similis* ♂ ; clear traces of the cribellum remain. Text-fig. 16, B shows those of *Dictyna puella* ♂ where the cribellum is represented by a barely perceptible chitinous ridge. In both cases the area of short hairs just anterior to the cribellum remains.

NOTE (3). The eye arrangement in the genus *Zora* (CLUBIONIDÆ) is the same, but these spiders have only two foot claws (with a well developed claw tuft) (Text-fig. 16, D). A very similar eye arrangement is found too in *Textrix* (AGELENIDÆ), which however is at once distinguished by the spinners peculiar to that family (see Text-fig. 11, C). Other spiders (e.g. CLUBIONIDÆ, SPARASSIDÆ and two species of the GNAPHOSIDÆ, *Drassodes lapidosus* and *D. pubescens*) also possess

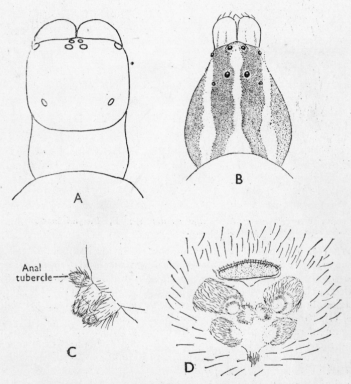

Anal
tubercle

TEXT-FIG. 15.—Carapace and eyes : A, *Eresus;* B, *Uloborus.*
    C, D, Spinners of *Uloborus.*

deeply notched trochanters, but the eye arrangement in these families is so different (two rows of eyes of much more uniform size) that confusion is impossible.

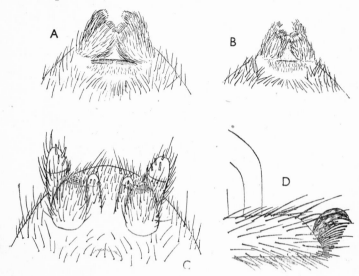

TEXT-FIG. 16.—Spinners: A, *Ciniflo similis* ♂; B, *Dictyna puella* ♂; C, *Cicurina cinerea;* D, foot of *Zora.*

NOTE (4). The apical segment of the posterior spinners is not so characteristic in the genera *Cicurina, Argyroneta* and *Cryphoeca,* and might escape recognition. In the first two genera especially it is rounded at the apex and not characteristically elongated (Text-fig. 16, C) The trichobothria on the tarsi are however quite typical (Text-fig. 11, F, G), though small in *Argyroneta,* and (bearing in mind the eye arrangement and the presence of three foot claws) they should provide for the recognition of these genera, which contain one British species each. *Cicurina cinerea* has the abdomen a uniform light grey colour and is about 6 mm. long. *Argyroneta aquatica* (Clk.) is the water spider, measuring about 10–12 mm. It is not a very typical Agelenid and has sometimes been placed in a separate family. *Cryphoeca silvicola* is about 2½ mm. long, has annulated legs and a clear abdominal pattern. In *Textrix* the eye arrangement is similar to that in the LYCOSIDÆ, but as the posterior spinners are very long and the trochanters have no notches, confusion cannot arise.

NOTE (5). The eyes of *Pholcomma gibbum* are similarly arranged; but this is a very small, short legged species belonging to the family THERIDIIDÆ and confusion with any of the PHOLCIDÆ is not possible.

NOTE (6). *Thanatus, Tibellus* and, to a lesser extent *Philodromus,* are not altogether typical in the arrangement of the legs, which are not markedly laterigrade. (These genera should be looked up before proceeding). Their eyes however, particularly the second row, are strongly recurved and confusion could not well arise with any of the GNAPHOSIDÆ, CLUBIONIDÆ, SPARASSIDÆ or ANYPHÆNIDÆ. (The posterior row of eyes is recurved in *Gnaphosa*, *Liocranum* and especially in *Zora*, but these all possess cheliceral teeth). On the other hand the legs of *Micrommata* (SPARASSIDÆ) may appear laterigrade in some positions (see NOTE 9).

NOTE (7). The anterior spinners of *Micaria* are not separated very distinctly. Reference should be made to this genus ; they are small spiders resembling at first sight *Phrurolithus* (CLUBIONIDÆ).

NOTE (8). In some species, particularly of *Clubiona*, the anterior medians appear slightly darker than the others ; the effect is one of degree, but is almost always more marked in the GNAPHOSIDÆ than in the CLUBIONIDÆ.

NOTE (9). This family is related closely to the CLUBIONIDÆ, in which it has been included by some authors (e.g. E. Simon in his " Histoire Naturelle des Araignées " 1892). But the single species is so striking that confusion could never arise with a fresh specimen, although the colour fades on preservation. The female is 9–11 mm. long, has very dense thick tarsal scopulæ and a peculiar scopula on the maxilla (Text-fig. 84, A). Palps and epigyne (Text-fig. 84, B, C).

NOTE (10). The serrations are obvious enough on these bristles in the larger species, but are very often hard to see on the small ones, when a high magnification reveals them as reduced to little more than irregularities along the surface.

NOTE (11). The term " rebordered " is borrowed from E. Simon (" Les Arachnides de France " Tome VI. p. 118). The labium of a spider of the families LINYPHIIDÆ, ARGIOPIDÆ, TETRAGNATHIDÆ appears almost to consist of two parts, the basal, hinged to the sternum and often darker, and an apical, usually lighter, almost sausage-shaped part, frequently bearing a few hairs (Text-fig. 13, C). This is absent in the THERIDIIDÆ in which the labium is flat and uniform (Text-fig. 13, B).

NOTE (12). The web of *Stearodea bipunctata* in course of time develops a rather indefinite sheet, but this spider is easily seen to be of the THERIDIIDÆ by its structural characters.

NOTE (13). *Pachygnatha* (TETRAGNATHIDÆ) lives at ground level and these species appear to spin no web.

NOTE (14). The legs of *Tetragnatha*, especially, are furnished liberally with these trichobothria. Those mentioned here form a regular series on the dorsal side of the base of the segment. They may run further, particularly on the legs IV., and their number is variable, apparently even for the same species. *Pachygnatha* has but a few, sometimes one or two, but they can always be made out without difficulty.

NOTE (15). The anal tubercle is reduced in the mature male of *Uloborus*, but the distinction from *Eresus* and the DICTYNIDÆ is very clear in any case.

VI. DESCRIPTION OF THE SPECIES

Class ARACHNIDA
Order ARANEÆ (ARANEIDA)
Sub-Order MYGALOMORPHÆ

1. Family ATYPIDÆ.

Atypus affinis Eich. is the only British representative of this family and of the Sub-order MYGALOMORPHÆ. Thus it differs from the rest of the British spider fauna in the characters which distinguish the MYGALOMORPHÆ from the Sub-order ARANEOMORPHÆ. The two conspicuous differences between these two Sub-orders are in the chelicerae and the respiratory organs. The former have an upward and downward instead of an inward and outward movement. The latter comprise two pairs of lung-books but no tracheae. These characters, together with the long three-segmented posterior spinners, and the general appearance, make confusion with any other species impossible (Text-figs. 8, A, B, and 18, A, B, C.).

Genus **ATYPUS** Eichwald 1830.

CHARACTERS OF GENUS. CARAPACE and EYES: Text-fig. 17, A. ABDOMEN: Text-figs. 17, and 18, C. Two pairs of lung spiracles conspicuous on ventral surface. Anal tubercle well removed from spinners. Posterior spinners 3–4 segmented, curling upwards close to abdomen (Text-fig. 8, B. p. 33). CHELICERÆ: Text-fig. 8, A p. 33). LABIUM: fused (not hinged) to sternum. LEGS: Short and stout (Text-fig. 17).

Atypus affinis Eichwald.
(Text-figs. 8, A, B., 17, 18.)

Atypus affinis E. Eichwald, 1830, p. 73. *A. sulzeri* J. Blackwall, 1861–4, p. 14. *A. blackwalli* E. Simon, 1873, p. 110. *A piceus* O. P.-Cambridge, 1879–81, p. 2 (and other British authors). *A. affinis* C. Chyzer and L. Kulczynski, 1891–7, II, p. 280 ; E. Simon, 1914, p. 23 ; W. S. Bristowe, 1933 (1), p. 289.

DESCRIPTION. LENGTH : ♀: c. 12 mm. ♂ : c. 8–9 mm. CARAPACE : Pale greenish brown in living specimens, becoming yellow on preservation. ABDOMEN : Brown, clothed with short hairs. Posterior spinners with three segments (Text-fig. 8, B). CHELICERÆ : Those of adults with 10–13 teeth (usually 11) on inner and one minute tooth on outer margin (opposite tip of folded fang). LEGS : Coloured as carapace. EPIGYNE : None. MALE PALP : Text-fig. 18, D.

OCCURRENCE : Only in the more southern counties. The spider makes a burrow, eight inches or more in depth, which it lines with a

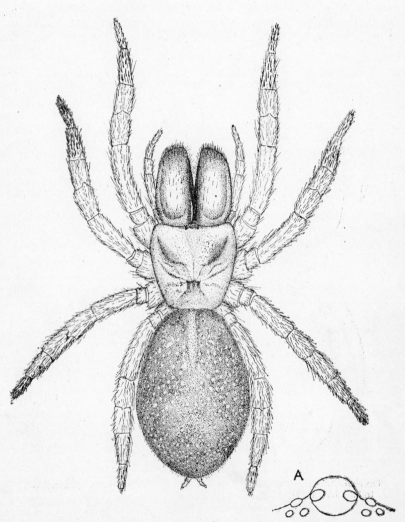

Text-fig. 17.—*Atypus affinis* ♀ (Atypidæ) : A, arrangement of eyes.

silken tube. The closed end of this tube extends some one to two inches from the entrance of the burrow, but is usually hanging or amongst grass stems, and not sticking out straight. By searching for this extension, which is usually covered with adherent particles of earth, the burrow may be found, usually under herbage, especially heather on banks in sandy places. The male is much less common than the

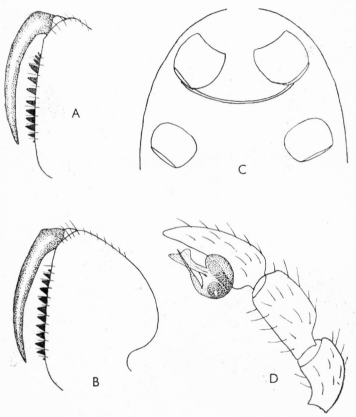

Text-fig. 18.—*Atypus affinis:* A, chelicera of ♂; B, do. of ♀; C, entrances to lung books; D, male palp.

female and has a very short season ; it is usually found in the female's burrow, or in the vicinity, in autumn or in spring. (Note : *Atypus piceus* Sulz. has been recorded for Britain, but almost certainly in error (Bristowe, W. S. 1933 (1), p. 289).

Sub-Order ARANEOMORPHÆ (Arachnomorphæ).

2. Family ERESIDÆ.

Genus **ERESUS** C. A. Walckenaer 1805.

CHARACTERS OF FAMILY AND OF GENUS. CARAPACE : Very wide in front (resembling at first sight that of SALTICIDÆ). Head very convex, descending steeply behind to thoracic region, which has no fovea. EYES : Disposed as in Text-fig. 15, A ; all dark. CLYPEUS : Very narrow, bearing a small projection between bases of cheliceræ. CHELI-CERÆ : Robust : inner margin without teeth or ridge ; outer margin sharply angular at apical end, where it bears a tooth and also a thick scopula. STERNUM : Long and narrow. LABIUM : Much longer than wide. LEGS : Short, rather thick ; tarsi with three claws. Metatarsus

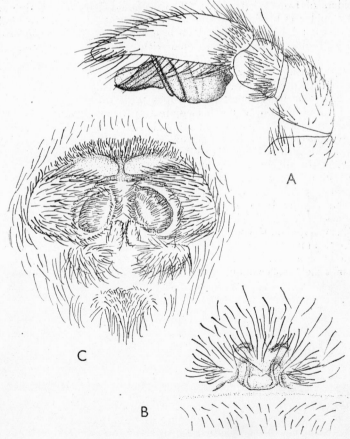

TEXT-FIG. 19.—*Eresus niger:* A, male palp ; B, epigyne ; C, spinners.

IV with a calamistrum which is poorly developed in the male. Female PALPAL TARSUS with a claw. CRIBELLUM : Divided by a thin ridge (Text-fig. 19, C) ; degenerate in the male. ANAL TUBERCLE: Short but well developed.

Eresus niger (Petagna).

(Text-figs. 15, A; 19)

Aranea nigra V. Petagna, 1787, p. 34. *A. cinnabarinus*, G. A. Olivier, 1789, p. 221. *Eresus cinnabarinus* J. Blackwall, 1861–4, p. 46 ; O. P.-Cambridge, 1879–81, p. 45 and 1893, p. 147 ; C. Chyzer and L. Kulczynski, 1891–7, I, p. 152. *E. niger* E. Simon, 1914, p. 69 ; W. S. Bristowe, 1939, p. 11.

DESCRIPTION. LENGTH : c. 8 mm. This spider could not well be mistaken for any other British species. Fresh specimens from this country are not available (none having been taken since 1906) and the following description of the male is quoted from O. Pickard-Cambridge's " Spiders of Dorset " (p. 46). " The cephalo-thorax of this fine and showy spider is black with a short red tapering band on the hinder part of each lateral margin. The legs are short, strong and black, annulated with white, and furnished with red hairs on the femora of the second, third and fourth pairs. The palpi are also black with white annuli, and the abdomen, which (as well as the rest of the spider) is thickly clothed with short hairs, has the upper side of a bright scarlet red, with four large black spots, edged with white hairs, forming a square ; and often between this square and the spinners are two other similar, but smaller, spots in a transverse line ; the underside is black with a white spot near its hinder extremity, and the spiracular plates are clothed with red hairs ". (The red colour fades in spirit). The female is almost completely black and the abdomen is covered with black silky pubescence. EPIGYNE : Text-fig. 19, B. MALE PALP : Text-fig. 19, A.

OCCURRENCE : It has been taken at Parley Heath (Dorset), Bournemouth and Poole. The latter localities at least are now built over. Heathery slopes on the south coast are the most likely habitat in which the species might be rediscovered. The female makes a burrow in the ground with a blackish matted web above the surface ; this is in the form of a sheet with a tubular retreat leading away from the under side.

3. Family DICTYNIDÆ.

This family contains most of the British cribellate species.

CHARACTERS OF FAMILY. CARAPACE : Head wide in front and more or less elevated (notably in *Dictyna*). The thoracic region has a fovea. EYES : In two nearly parallel rows, with no very marked curvature ; they are all pearly white, except for the anterior medians which are usually darker. CHELICERÆ : Strong and often rounded, sometimes modified in shape in the male (Text-fig. 23, A), bearing a lateral condyle ;

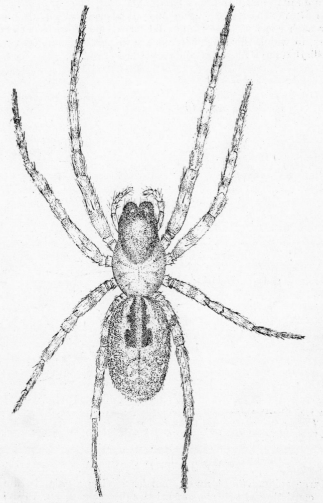

TEXT-FIG. 20.—*Ciniflo similis* ♀ (DICTYNIDÆ).

the inner and outer margins of the basal segment bear one or more teeth.
LEGS : Robust, of roughly equal length, without a regular scopula
(although hairs may be more numerous on the tarsi) ; three foot
claws, the paired claws always, the median generally, toothed ; no
claw tufts. CALAMISTRUM, on metatarsi IV, straight, consisting of one
or, in *Ciniflo,* two rows of bristles. The female PALPAL TARSUS bears a
pectinate claw. The anterior SPINNERS are set well apart ; the
CRIBELLUM is nearly parallel sided, sometimes divided into two areas
by a little chitinous ridge. In mature males the cribellum and calamistrum are reduced and may be absent. (see *Note* (2) p. 42).

The DICTYNIDAE live in varying situations, which are indicated
under each species. They all build webs characteristic of cribellate
spiders, in which the main threads are in part surrounded by flocculent silk, having a bluish appearance when fresh.

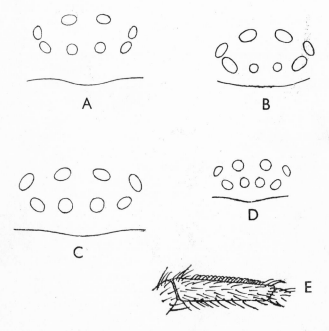

TEXT-FIG. 21.—Arrangements of eyes (seen from in front) : A, *Dictyna;*
B, *Lathys;* C, *Protadia;* D, *Argenna.*
E, Calamistrum of *Dictyna.*

KEY TO THE GENERA

1. Large spiders (5–14 mm.), females having a calamistrum
   consisting of two rows of bristles (Text-fig. 8, D). Tarsi
   with a row of trichobothria . . . . . . (1) **Ciniflo**

——Small spiders (less than 4 mm.), females having a calamistrum consisting of a single row of bristles (Text-fig. 21, E). Tarsi with a single trichobothrium, or none 2

2. ♀: tibiæ I, II and III with spines. ♂: tibia III with a single stout curved spine (Text-fig. 30, B) ; metatarsus I with two single short ventral spines. Labium drawn to a point . . . . (6) **Altella**

——Legs without spines (except those on the patellæ and bases of the tibiæ in *Lathys*). Labium blunt or rounded at the tip 3

3. Clypeus wider than twice the diameter of the anterior median eyes (Text-fig. 21, A). No trichobothria on the tarsi or metatarsi . . . . (2) **Dictyna**

——Clypeus narrow (Text-fig. 21, B, C, D). A trichobothrium present on the tarsus and apical end of the metatarsus of the IVth legs at least. 4

4. Anterior median eyes much smaller than anterior laterals (Text-fig. 21, B) . . . . (3) **Lathys**

——Anterior median eyes, if the smallest, not much smaller than anterior laterals (Text-fig. 21, C, D) 5

5. The trapezium formed by the median eyes noticeably wider at the back than in front. The eyes grouped closely . . . . (4) **Argenna**

——The trapezium formed by the median eyes almost the same width behind as in front. The eyes more widely spaced (Text-fig. 21, C). Slightly larger spider (see description) . . . . (5) **Protadia**

1. Genus **CINIFLO** J. Blackwall 1841.

CHARACTERS OF GENUS. ABDOMEN : Bears a characteristic pattern (Text-fig. 20) (not well defined in *C. ferox*). CRIBELLUM : Divided distinctly into two areas (Text-fig. 8, C) (also found in a few species of *Dictyna*). CHELICERÆ : Gibbous, rounded in front and dark in colour. LEGS : In their normal positions, coxæ IV are nearly touching. CALAMISTRUM : consists of two rows of bristles (Text-fig 8, D). Tarsi have a row of trichobothria dorsally.

The three British species, *Ciniflo fenestralis* (Stroem), *C. similis* Bl. and *C. ferox* (Walck.) are alike in general appearance, especially the first two. The males are easily distinguished by the forms of the palpal tibiæ, which are best viewed from above (Text-fig. 22). The epigynes of the first two species are somewhat variable and are occasionally rather alike, but there is usually not much difficulty in separating them.

Ciniflo fenestralis (Stroem).
(Text-fig. 22, C, F)

Aranea fenestralis H. Stroem, 1768, p. 362.   *A. atrox* C. Degeer, 1778, p. 253;
Ciniflo atrox J. Blackwall, 1841, p. 607 and 1861–4, p. 140.   *Amaurobius fenestralis*
O. P.-Cambridge, 1879–81, p. 56 ;   C. Chyzer and L. Kulczynski, 1891–7, I, p. 165 ;
E. Simon, 1914, pp. 37, 40 ;   C. F. Roewer, 1928, p. 119.   *Ciniflo fenestralis* W. S.
Bristowe, 1939–41, p. 13.

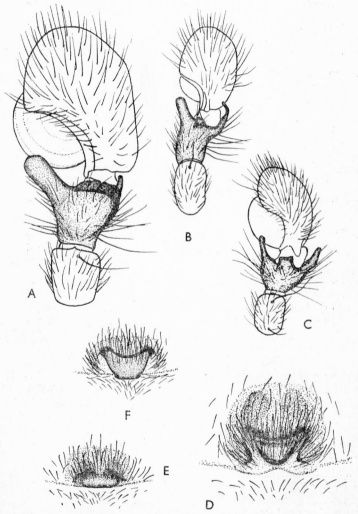

TEXT-FIG. 22.—Male palps (above): A, *Ciniflo ferox;* B, *C. similis;* C, *C.
fenestralis.*
    Epigynes: D, *Ciniflo ferox;* E, *C. similis;* F, *C. fenestralis.*

DESCRIPTION. LENGTH : ♀ : 7–8 mm. ♂ : 4.5–7 mm. CARAPACE : Red-brown, darker on head ; often with divergent wedge-shaped markings radiating from fovea. ABDOMEN : ♀ : Dorsal median dark mark on anterior half usually distinct, wider behind than in front, flanked by light areas and followed by an almost oblong light region and then by a series of obscure darker chevrons. Sides mottled with dark colour. The depth of colour throughout rather variable. ♂ : abdomen rather darker, but with a similar pattern. STERNUM : Coloured as the carapace, sometimes darkened at the edges. A median dark streak proceeds forward from the posterior end. CHELICERÆ : Swollen and rounded in front, very dark (becoming reddish on preservation). LEGS : Annulated. EPIGYNE : Text-fig. 22, F. This is rather variable, but the form of the anterior margin is constant. MALE PALPAL TIBIA : Text-fig. 22, C.

OCCURRENCE : Under bark of trees, in crevices, under stones, etc., dense gorse bushes. Found more frequently in the north, where it is common. It seems to be replaced largely in the south by *C. similis*, but both species may be found together. Adult probably all the year round.

Ciniflo similis Blackwall.
(Text-figs. 20 ; 22, B, E)

Ciniflo similis J. Blackwall, 1845, p. 116 and 1861–4, p. 141. *Amaurobius similis* O. P.-Cambridge, 1879–81, p. 54 ; E. Simon, 1914, pp. 38, 40. *Ciniflo similis* W. S. Bristowe, 1939–41, p. 13.

DESCRIPTION. LENGTH : ♀ : 9–12 mm. ♂ : 6–8 mm.

This resembles the preceding species but is larger and it is met with more commonly in the south.

ABDOMEN : ♀ : Central stripe usually divided more definitely than in *C. fenestralis* by a longitudinal lighter streak, which is sometimes extended backwards nearly to the spinners, and light lateral streaks may proceed from it backwards and outwards at intervals. ♂ : somewhat darker but with a similar pattern. STERNUM : The dark median streak from the posterior end is usually present but less well defined than in *C. fenestralis*. LEGS : Annulated. EPIGYNE : Text-fig. 22, E. MALE PALPAL TIBIA : Text-fig. 22, B.

OCCURRENCE : Distributed all over the British Isles and common in most places, especially in the south. In holes in walls, outhouses and window frames, as well as under stones and bark.

Ciniflo ferox (Walckenaer).
(Text-fig. 22, A, D)

Clubiona ferox C. A. Walckenaer, 1825, p. 150. *Ciniflo ferox* and *C. mordax* J. Blackwall, 1861–4, p. 142. *Amaurobius ferox* O. P.-Cambridge, 1879—81, p. 56 , C. Chyzer and L. Kulczynski, 1891–7, I, p. 165 ; E. Simon, 1914, pp. 36, 39 ; C. F, Roewer, 1928, p. 118 ; B. J. Kaston, 1948, p. 517. *Ciniflo ferox* W. S. Bristowe. 1939–41, p. 13.

DESCRIPTION. LENGTH : ♀ : 11.5–14 mm. ♂ : 8.5–10 mm. CARAPACE : Darker than in *C. similis*. ABDOMEN : ♀ : Usually a

E

deep dusky grey, almost black. The rectangular dark mark on the fore-part usually invisible or merged with dark colouring of sides, the longitudinal, lighter, dividing streak being maintained and followed, in the posterior half, by light chevrons. ♂ : Much more distinctly marked, the light stripe on the anterior half being flanked by light regions on which are wavy bars (corresponding to the pattern in the other species). LEGS : Not annulated as in the other species. The spider has a dark sinister appearance and is decidedly fierce. It is not likely to be mistaken for another species. The white colour of the palpal bulb in the male is striking. EPIGYNE : Text-fig. 22, D. MALE PALPAL TIBIA : Text-fig. 22, A.

OCCURRENCE : In situations similar to the last species. Quite common in the south, rather rare in the north.

2. Genus **DICTYNA** C. J. Sundevall 1833.

CHARACTERS OF GENUS. Small spiders, length not more than 4 mm. CARAPACE : Markedly elevated in front. Rows of light hairs (five can usually be made out) run forward from the region of the fovea to the front of the head, converging a little in front and behind. EYES : Seen from in front, disposed as in Text-fig. 21, A, evenly and rather widely spaced ; the clypeus wide. LEGS : Tarsi and metatarsi lack the trichobothria found in the succeeding genera.

The eight spiders of the genus fall naturally into two groups :—

Group I. *Dictyna arundinacea* (L.), *D. pusilla* Thor., *D. major* Menge, *D. uncinata* Thor., *D. latens* (Fabr.). These have the carapace dark brown, the abdomen with dark brown or black markings. The male chelicerae are excavated along their inner margins (Text-fig. 23, A). The male palpal tibia has an apophysis, the patella none. The cribellum is undivided.

Group II. *Dictyna puella* Sim., *D. flavescens* (Walck.), *D. viridissima* (Walck.). The carapace in these species is a lighter brown, with a row of semicircular light patches along the posterior part of each margin (absent in Group I). The abdomen is light yellow, green or reddish but not marked deeply with brown (in the female of *D. puella* it bears a longitudinal carmine stripe). The male chelicerae are not excavated as in Group I, but have a swelling near the base (Text-fig. 23, B). (During copulation, the female seizes the male's chelicerae with her own and these swellings ensure that she does this in the correct position (Jeanne Berland, 1916).) The palpal tibiae have no apophysis (only a ridge marked with a double row of fine hairs) ; the patella bears a tooth dorsally and a little to the outside. The cribellum is divided by a fine ridge (which, however, it is often extremely difficult to see). The legs are a uniform yellow-brown or rust colour.

Group I *Dictyna arundinacea* (L.), *D. pusilla* Thor., *D. major* Menge, *D. uncinata* Thor., *D. latens* (Fabr.).

The males are separated fairly easily by the form of the tibial apophysis on the palp. The females, however, present some difficulty, since the epigynes are not well defined and hairs tend to make the parts difficult to see ; moreover, there is often a good deal of variation between individuals of the same species. Fortunately the two sexes are found frequently together occupying the same web, when the

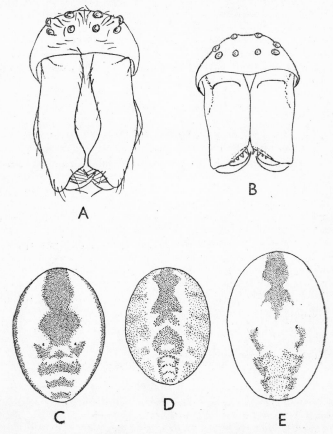

TEXT-FIG. 23.—Cheliceræ : A, *Dictyna arundinacea* ♂ ; B, *Dictyna puella* ♂. Abdominal patterns : C, *D. arundinacea;* D, *D. pusilla;* E, *D. major.*

male serves to identify the species. (The descriptions given under each species are of the females. The coloration of the males is essentially similar but is frequently darker with the abdominal pattern then less distinct.) The most useful distinguishing characters are summarised below.

MALES

(1) The twisted process at the base of the palpal tarsus pointing upwards, towards the tibia (Text-fig. 24, A, B, C, D) : *D. arundinacea* and *D. pusilla.*

These two species may then be distinguished (a) by the proportions and position of the tibial apophysis (Text-fig. 24, A, C) ; (b) by the sexual organs as viewed from inside and somewhat below (Text-fig. 24, B, D).

(2) The twisted process pointing backwards and downwards (Text-fig. 24, E, F) : *D. uncinata, D. major, D. latens.*

The tibial apophyses will then separate these species. In addition, *D. latens* is of a blackish colour with many white hairs ; the median dark mark on the front part of the abdomen is trifid behind (as in the female) in *D. major.*

FEMALES

(1) The septum between the depressions of the epigyne broad (Text-fig. 25, C, G) : *Dictyna latens* and *D. uncinata.* The former is a dark sooty grey or black with white pubescence, the latter is marked rather like *D. arundinacea,* but with no darkening of tarsi I and II.

(2) The septum between the depressions of the epigyne narrow (Text-fig. 25, D, E, F) :

D. major: The posterior end of the median mark on the fore part of the abdomen trifid (Text-fig. 23, E) ; tarsi I and II not darkened.

D. arundinacea: The abdominal pattern variable, but the region between the median mark and the marks on the sides usually clear (Text-fig. 23, C). Tarsi I and II darkened to about half way.

D. pusilla: Abdominal pattern (Text-fig. 23, D) variable (see description of the species.) Tarsi I and II darkened only at the tips, if at all. Annulations usually distinct at the ends of the segments.

D. uncinata, D. arundinacea and *D. pusilla* are often very difficult to distinguish, since the septa of their epigynes can vary in width and the colours are often very similar.

Dictyna arundinacea (Linnaeus).
(Text-figs. 23, A, C ; 24, A, B ; 25, D)

Aranea arundinacea Linnaeus, 1758, p. 620. *A. benigna* C. A. Walckenaer, 1802. p. 209. *Ergatis benigna* J. Blackwall, 1861–4. p. 146. *Dictyna arundinacea* O. P.-Cambridge, 1879–81, p. 49 ; C. Chyzer and L. Kulczynski, 1891–7, I, p. 158 ; E. Simon, 1914, pp. 55, 58 ; C. F. Roewer, 1928, p. 52.

DESCRIPTION. LENGTH : ♀ : 2·5–3 mm. ♂ : c. 2·5 mm. CARAPACE: Deep brown. ABDOMEN : Pattern (Text-fig. 23, C) deep brown, sometimes greyish, the light region yellowish white or sometimes with a grey tint. STERNUM : Dark brown. CHELICERÆ : Deep brown. LEGS : There are sometimes very faint traces of annulations. Tarsi I, II and III tinted deeper brown than the remaining segments from the tips to about their mid points. Tarsus IV may be tinted for its whole length, as well as tip of metatarsus. EPIGYNE : Text-fig. 25, D. MALE PALP : Text-fig. 24, A, B.

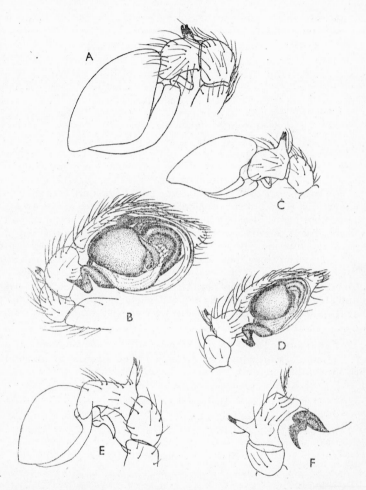

TEXT-FIG. 24.—Male palps : A, *Dictyna arundinacea* (side) ; B, do. (inside and a little below) ; C, *Dictyna pusilla* (side) ; D, do. (inside and a little below) ; E, *Dictyna uncinata* (side) ; F, do. (inside).

OCCURRENCE : Common and widespread. The web is built on the heads of plants (living or dead) and in bushes, gorse, etc. The male is frequently found with the female. Mature May to June.

Dictyna pusilla Thorell.
(Text-figs. 23, D ; 24, C, D ; 25, E)

Dictyna pusilla T. Thorell, 1856, p. 82 ; C. Chyzer and L. Kulczynski, 1891–7, I; p. 158 ; O. P.-Cambridge, 1879–81, p. 426 ; E. Simon, 1914, pp. 54, 58 ; C. F. Roewer. 1928, p. 52.

DESCRIPTION. LENGTH : ♀: 1·75–2·5 mm. ♂: c. 2 mm. This species often resembles *D. arundinacea* closely. The males can be separated by the form and proportions of the tibial apophysis (Text-fig. 24, D) and by inspecting the sexual organs from inside and a little below (Text-fig. 24, B, D). Although these are alike in the two species, everything in *D. pusilla* is on a smaller scale and, as seen from this position they give a definite separation. The females present more difficulty, especially after preservation ; but consideration of the following characters should enable a separation to be made. (1) Size. (2) The epigyne (Text-fig. 25, E) is usually surrounded by a deeper pigment and the horizontal chitinised ridges outside the two depressions (almost always clear in *D. arundinacea*) are here less definite and often not visible. (3) The abdominal pattern (Text-fig. 23, D) is variable and can approach that of *D. arundinacea*, but the colouration of the sides (characteristically brown) usually invades the lighter area surrounding the median band. Sometimes the markings on the posterior half are wholly absent, often there is a light, almost white, border on either side of the anterior and posterior median dark marks, in sharp contrast to them ; when this occurs it is striking. Northern specimens at any rate often have the pattern much less distinct, the white portions being obscured, and there is more dark covering hair. (4) The legs are usually annulated distinctly at the ends of the segments. The deeper brown of the tarsi occurs, if at all, on the tips of I and II, not half way along as in *D. arundinacea*.

OCCURRENCE : Rather rare in the south ; locally abundant in parts of Scotland (*e.g.* Abernethy Forest). Found on low plants and by beating bushes. Adult spring and summer.

Dictyna major Menge.
(Text-figs. 23, E ; 25, B ; 25, F)

Dictyna major A. Menge, 1866–79, III, p. 247.   *D. cognata* O. P.-Cambridge, 1885, (2), p. 237.   *D. arenicola* O. P.-Cambridge, 1894 (2), p. 589.   *D. major* E. Simon, 1914, pp. 55, 57 ;   C. F. Roewer, 1928, p. 52 ;   A. R. Jackson, 1931, p. 639 ;   J. Braendegaard, 1940, p. 10.

(*Note.*—Confusion in the records abroad of this species with *D. borealis* Camb. is dealt with by A. R. Jackson (1934, p. 611) and by J. Braendegaard (1940), although in this latter paper *D. borealis* Camb. is wrongly shown as a synonym of *D. hamifera* Thor. (1872), which Braendegaard (1946) later recognised as a synonym of *D. major* Menge.)

DESCRIPTION. LENGTH : ♀: 3·0–3·5 mm. ♂: 2·5–3 mm.

This species resembles *D. arundinacea* in general appearance. The male is identifiable by the palpal tibial apophysis (Text-fig. 25, B) which springs from the extreme end of the segment. For the female reliance must be placed on the trifid abdominal marking (Text-fig. 23, E) and on the legs, which lack the dark markings on the tarsi. The ventral dark band on the abdomen is well defined, with two pairs of pale spots (sometimes confluent) on its anterior half. These, if present, are seldom so well defined in the other species. Fresh specimens are not available, but the spider would seem to have a lighter appearance than others in this Group, especially the female. EPIGYNE : Text-fig. 25, F. MALE PALP : Text-fig. 25, B.

OCCURRENCE : Scotland : Aberlady (Haddingtonshire). The males have been found running over warm sand, the females were concealed with their egg-cocoons in pieces of dried seaweed (*Fucus*) and withered leaves lying on the sand. Also on the shores of Loch Morlich, at 1,040 ft. (Inverness) and in Morayshire.

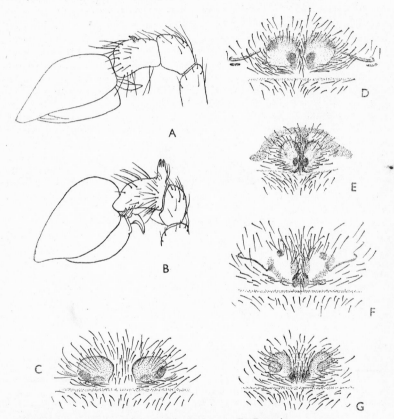

TEXT-FIG. 25.—Male palps : A, *Dictyna latens;* B, *D. major.*
Epigynes : C, *Dictyna latens;* D, *D. arundinacea;* E, *D. pusilla;* F, *D. major;* G, *D. uncinata.*

Dictyna uncinata Thorell.
(Text-figs. 24, E, F ; 25, G)

Dictyna uncinata T. Thorell, 1856, p. 82. *Ergatis arborea* O. P.-Cambridge, 1862, p. 7959. *D. uncinata* C. Chyzer and L. Kulczynski, 1891–7, I, p. 157 ; E. Simon, 1914, pp. 55, 56 ; C. F. Roewer, 1928, p. 52.

DESCRIPTION. LENGTH : ♀ : 2·5–2·75 mm. ♂ : 2–2·5 mm.
This species again resembles *D. arundinacea* in general appearance.
The anterior median dorsal mark on the abdomen is rather less well
defined and more brown in colour and the mottling from the sides
tends to invade the lighter areas on either side of it. The legs are yellow
brown with no annulations nor darkening of the tarsi. The males are
easy enough to distinguish (Text-fig. 24, A, B and E, F). The septum
between the depressions of the epigyne of the female is normally
broader than in *D. arundinacea*, but variation can occur, making
distinction between the species difficult at times. EPIGYNE : Text-fig.
25, G. MALE PALP : Text-fig. 24, E, F.

OCCURRENCE : In places similar to those in which *D. arundinacea* is
found. A common and widespread species. Adult spring and summer.

Dictyna latens (Fabricius).
(Text-fig. 25, A, C.)

Aranea latens J. C. Fabricius, 1775, p. 432. *Ergatis latens* J. Blackwall, 1861–4,
p. 149. *Dictyna lugubris* O. P.-Cambridge, 1879–81, p. 50. *D. latens* C. Chyzer and
L. Kulczynski, 1891–7, I, p. 158 ; E. Simon, 1914, p. 52 ; C. F. Roewer, 1928, p. 51.

DESCRIPTION. LENGTH : ♀ : 2·5–3·5 mm. ♂ : 1·75–2·5mm.
The dark colour, often black, with the covering of white hairs
and the absence of a definite abdominal pattern, make separation of
this species relatively easy. EPIGYNE : Text-fig. 25, C. MALE PALP :
Text-fig. 25, A.

OCCURRENCE : Widespread. In the same situations as *D. arundinacea* and *D. uncinata*, but much less common. Adult in spring and
summer.

Group II. *Dictyna puella* Sim., *D. flavescens* (Walck.), *D. viridissima* (Walck.).

There is little difficulty about the separation of these species as
long as their colours have been noted before preservation, but with
preserved specimens considerable difficulty arises with the females,
although the males can still be identified with tolerable certainty.
The most useful characters are summarised as follows.

MALES

The ridges at the base of the cheliceræ are usually quite distinct
as seen from above (*D. puella:* Text-fig. 27, A. *D. flavescens:* Text-
fig. 27, C. *D. viridissima:* Text-fig. 27, B). Those of *D. flavescens*
sometimes resemble those of *D. viridissima*, but the relative size and
distance apart of the anterior eyes, as in the females (see below),
affords another distinguishing character. *D. puella* is again recognisable by the larger tooth borne on the tibial patella (Text-fig. 26, A, B) ;
in *D. flavescens* and *D. viridissima* this is alike (Text-fig. 26, C, D)
but much smaller than in *D. puella*.

FEMALES

Dictyna viridissima is separated from the other two species as follows :
The impression on either side of the septum of the epigyne is oval

(Text-fig. 26, F). The median anterior eyes are separated by less than two diameters of one of these eyes, and from the adjacent laterals by one diameter of a lateral. The trapezium formed by the four median eyes is distinctly wider behind than in front. Length : about 4 mm.

D. puella and *D. flavescens:* The impressions on either side of the septum of the epigyne are nearly circular. The median anterior eyes separated by $3\frac{1}{2}$–4 diameters of one of them and from the adjacent laterals by a little more than a diameter of a lateral eye. The trapezium formed by the four median eyes no wider, or slightly narrower, behind than in front. Length : 2·5–3 mm.

It is extremely difficult to find reliable characters for distinguishing between long preserved specimens of these two species, whose epigynes are very similar, especially when bleached. In all the specimens examined, the anterior median eyes are only slightly smaller than, or equal to, the anterior laterals in *D. puella*, whereas the medians have only about half the diameter of the laterals in *D. flavescens*. In the former species traces of the abdominal stripe may remain as darker markings, as opposed to the more uniform reticulated surface of *D. flavescens*. The sides of the carapace are usually deeper in colour in *D. puella*.

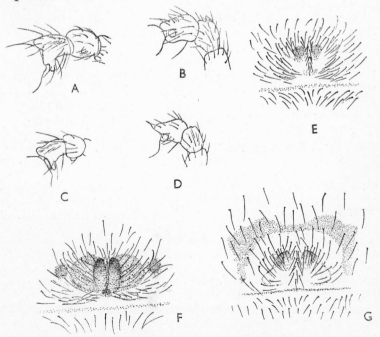

TEXT-FIG. 26.—Male palpal patellæ and tibiæ : A, *Dictyna puella* (above) ; B, do. (side) ; C, *D. viridissima* and *flavescens* (above) ; D, do. (side). Epigynes : E, *Dictyna puella;* F, *D. viridissima;* G, *D. flavescens*.

Dictyna puella Simon.
(Text-figs. 23, B ; 26, A, B, E ; 27, A)

Dictyna puella E. Simon, 1870, p. 31 ; 1914, p. 51. *Ergatis pallens* J. Blackwall, 1861–4, p. 148. *Dictyna variabilis* O. P.-Cambridge, 1879–81, p. 466.

DESCRIPTION. LENGTH : ♀ : 2·5–3 mm. ♂ : 2–2·75 mm. CARAPACE Light yellow-green or brown along the central area as far as the front of the head, on which are long, forward-pointing white hairs. This almost parallel-sided region is flanked by darker areas on which are the light semicircular marginal patches characteristic of the Group (see p. 56). ABDOMEN : A longitudinal carmine stripe, on a light greenish yellow ground, serves to identify the females, but it fades on preservation in spirit and is absent in adult males. EPIGYNE : Text-fig. 26, E. MALE PALPAL PATELLA AND TIBIA : Text-fig. 26, A, B.

OCCURRENCE : Local in southern counties. Usually found on low bushes and shrubs from May until August, and probably later.

Dictyna flavescens (Walckenaer).
(Text-figs. 26, C, D, G ; 27, C)

Drassus flavescens C. A. Walckenaer, 1825, p. 179. *Dictyna flavescens*, C. Chyzer and L. Kulczynski, 1891–7, I, p. 158 ; E. Simon, 1914, p. 51 ; A. R. Jackson, 1924, p. 109. (*Note.*—County records, other than Co. Durham, in W. S. Bristowe, 1939–41, p. 12, refer to *D. puella* Sim.)

DESCRIPTION. LENGTH : ♀ : 2·5 mm. ♂ : 2·25 mm. (Fresh specimens have not been available for examination). CARAPACE : In preserved specimens : similar to that of *D. puella*, but not so dark along the sides. ABDOMEN : Yellowish, perhaps with a reddish tinge, becoming nearly white on preservation and then very often covered with reticulations. EPIGYNE : Text-fig. 26, G. MALE PALPAL PATELLA AND TIBIA : Text-fig. 26, C, D.

The species has been confused with *D. puella* in this country.

OCCURRENCE : Gibside (Co. Durham), 1909.

Dictyna viridissima (Walckenaer).
(Text-figs. 26, C, D, F ; 27, B)

Aranea viridissima C. A. Walckenaer, 1802, p. 212. *Dictyna viridissima* O. P, Cambridge, 1879, p. 210 ; 1879–81, p. 589 ; 1899, p. 5 ; C. Chyzer and L. Kulczynski. 1891–7, I, p. 158 ; E. Simon, 1914, p. 51.

DESCRIPTION. LENGTH : ♀ : 4 mm. ♂ : 3–4 mm. (Fresh specimens have not been available for examination.)

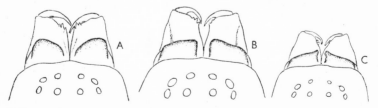

TEXT-FIG. 27.—Male cheliceræ (above) : A, *Dictyna puella;* B, *D. viridissima;* C, *D. flavescens.*

From descriptions of continental specimens it appears that the female is pale green while the male has the abdomen green but the cephalothorax and legs a rusty brown. EPIGYNE : Text-fig. 26, F. MALE PALPAL PATELLA AND TIBIA : not distinguishable from that of *D. flavescens*.

OCCURRENCE : Box Hill (Surrey) ; Kew. It has not been taken for many years. On the continent it has been observed to build its web and retreat on the upper sides of large leaves. Probably adult in late summer and autumn.

3. Genus **LATHYS** E. Simon 1884.

The chief distinguishing characters for this genus are the eyes, of which the median anteriors are much the smallest (Text-fig. 21, B) and the possession of a number of small but definite spines on the patellæ and bases of the tibiæ of the legs. As in the genera *Argenna* and *Protadia*, the tarsi and apical ends of the metatarsi of the legs are furnished each with a long trichobothrium. The cheliceræ in the males are tapering and the fangs very long.

Lathys humilis (Blackwall).
(Text-figs. 28, A, C)

Ciniflo humilis J. Blackwall, 1855, p. 120, and 1861–4, p. 145. *Lethia humilis* O. P.-Cambridge, 1879–81, p. 51. *Lathys humilis* C. Chyzer and L. Kulczynski, 1891–7, I, p. 161 ; E. Simon, 1914, p. 44 ; C. F. Roewer, 1928, p. 53 ; W. S. Bristowe, 1947, pl. 1.

DESCRIPTION. LENGTH : ♀ : 2–2·5 mm. ♂ : 1·75–2 mm. CARAPACE Light brown with darker veinings on the fore part, and dark radiating wedge-shaped marks on the thoracic region. ABDOMEN : ♀ : Light greenish brown with white mottling, often having a reticulate appearance. Pattern variable but fairly distinct, consisting of pairs of longitudinal darker bars running from end to end, with a thin line of the greenish brown ground colour running between them. The sides darker or at least with fewer white spots. ♂ : colour much deeper, often almost black, with fewer white spots dorsally and with the dark bars dilated laterally. LEGS : Yellow brown ; distinctly annulated in both sexes. EPIGYNE : Text-fig. 28, C. MALE PALP : Text-fig. 28, A.

OCCURRENCE : A southern species, common locally. Usually beaten from bushes, also found among dead leaves. Mature in April, May and June.

Lathys stigmatisata (Menge).
(Text-figs. 28, B, D)

Lethia stigmatisata A. Menge, 1869, p. 250. *Lathys puta* E. Simon, 1914, p. 45 (not O. P.-Cambridge, 1863, etc.) ; C. F. Roewer, 1928, p. 53. *Lathys stigmatisata* A. R. Jackson, 1924, p. 109.

DESCRIPTION. LENGTH : ♀ : 2·25–2·75 mm. ♂ : c. 2 mm. This species differs from the last, apart from its being slightly larger, in the following respects. ABDOMEN : Almost uniform brown, lacking the

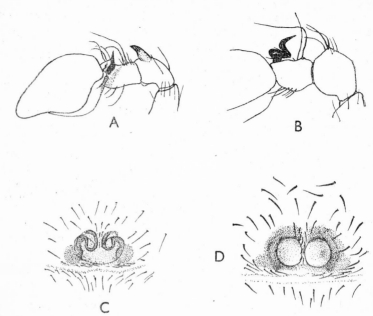

TEXT-FIG. 28.—Male palps : A, *Lathys humilis;* B, *L. stigmatisata.*
Epigynes : C, *Lathys humilis;* D, *L. stigmatisata.*

white spots and pattern of *L. humilis*, sometimes dark brown with faint divergent bars on the posterior half. The colour is again darker in the male. LEGS : Light brown, with no annulations. EPIGYNE : Text-fig. 28, D. There are two circular depressions separated by a narrow septum ; the seminal ducts, usually quite clear in *L. humilis*, are rarely at all clearly visible in this species. MALE PALP : The apophysis at the front of the tibia is contorted into a spiral and is quite unmistakable. Text-fig. 28, B. (This drawing was made from a foreign specimen.)

OCCURRENCE : The Lizard (Cornwall) in 1922 and Kynance (Cornwall) amongst grass and thrift in 1924. Lundy, in heather in 1929. Only the female has been taken in this country.

4. Genus **ARGENNA** T. Thorell 1870 and
5. Genus **PROTADIA** E. Simon 1893.

There is but one representative of each of these genera, and the differences are hardly sufficient to warrant their being thus separated.

CHARACTERS OF GENERA. CLYPEUS : Narrow (cf. *Dictyna*). EYES : The anterior medians are not very different in size from the rest (cf. *Lathys*). LEGS : The tarsi and apical ends of the metatarsi each bear a trichobothrium (cf. *Dictyna*). The two species differ from each other in the arrangement of the eyes (see Key to the Genera, p. 53, Text-fig. 21).

Argenna subnigra (O. P.-Cambridge).
(Text-figs. 21, D ; 29, A, B, E)

Drassus subniger O. P.-Cambridge, 1861, p. 420. *Ciniflo puta* O. P.-Cambridge, 1863, p. 8570. *Ciniflo mengei* O. P.-Cambridge, 1873 (1), p. 441. *Lethia albospiraculis* O. P.-Cambridge, 1878, p. 109. *Argenna minima* C. Chyzer and L. Kulczynski, 1891-7, I, p. 159. *Protadia subnigra* L. Kulczynski, 1898, p. 54 ; *Argenna subnigra* E. Simon, 1914, p. 48.

DESCRIPTION. LENGTH : ♀ : 1·75-2·5 mm. ♂ : 1·5-1·75 mm. CARAPACE : Brown, variable in depth of colour, sometimes with a faint darker borderline and often darker on the head. Dark veinings usually radiate from the fovea. EYES : Text-fig. 21, D. ABDOMEN :

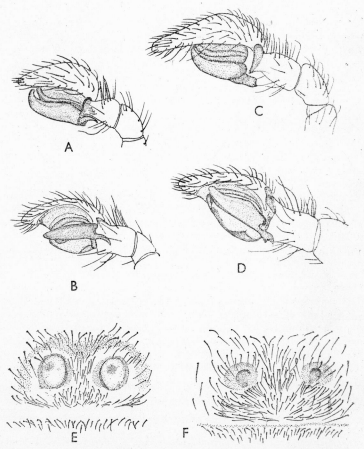

TEXT-FIG. 29.—Male palps : A, *Argenna subnigra* (side) ; B, do. (a little below) ; C, *Protadia patula* (side) ; D, do. (a little below).
Epigynes : E, *Argenna subnigra;* F, *Protadia patula.*

Light or dark brown to dark grey with whitish hairs, three pairs of yellowish spots, in depressions along the middle.   These are succeeded by three to four faint yellow chevrons, whose vertices and extremities are marked each with a minute tuft of white hairs.   There are thus three longitudinal and nearly parallel lines of these tufts, which are very distinct though liable to be rubbed off.   The colour is much darker in the male, sometimes with indistinct light angular bars across the middle.   CHELICERÆ : Coloured as the carapace ; somewhat more tapering in the male.   LEGS : Rather lighter than the carapace, with no annulations.   EPIGYNE : Text-fig. 29, E. There are two depressions, each filled with a grey or white membranous body (of variable size) which can be very striking.   MALE PALP : Text-fig. 29, A, B.   This has a projection pointing backwards from the base of the bulb (somewhat resembling that of *Dictyna uncinata*).   There are no apophyses on the patella or tibia.

OCCURRENCE : A rare, southern species.   Found under stones but also on bushes ; it has occurred on railings.

Protadia patula (Simon).
(Text-figs. 21, C ; 29, C, D, F)

Dictyna patula E. Simon, 1874, I, p. 197.   *Lethia patula* O. P.-Cambridge, 1878, p. 108.   *Protadia patula* A. R. Jackson, 1913 (2), p. 20 ; E. Simon, 1914, p. 48.

DESCRIPTION.   LENGTH :   ♀ :   2·75–3 mm.   ♂ :   2·5–2·75 mm. This species resembles *Argenna subnigra*, but, apart from its paler colour and rather larger size, differs from it notably in the following respects :

EYES : Text-fig. 21, C.   EPIGYNE : Text-fig. 29, F.   The depressions lack the membranous bodies so characteristic of the last species. MALE PALP : Text-fig. 29, C, D.   The projection at the base of the bulb takes a different form.

OCCURRENCE : Rare.   Among detritus by the banks of tidal rivers.

6. Genus **ALTELLA** E. Simon 1884.

CHARACTERS OF GENUS.   EYES : Anteriors sub-contiguous. Posterior medians separated by about one diameter, being closer than this to adjacent laterals.   LABIUM : Drawn out anteriorly almost to a point. LEGS : ♂ : Tibia III with a long ventral curved spine directed forwards (Text-fig. 30, B).   Metatarsus I with two single short black spines ventrally.   CRIBELLUM : Undivided.

A single male specimen of *Altella lucida* (Sim.) constitutes the only British record of this genus.

Altella lucida Simon.
(Text-fig. 30, A, B)

Lethia lucida E. Simon, 1874, I, p. 203.   *Lethia spinigera* O. P.-Cambridge, 1879–81, p. 468.   *Amphissa spinigera* O. P.-Cambridge, 1882, p. 3.   *Altella lucida* C. F. Roewer, 1928, p. 51.

DESCRIPTION.   LENGTH : ♂ : c. 1 mm.   The only British specimen is now much bleached, but when fresh, the general coloration is yellow

brown. ABDOMEN : Seen in spirit under a lens, minutely spotted with
dull reddish-yellow points ; and several transverse angular lines are
visible on the hinder part of the upper side. LEGS : Femora, especially
of I, strongly tinged with blackish-brown. MALE PALPAL TIBIA :

TEXT-FIG. 30.—*Altella lucida:* A, male palp, in outline (above) ; B, male patella
and tibia III.

Text-fig. 30, A. This is shown in outline as seen from above. There is a
blunt-ended apophysis on the retrolateral side. (The palps cannot be
viewed in this unique specimen without risk of damage to the legs.)

OCCURRENCE : A male was found in his house at Hoddesdon (Hertfordshire), by F. M. Campbell in the early part of 1880.

4. Family ULOBORIDÆ.

CHARACTERS OF FAMILY. CARAPACE : Form (and disposition of eyes) Text-fig. 15, B. There is no thoracic fovea. EYES : All dark in colour. CHELICERÆ : Moderately robust, nearly parallel-sided. LEGS : The anterior are the longest (notably in *Uloborus*). Femora with dorsal trichobothria ; tarsi with three foot claws. Metatarsus IV, bearing the calamistrum (degenerate in males), somewhat curved (Text-fig. 32, E), at least along its dorsal edge ; it bears a series of short thick spines ventrally, narrowed at their bases and also present on the tarsus. CRIBELLUM : Clear enough in females (Text-fig. 15, D) ; absent or degenerate in adult males. ANAL TUBERCLE : Well developed in *Uloborus* (Text-fig. 15, C) but less conspicuous in *Hyptiotes*, being close to posterior spinners.

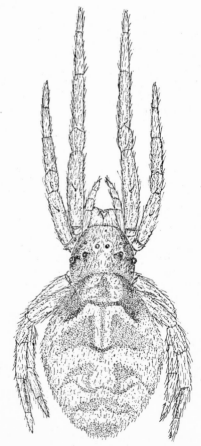

TEXT-FIG. 31.—*Hyptiotes paradoxus* ♀ (ULOBORIDÆ).

The representatives of each of the two genera, *Uloborus* and *Hyptiotes*, differ from one another considerably in general appearance, the former having rather long legs (the first pair being longest), while those of *Hyptiotes* are very short (Text-fig. 31). There is no difficulty in separating them, each having a characteristic and peculiar appearance.

1. Genus **ULOBORUS** P. A. Latreille 1806.

CHARACTERS OF GENUS. CARAPACE and EYES : Text-fig. 15, B. ABDOMEN : Anal tubercle prominent in the female (Text-fig. 15, C), diminished in the male. LEGS : First pair much longer and stronger than the rest. ♂ : Tibia I with six to seven dorsal spines, almost in the form of teeth.

Uloborus walckenaerius Latreille.
(Text-figs. 15, B ; 32, A, B)

Uloborus walckenaerius P. A. Latreille, 1806, p. 110. *Veleda lineata* J. Blackwall, 1861–4, p. 150. *Uloborus walckenærii* C. Chyzer and L. Kulczynski, 1891–7, I, p. 147. *U. walckenærius* O. P.-Cambridge, 1879–81, pp. 285, 580 ; E. Simon, 1914, p. 27 ; C. F. Roewer, 1928, p. 108.

DESCRIPTION. LENGTH : ♀ : 3·5–6 mm. ♂ : 3–4 mm. CARAPACE : Brown, with lighter median and lateral bands (Text-fig. 15, B) covered thickly with light hairs (not shown in the fig.). ABDOMEN : Whitish with a darker grey-green median and two lateral longitudinal stripes ; mottled on the sides. Ventrally : covered with an oblong deep brown area. Anal tubercle prominent in the female (Text-fig. 15, C) but diminished in the male. STERNUM : Deep brown. LEGS : Femur I brown, femora II, III and IV brown only at the tips, the rest whitish. The remaining segments brown with a few whitish annulations (except I). There is some variation in this colouring. EPIGYNE : Text-fig. 32, B. (The whitish finger-like processes are variable in size.) MALE PALP : Text-fig. 32, A.

OCCURRENCE : The spider is found, but rarely, by sweeping heather in southern counties (*e.g.* Dorset ; also in the New Forest). The web is a complete orb, usually horizontal. (See Bristowe, 1939–41, p. 245.)

2. Genus **HYPTIOTES** C. A. Walckenaer 1833.

CHARACTERS OF GENUS. General appearance as in Text-fig. 31 LEGS : Much shorter than in *Uloborus*. MALE PALPAL ORGANS : These are most remarkable, being nearly as large as the carapace (Text-fig. 32, D).

Hyptiotes paradoxus (C. L. Koch).
(Text-figs. 31 ; 32, C, D, E, F.)

Mithras paradoxus C. L. Koch, 1834 (3), **9**, p. 123, and 1845, XII, p. 94. *Hyptiotes paradoxus* O. P.-Cambridge, 1879–81, p. 532 ; C. Chyzer and L. Kulczynski, 1891-7, I, p. 148 ; E. Simon, 1914, p. 29 ; C. F. Roewer, 1928, p. 108.

DESCRIPTION. LENGTH : ♀ : 5–6 mm. ♂ : c. 4 mm. This spider (Text-fig. 31) could not be confused with any other British species. The colour is very variable, from ginger to dark brown, with deeper almost black, markings. In some specimens the light regions are greatly emphasised, but this is by no means always the case. The legs are

F

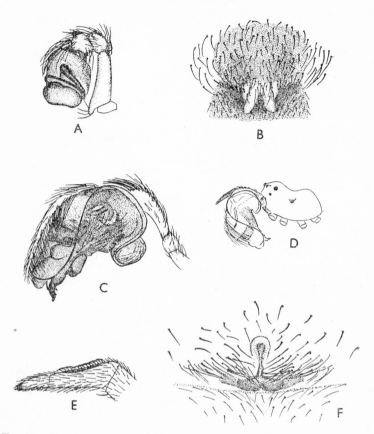

TEXT-FIG. 32.—*Uloborus walckenœrius:* A, male palp; B, epigyne.
Hyptiotes paradoxus: C, male palp; D, do. and carapace; E, calamistrum;
F, epigyne.

remarkably short. EPIGYNE: Text-fig. 32, F. MALE PALPS: Text–
fig. 32, C, D. The great size of these is very remarkable.

OCCURRENCE: The species is very local and may be found by beating
yew or box (New Forest, West Walk (Hants) and Box Hill (Surrey)).
The web, which has been observed by the authors at Box Hill, is very
characteristic, consisting of a segment (about one-sixth) of an orb web
as constructed by the ARGIOPIDÆ. The spider sits upside down just
under a leaf or twig, from which a single thread leads to the apex
of the segment, which is spread directly below in a vertical plane
The threads between the radii of the segment are of the typical cribellate
type, spaced about ¾ in. apart, the whole web measuring about 10 ins.
across. (The form and method of construction are fully described
by Wiehle, 1927, Marples, 1937, and Peters, 1938.)

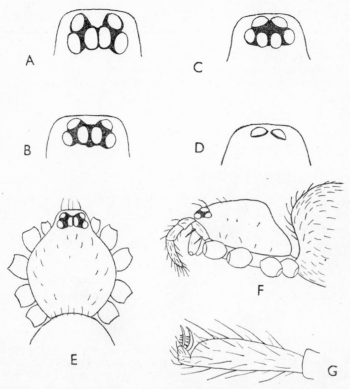

TEXT-FIG. 33.—Arrangements of eyes: A, *Oonops;* B, *Triæris;* C, *Ischnothyreus;* D, *Diblemma.* E, F, carapace of *Oonops.* G, onychium of *Oonops.*

5. Family OONOPIDÆ.

CHARACTERS OF FAMILY. CARAPACE : Smooth, with no thoracic fovea or impressions ; markedly narrowed in front (Text-fig. 33, E). EYES : Normally six in number (except *Diblemma,* which has two) ; all light in colour, fairly large and in a compact group, which is nearly as wide as the head. ABDOMEN : Oval, long, pale yellowish-brown or pink, with no pattern. Hard chitinous shields (*scuta*) are present, dorsally and ventrally, in the hot-house species, and are usually larger in the males (Text-fig. 35). There are two pairs of spiracles close together, one on each side of the epigastric fold ; the posterior pair lead to trachæe (and in *Oonops* are difficult to see). STERNUM : Wide, narrowing posteriorly and separating coxæ IV (Text-fig. 34). CHELICERÆ : Normally with no teeth. MAXILLÆ : Inclined distinctly inwards (Text-fig. 34). FEMALE PALP : With no claw. LEGS : Devoid of scopulæ. Tibiæ and tarsi usually with a series of paired spines (Text-figs. 36, 37). All tarsi with a distinct *onychium* (Text-fig. 33, G) bearing two claws, each with two rows of teeth (one of these rows may be small and difficult to see). No claw tufts, but a few plumose hairs close to the claws. Females have no EPIGYNE and the PALPAL ORGANS of the males are of a primitive type.

The British OONOPIDÆ comprise five species of small, pale-coloured spiders ranging in length from 1½ to 2½ mm. when adult. Only two, of the genus *Oonops*, are truly native; the remainder occur in hot-houses.

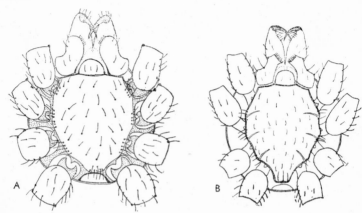

TEXT-FIG. 34.—Ventral view of cephalothorax : A, *Triceris stenaspis;* B, *Diblemma donisthorpei*.

KEY TO THE GENERA AND SPECIES

1. Soft abdomen with no scutum   2
——Abdomen with hard chitinous scuta (Text-fig. 35) (hot-house species)   3

2. Eyes as in Text-fig. 33, **A**. Tibiæ and metatarsi I and II with a series of paired spines (Text-fig. 36) . Male palpal organs : Text-fig. 38, A, B . . . . . . (1) **Oonops**
——Tibia I with four pairs of ventral spines (Text-fig. 36, A) . . . . *O. pulcher* p. 76
——Tibia I with five pairs of ventral spines (Text-fig. 36, B) . . . . *O. domesticus* p. 76

3. Eyes two, nearly touching (Text-fig. 33, D). Tibiæ I and II with bristles but no spines (Text-fig. 37, C). Carapace and sternum not joined by chitinous strips between coxæ (Text-fig. 34, B) . . . . (2) **Diblemma**
——Eyes six. Tibiæ I and II with paired spines (Text-fig. 37, A, B). Carapace and sternum joined by chitinous strips between the coxæ (Text-fig. 34, A)   4

4. Eye arrangement similar to that of *Oonops;* anterior laterals separated by more than an eye diameter (Text-fig.

33, B). A small ventral scutum lies posterior to the epigastric fold (Text-fig. 35, B). Patellæ I very long ; progressively shorter in II, III and IV. Patellæ (but not metatarsi) I and II with three pairs of ventral spines . . . . (3) **Triaeris**

—Anterior lateral eyes touching (Text-fig. 33, C). No scutum lies posterior to the epigastric fold (Text-fig. 35, A). Patellæ all similar, without ventral spines, but metatarsi I and II with a series of paired spines (Text-fig. 37, A) . . . . (4) **Ischnothyreus**

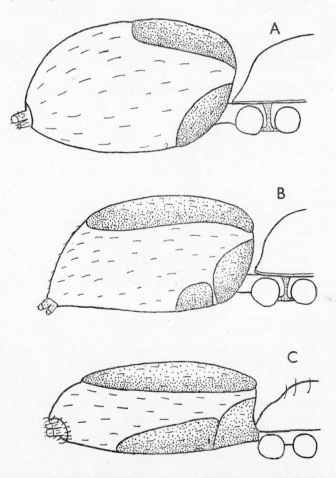

TEXT-FIG. 35.—Abdomen, showing scuta : A, *Ischnothyreus velox;* B, *Triæris stenaspia;* C, *Diblemma donisthorpei.*

1. Genus **OONOPS** R. Templeton 1834.

Oonops pulcher Templeton.

(Text figs. 36, A; 38, A)

Oonops pulcher R. Templeton, 1835, p. 404 ; J. Blackwall, 1861–4, p. 377 ; O. P.-Cambridge, 1879–81, p. 9 ; R. de Dalmas, 1916, p. 246 ; W. S. Bristowe, 1948, p. 890. (*Note.*—Many Continental records including those of E. Simon, 1914, p. 91, and J. Braendegaard, 1932, p. 680, refer to other species.)

DESCRIPTION. LENGTH : c. 1·5–2 mm. Colouration pink to light brick-red. EYES : Text-fig. 33, A. ABDOMEN : Soft with no scutum. LEGS : Tibia I with four pairs of ventral spines (Text-fig. 36, A) (cf. *O. domesticus*). There is no epigyne. MALE PALP : Text-fig. 38, A.

OCCURRENCE : Widespread. Found under stones and amongst dry matted vegetable detritus, leaves and moss. Adult in spring.

Oonops domesticus de Dalmas

(Text-figs. 36, B ; 38, B)

Oonops domesticus R. de Dalmas, 1916, p. 247 ; W. S. Bristowe, 1922, p. 4, and 1948, p. 890.

DESCRIPTION. Very like *O. pulcher.* Tibia I with five pairs of ventral spines (Text-fig. 36, B). MALE PALP : Text-fig. 38, B.

OCCURRENCE : Recorded from Merioneth and from 17 English counties as far north as Lancashire ; also in Argyll. Found in houses walking with characteristic short rushes on walls, etc., especially after dark.

2. Genus **ISCHNOTHYREUS** E. Simon 1892.

Ischnothyreus velox Jackson.

(Text-figs. 33, C ; 35, A ; 37, A ; 38, C, E)

Ischnothyreus velox A. R. Jackson, 1908, p. 51 ; O. P.-Cambridge, 1908, p. 165 ; W. S. Bristowe, 1948, p. 890.

DESCRIPTION. LENGTH : Nearly 2 mm. CARAPACE : Dark yellow-brown (darker than abdomen or legs, but depth of colour variable). Surface granular. ABDOMEN : Greyish yellow-brown or clay colour ; covered with long hairs. Ventral scutum (Text-fig. 35, A) of nearly same colour as surroundings. LABIUM : Slightly concave anteriorly (cf. *Triæris*). LEGS : Clear yellow-brown. Patellæ without spines. Tibia I and II with four pairs of strong ventral spines. Metatarsi I and II with two pairs of ventral spines (cf. *Triæris*). There is no epigyne. MALE PALPS : Text-fig. 38, C.

OCCURRENCE : Established in hot houses at Kew, Chester and Alnwick.

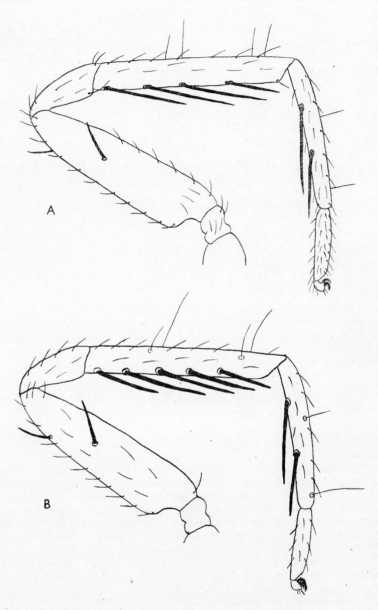

TEXT-FIG. 36.—Leg I : A, *Oonops pulcher;* B, *O. domesticus.*

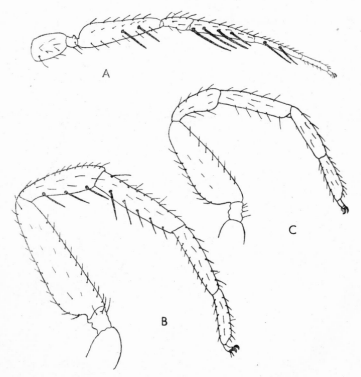

TEXT-FIG. 37.—Leg I: A, *Ischnothyreus velox;* B, *Triæris stenaspis;* C, *Diblemma donisthorpei.*

3. Genus **TRIÆRIS** E. Simon 1891.

Triæris stenaspis Simon.

(Text-figs. 33, B ; 34, A ; 35, B ; 37, B)

Triæris stenaspis E. Simon, 1891, p. 561 ; A. R. Jackson, 1909, p. 419 ; O. P.-Cambridge, 1909 (1), p. 100 ; W. S. Bristowe, 1948, p. 890.

DESCRIPTION. LENGTH : c. 1·8 mm. The spider has a strong superficial resemblance to *Ischnothyreus velox,* but is generally redder. ABDOMEN : Dorsal scutum (Text-fig. 35, B) reddish-brown (darker than in *I. velox*). There is a small ventral scutum posterior to the epigastric fold. EYES : Arranged as in *Oonops* (Text-fig. 33, B). LABIUM : Semicircular (cf. *Ischnothyreus*). LEGS : Patella I very long (nearly equal to the tibia), progressively shorter in II, III and IV. Patellæ I and II with three pairs of ventral spines ; tibiæ I and II with five pairs (metatarsi have none) (cf. *Ischnothyreus*). There is no epigyne. The male is not known.

OCCURRENCE : Established in hot-houses at Dublin and, at one time, at Nunwick Hall, near Penrith.

4. Genus **DIBLEMMA** O. P.-Cambridge 1908.

Diblemma donisthorpei O. P.-Cambridge.

(Text-figs. 33, D ; 34, B ; 35, C ; 37, C ; 38, D)

Diblemma donisthorpei O. P.-Cambridge, 1908, p. 166 ; W. S. Bristowe, 1948, p. 890.

DESCRIPTION. LENGTH : ♀ ♂ : c. 2·5 mm. CARAPACE : Yellowish-brown. Not so high in profile as in most OONOPIDÆ. On each side of

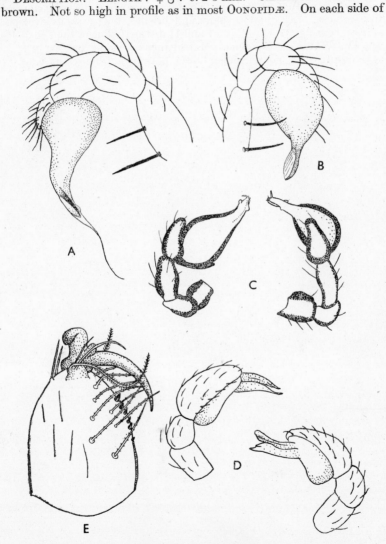

TEXT-FIG. 38.—Left male palps : A, *Oonops pulcher;* B, *O. domesticus;* C, *Ischnothyreus velox;* D, *Diblemma donisthorpei.*
E, chelicera of *Ischnothyreus velox.*

median line is a curved longitudinal line of bristles on minute tubercles. EYES : Two, of moderate size, nearly touching (Text-fig. 33, D). ABDOMEN : Bearing yellowish-brown scuta (Text-fig. 35, C) longer in ♂ than in ♀. Soft parts yellowish-white. Spinners encircled by a narrow chitinous collar. STERNUM : With small slits suggesting segmentation (Text-fig. 34, B). No chitinous strips connecting sternum to carapace. LEGS : With hairs and bristles, but no well-developed spines (Text-fig. 37, C). Coxæ I and II distinctly longer than coxæ III and IV. There is no epigyne. MALE PALPS : Text-fig. 38, D.

OCCURRENCE : Found under flower pots in hot-houses at Kew.

6. Family DYSDERIDÆ.

CHARACTERS OF FAMILY. CARAPACE : Smooth, with no thoracic fovea or impression. EYES : six ; all light coloured ; arranged in a compact group or, where in three groups of two, not widely separated

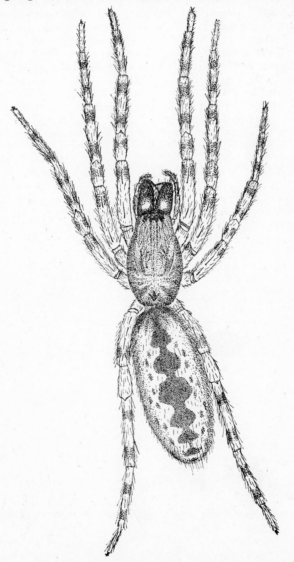

TEXT-FIG. 39.—*Segestria senoculata* ♀ (DYSDERIDÆ).

(Text-fig. 40, A, B, C). Ocular area not nearly as wide as head (cf. OONOPIDÆ). ABDOMEN : Cylindrical or oval, with two distinct pairs of spiracles on ventral surface ; the anterior pair lead to lung books the posterior pair (situated close behind the epigastric fold) to tracheae (Text-fig. 41, A). There is a distinct pattern in the Genus *Segestria* (Text-fig. 39). STERNUM : Elongate-oval with deep lateral impressions. CHELICERÆ : One or two rows of teeth and no lateral condyle. MAXILLÆ : Nearly straight, or only slightly inclined inwards (Text-fig. 40, D, E, F). FEMALE PALP : With an untoothed claw. LEGS : These bear scopulæ at least on III and IV. Coxæ I and II are distinctly longer than coxæ III and IV. The tarsi, less than one-third the length of metatarsi, bear two claws and a claw tuft (Text-fig. 41, B, C, D, E) or three claws and no claw tuft ; the paired claws are pectinate. EPIGYNE : None. MALE PALPAL ORGANS : Variable in structure, but always simple and exposed.

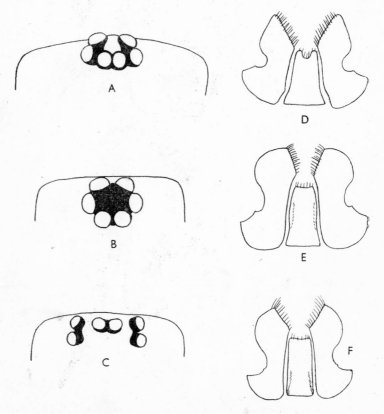

TEXT-FIG. 40.—Arrangement of eyes : A, *Dysdera;* B, *Harpactea;* C, *Segestria.* Maxillæ and labium : D, *Dysdera;* E, *Harpactea;* F, *Segestria.*

KEY TO THE GENERA

1. Eyes in a compact group (Text-fig. 40, A, B). Sternum connected to carapace by chitinous strips passing between the legs. No abdominal pattern   2
——Eyes in three separate pairs (Text-fig. 40, C). Sternum not connected to carapace by chitinous strips. Abdomen with a pattern of form shown in Text-fig. 39 (which may be obscured by dark pigmentation of entire abdomen) . . . . (3) **Segestria**
2. Eyes as in Text-fig. 40, A. Carapace red. Large spiders; length about 8–15 mm. . . . . (1) **Dysdera**
——Eyes as in Text-fig. 40, B. Carapace dark brown. Length about 5–7 mm. . . . .(2) **Harpactea**

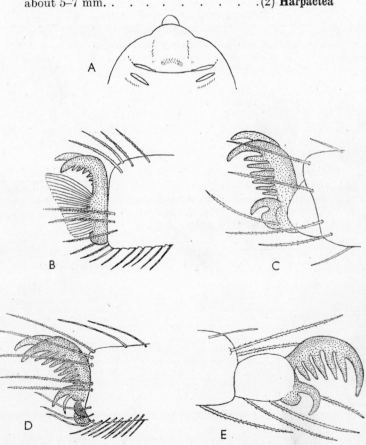

TEXT-FIG. 41.—A. *Dysdera crocata:* ventral side of anterior part of abdomen, showing spiracles and genital marking. Feet of Leg I: B, *Dysdera;* C, *Harpactea;* D, *Segestria.* E, foot of Leg IV of *Harpactea.*

1. Genus **DYSDERA** P.A.Latreille 1804.

CHARACTERS OF GENUS. EYES : Text-fig. 40, A. Sternum connected to carapace by chitinous strips passing between coxæ. CHELICERÆ : Very strong and projecting in front. Basal segment with one row of teeth (usually three) ; fang exceptionally long. LABIUM : Anterior margin deeply excavated in shape of a half circle (Text fig. 40, D). LEGS : Bearing spines. Scopulæ more or less restricted to apical portions of metatarsi III and IV. Two tarsal claws and dense claw tufts (Text-fig. 41, B). The colouring of the two British species is dull red to deep orange, with a nearly hairless light grey or nearly white abdomen.

Dysdera erythrina (Walckenaer).
(Text-fig. 42, A, D)

Aranea erythrina C. A. Walckenaer, 1802, p. 224. *Dysdera erythrina* J. Blackwall' 1861–4, p. 270. *D. cambridgei* T. Thorell, 1873, p. 455 ; O. P.-Cambridge, 1879–81, p. 6 ; C. Chyzer and L. Kulczynski, 1891–7, p. 268. *D. erythrina* E. Simon, 1914, p. 99.

Dysdera crocata C. L. Koch.
(Text-figs. 41, A ; 42, B, C, E)

Dysdera crocata C. L. Koch, 1839 (1), V, p. 81. *D. rubicunda* J. Blackwall, 1861–4, p. 371 (not C. L. Koch or A. Menge). *D. crocata* O. P.-Cambridge, 1879–81, p. 6 ; E. Simon, 1914, p. 95 ; B. J. Kaston, 1948, p. 62.

D. erythrina and *D. crocata* are among our larger spiders ; they resemble one another closely, but the following characters will usually serve to separate them, although it has been found that the spines alone are not absolutely reliable. The chitinous parts are red to deep orange, the abdomen grey or nearly white.

	D. erythrina	*D. crocata*
Length . .	♂: c. 8 mm. ♀: c. 10 mm.	♂: 9–10 mm. ♀: 11–15 mm.
Femur IV . .	No dorsal spines	Short spines (usually 2) dorsally, close to basal end. Text-fig. 42, C.
Tibia IV . .	Usually with 2 ventral spines in basal half (apart from the lateral and apical spines). Text-fig. 42, D.	Usually with 1 ventral spine in basal half (apart from the lateral and apical spines). Text-fig. 42, E.
♀ genital markings.	No distinct subcutaneous genital marking.	In preserved specimens a small subcutaneous genital marking usually visible anterior to epigastric fold. Text-fig. 41, A.
♂ palpal organs	Text-fig. 42, A.	Text-fig. 42, B.

OCCURRENCE : Both species are met with fairly frequently, although *D. erythrina* is not recorded north of Lancashire. They build no snare, but live under stones, often in silk cells, and emerge on hunting excursions at night. They like warm situations, *e.g.* stones heated by the sun, rubbish dumps, etc. Adult in early summer.

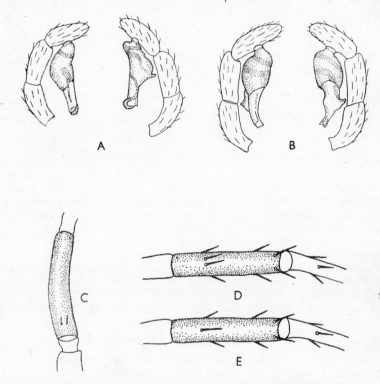

TEXT-FIG. 42.—Left male palps : A, *Dysdera erythrina;* B, *D. crocata;* C, Femur IV (above) of *D. crocata.* D, Tibia IV (below) of *D. erythrina.* E, do. of *D. crocata.*

2. Genus **HARPACTEA** Bristowe 1939.

CHARACTERS OF GENUS. Like *Dysdera*, from which it differs in the arrangement of the eyes (Text-fig. 40, B) and the shape of the apex of the labium (Text-fig. 40, E).

Harpactea hombergi (Scopoli).
(Text-figs. 40, B, E ; 41, C, E ; 43)

Aranea hombergi J. A. Scopoli 1763, p. 403. *Dysdera hombergii* J. Blackwall, 1861–4, p. 371. *Harpactes hombergi* O. P.-Cambridge, 1879–81, p. 7 ; C. Chyzer and L. Kulczynski, 1891–7, II, p. 273 ; E. Simon, 1914, p. 104.

TEXT-FIG. 43.—Left male palp of *Harpactea hombergi*.

DESCRIPTION. LENGTH : ♀: 6–7 mm. ♂: 5–6 mm. CARAPACE : Dark brown, narrowing anteriorly more than in *Dysdera*. EYES : Text-fig. 40, B. ABDOMEN : Tubular, very slender and attenuated, especially in the male ; pale dull grey or brown. CHELICERÆ : With two teeth in the outer and two or three teeth in the inner row ; fangs long, but not exceptionally so. LABIUM : Anterior margin nearly straight, only slightly concave (Text-fig. 40, E). LEGS : With three tarsal claws, with no claw tuft. Tarsus IV with a distinct onychium. (Text-fig. 41, E). EPIGYNE : None. MALE PALP : Text-fig. 43.

OCCURRENCE : Widely distributed and commonly found in silk cells under bark of trees or stones or among dry matted vegetation, often in woods. Adult apparently at all seasons.

3. Genus **SEGESTRIA** P.A.Latreille, 1804.

CHARACTERS OF GENUS. The general appearance of the female is shown in Text-fig. 39 ; the males are similar but with relatively longer legs. They are large spiders. EYES : Text-fig. 40, C. ABDOMEN : Pattern, as in Text-fig. 39, is characteristic (obscure or indiscernible in adult females of *S. florentina*). STERNUM : Elongated and somewhat attenuated in front. CHELICERÆ : With two rows of teeth ; outer row with three teeth, central tooth being much the largest ; inner row with two teeth. LABIUM : Anterior margin nearly straight, slightly concave. MAXILLÆ : Straight, inner margins scarcely inclined inwards (Text-fig. 40, F). LEGS : I and II noticeably thicker and stronger than III and IV. Metatarsi and tarsi I and II with thick scopulæ throughout entire length of ventral surface. There are three tarsal claws and no claw tufts (Text-fig. 41, D).

The three species of the genus live in silk tubes constructed in crevices in walls, under bark or under stones. About a dozen threads radiate from the entrance of the tube.

Segestria senoculata (Linnaeus).

(Text-figs. 39 ; 44, A, F)

Aranea senoculata Linnaeus, 1758, p. 622. *Segestria senoculata* J. Blackwall, 1861–4,
p. 374 ; O. P.-Cambridge, 1879–81, p. 7 ; C. Chyzer and L. Kulczynski, 1891–7, II,
p. 263 ; E. Simon, 1914, p. 110.

DESCRIPTION. LENGTH : ♀ ♂ : 7–10 mm. The female is shown in
Text-fig. 39 ; the abdominal pattern is conspicuous. The male is
similar with relatively longer legs. LEGS : Metatarsi I, seen ventrally,
with one short median spine at apex and *three pairs* of ventrolateral
spines (apart from the unpaired prolateral spine in basal half, which is
usually present) (Text-fig. 44, F). EPIGYNE : None. MALE PALP :
Text-fig. 44, A. It tapers away into a long fine curved embolus.

OCCURRENCE : Widespread all over the British Isles and often very
common. In crevices in walls, amongst loose stones, under bark of
trees. Adult in April and May.

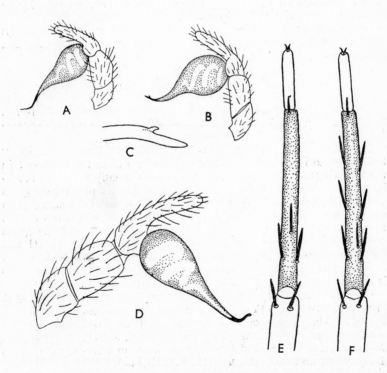

TEXT-FIG. 44.—Male palps· A. *Segestria senoculata;* B, *S. bavarica;* C, do.
(bifurcation of embolus) ; D, *S. florentina.*
Metatarsi I (ventral side) : E, *Segestria bavarica* and *S. florentina;* F, *S.*
senoculata.

Segestria bavarica C. L. Koch.
(Text-figs. 44, B, E)

Segestria bavarica C. L. Koch, 1843 (1), X, p. 93 ; O. P.-Cambridge, 1879–81, p. 8
C. Chyzer and L. Kulczynski, 1891–7, II, p. 263 ; E. Simon, 1914, p. 110.

DESCRIPTION. LENGTH : ♀ ♂ : 10–12 mm. ABDOMEN : Markings
as in the last species, except that centres of rounded lobes are pale in
colour. Remainder of dorsal surface greyish fawn, well spotted with
black. Ventrally : there is a distinct (or indistinct) broad black band.
STERNUM : Dark brown, distinctly darker than coxæ. CHELICERÆ :
Polished black or brown. LEGS : II, III and IV clearly annulated.
Metatarsi I viewed ventrally : each bear one short median spine at apex
and *one pair* of ventrolateral spines, close to basal margin (one or both
of these spines are usually absent in adult males, but are present on
leg II). Close to the pair, but a little further from the basal margin,
is a single median spine. A single retrolateral spine is sometimes
present in the apical half (Text-fig. 44, E). EPIGYNE : None. MALE
PALP : Text-fig. 44, B. The tip of the embolus is shorter than in the
last species and distinctly bifurcated.

OCCURRENCE : Very rare on the mainland. Recorded from Scilly
Islands, Lundy, Channel Islands, Berkshire and Dorset (Portland and
Ringstead) ; Cornwall (Tintagel).

Segestria florentina (Rossi).
(Text-fig. 44, D, E)

Aranea florentina P. Rossi, 1790, p. 133. *Segestria perfida* J. Blackwall, 1861–4,
p. 373. *S. florentina* O. P.-Cambridge, 1879–81, p. 459 ; C. Chyzer and L. Kulczynski,
1891–7, II, p. 263 ; E. Simon, 1914, p. 109.

DESCRIPTION. LENGTH : ♀ ♂ : 13–22 mm. (In this respect probably
the largest British spider.) This fine species differs from the last in
the following respects. ABDOMEN : In adults usually a uniform blackish-brown with the dorsal band indistinct or indiscernible (although in
young specimens it may be quite clear). The lobes of the band, when
visible, without pale centres. STERNUM : Reddish-brown to dark
brown, same colour as coxæ. CHELICERÆ : With a metallic green
sheen (sometimes bronze in the male). LEGS : I black ; II, III and
IV without annulations in adults. Metatarsi I as in *S. bavarica*.
EPIGYNE : None. MALE PALPS : Text-fig. 44, D. The embolus
is shorter than in *S. senoculata* and not bifurcated as in *S. bavarica*.

OCCURRENCE : Very local, almost always at or near a sea port
(Exeter, Tiverton, Plymouth, Bristol, Westminster, Bridport,
Fowey). Where it does occur, many specimens are often found together
within a small radius, inhabiting holes in walls, or living under stones.
Males have been observed to reach maturity in late July (A. A. D.
La Touche) and early August (W. S. Bristowe).

7. Family SCYTODIDÆ (SICARIIDÆ)

CHARACTERS OF FAMILY. EYES : Six in number. CARAPACE : Unusually high behind (Text-fig. 9, A). LABIUM : Fused to sternum. LEGS : Very slender.

Genus **SCYTODES** P.A. Latreille 1804.

The single species, *Scytodes thoracica* Latreille is our sole representative of this family.

Scytodes thoracica Latreille.
(Text-figs. 45, 46)

Scytodes thoracica P. A. Latreille, 1804 (2), p. 249 ; J. Blackwall, 1861–4, p. 380 ; O. P.-Cambridge, 1879–81, p. 75, and 1896, p. 57 ; E. Simon, 1914, p. 74 ; W. S. Bristowe, 1947, p. 24 ; B. J. Kaston, 1948, p. 65.

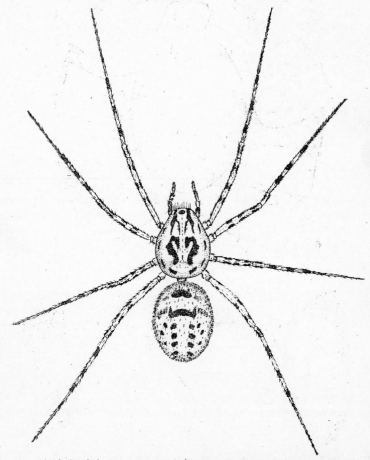

TEXT-FIG. 45.—*Scytodes thoracica* ♀ (SCYTODIDÆ).

DESCRIPTION. LENGTH : ♀ ♂ : ca. 5–6 mm. CARAPACE : With no thoracic fovea or impressions, very high posteriorly ; pale yellow with numerous blackish spots which sometimes join to form patterns or irregular lines (Text-fig. 45). EYES : Six in number, small and light-coloured, arranged in three widely-separated pairs, the median pair well in advance of the lateral pair. ABDOMEN : Short, coloured as the

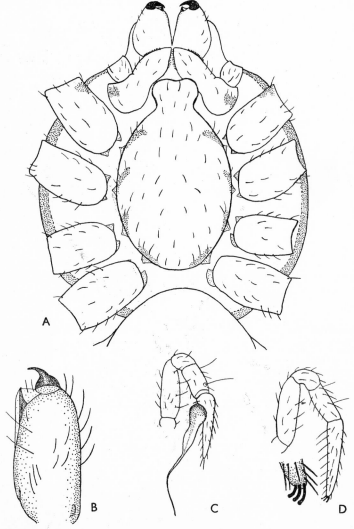

TEXT-FIG.46.—*Scytodes thoracica:* A, ventral view of cephalothorax; B, chelicera; C, male palp ; D, female palp.

carapace ; there is, on the ventral surface, an indistinct median tracheal spiracle closer to the spinners than to the epigastric furrow. SPINNERS : Small and preceded by a projecting and somewhat conical colulus. STERNUM : Oval, pale yellow with a short black lateral bar opposite each leg. LABIUM : Fused to the sternum, slightly darker in colour, short and with a slightly concave anterior margin. CHELICERÆ : With a very short squat fang and a conspicuous chitinous lamina on the outer margin of the basal segment (Text-fig. 46, B) giving the cheliceræ a chelate appearance. MAXILLÆ : Long, narrow and pointed, inclined inwards with their tips touching. LEGS : Slender, and annulated. EPIGYNE : None, but two slightly chitinised circular genital openings occur posterior to the epigastric furrow. MALE PALP : Text-fig. 46, C.

OCCURRENCE : Rare, in counties bordering the south coast ; it has been found as far north as Oxford. The spiders are to be seen in houses at night, slowly traversing walls and ceilings, especially after a hot day. They seem to make no snare but catch their prey by squirting gum from the cheliceræ at a distance of one quarter to one half an inch.

8. Family PHOLCIDÆ.

CHARACTERS OF FAMILY. EYES : Eight in number (six in some foreign species), arranged as in Text-fig. 12, B, C.   CHELICERÆ : Fused at the base (this is difficult to see), armed in both sexes with a long dark coloured tooth on the inner margin (Text-fig. 48, B) ; the males have additional teeth or bosses on the front.   LEGS : Extremely long and thin, the long tarsi having false segmentation lines (Text-fig.12,D.). The tarsi have three claws.   PALPS : Very short in both sexes ; that of the female is without a claw but has some serrated bristles at its extremity.   EPIGYNES : Very simple type.   MALE PALPAL ORGANS : Relatively complex though of the exposed type.

The two British species of this family are included in the two genera *Pholcus* and *Physocyclus;* they are readily separated by their size, general appearance and habitat.   In this country they occur only inside buildings.

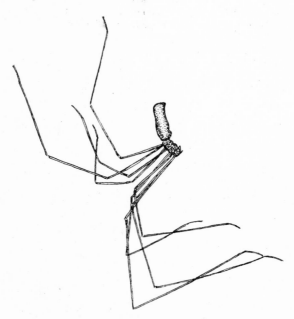

TEXT-FIG. 47.—*Pholcus phalangioides* ♀ (PHOLCIDÆ).

1. Genus **PHOLCUS** C. A. Wackenaer 1805.

CHARACTERS OF GENUS.   EYES : Anterior medians practically contiguous, but well separated from the laterals ; median ocular trapezium much wider than long.   ABDOMEN : long and cylindrical, with the spinners far removed from the epigastric fold.

Pholcus phalangioides (Fuesslin).
(Text-figs. 47 ; 48, A, B, C)

Aranea phalangioides J. C. Fuesslin, 1775, p. 61. *P. phalangioides* J. Blackwall, 1861–4, p. 208 ; C. Chyzer and L. Kulczynski, 1891–7, I, p 109 ; E. Simon, 1914, p. 237 ; B. J. Kaston, 1948, p. 68.

DESCRIPTION. LENGTH : 8–10 mm. in both sexes. CARAPACE : Considerably narrowed in front ; it is pale yellow with a central brown marking in the region of the fovea, and clothed with some fine hairs. EYES : Anterior medians almost contiguous but separated by about one diameter from the laterals (Text-fig. 12, B, C). ABDOMEN : Cylindrical in shape, about three times as long as wide. Grey, with no pattern, clothed with numerous short fine hairs. SPINNERS : Far removed from the epigastric fold (cf. *Physocyclus simoni*). CHELICERÆ : Armed in the male, in addition to the large tooth on the margin (characteristic of the family), with two extra tooth-like prominences (Text-fig. 48, B). LEGS : Very long, brown in colour and clothed with numerous long fine hairs. FEMALE PALP : Very short, armed at the tip with a blunt tooth and with some stout curved serrated bristles. EPIGYNE : Has a small tongue-shaped process anteriorly (Text-fig. 48, C). MALE PALP : Of very unusual appearance (Text-fig. 48, A).

OCCURRENCE : This spider is so characteristic in appearance and habitat that it will not be mistaken for any other species. It inhabits dwelling houses and outbuildings in the southern half of the country and is conspicuous hanging upside down in its web in the corners of rooms, etc., usually at ceiling level. The female may sometimes be found clasping its globular cocoon, which is ca. 5 mm. in diameter. It appears to be adult at most seasons.

2. Genus **PHYSOCYCLUS** E. Simon 1893.

CHARACTERS OF GENUS. EYES : Anteriors practically contiguous : median ocular trapezium as long as anterior width. ABDOMEN : Very globular and convex, higher than long ; spinners very close to epigastric fold.

Physocyclus simoni Berland.
(Text-fig. 48, D, E, F)

P. simoni L. Berland, 1911, p. 110 ; W. S. Bristowe, 1933 (2), p. 510.

DESCRIPTION. LENGTH : 2–2·5 mm. in both sexes. CARAPACE : Yellow-brown, with the head divided fairly sharply from the thoracic region. EYES : Very similar in arrangement to those of *Pholcus*, but with the anterior medians close to the laterals. ABDOMEN : Very globular, clothed with fine hairs. Grey in colour with a faint bluish tinge which sometimes becomes pronounced in spirit. SPINNERS : These lie very close to the epigastric fold. CHELICERÆ : Armed in the male, in addition to the large tooth on the margin, with a pronounced black tooth on the front (Text-fig. 48, E). LEGS : Very long, yellow to yellow-brown in colour and clothed with some fine hairs. FEMALE

PALP : Very short and armed at its extremity with some curved serrated
bristles.   EPIGYNE : Appears to be a simple transverse slit (Text-fig.
48, F).   MALE PALP : Text-fig. 48, D.

OCCURRENCE : This species has been found exclusively in dry wine
cellars, where it lives in angles and corners in an inverted position on
its web.   The female clasps its globular cocoon, which is 2–3 mm. in
diameter, in a somewhat similar manner to *Pholcus*.   Adults are probably to be found at most seasons.

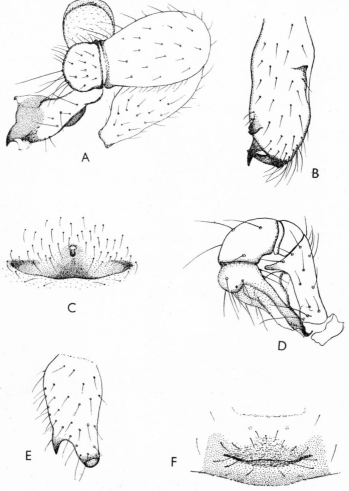

TEXT-FIG. 48.—*Pholcus phalangioides:* A, male palp (side) ; B, male chelicera ;
    C, epigyne.
    Physocyclus simoni: D, male palp (side) ; E, male chelicera ; F, epigyne.

9. Family GNAPHOSIDÆ.

CHARACTERS OF FAMILY. Typical appearance, Text-fig. 49. CARAPACE : Broad or attenuated in front, marked with a fovea (except in *Micaria*), not markedly convex. EYES : In two rows. Anterior medians generally distinctly darker than the rest ; posterior medians often irregular in shape (in the sense that they are not circular but

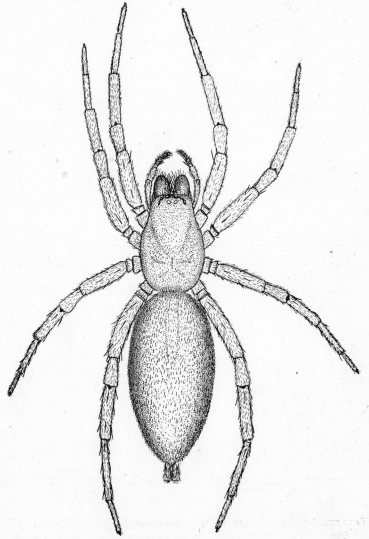

TEXT-FIG. 49.—*Drassodes lapidosus* ♀ (GNAPHOSIDÆ).

markedly oval or nearly triangular). ABDOMEN: Usually rather long and narrow, without very clear markings (except in *Phœocedus* and *Micaria*). SPINNERS: Projecting from posterior end of abdomen, the anteriors usually distinctly cylindrical and set apart from one another (Text-fig. 7, A, B). CHELICERÆ: Usually vertical and toothed; inner margin with one or more teeth (there is, in addition, a serrated

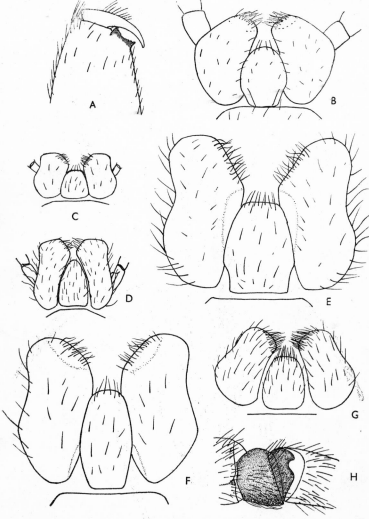

TEXT-FIG. 50.—A, Chelicera of *Gnaphosa*. Maxillæ and labium of: B, *Gnaphosa*; C, *Micaria*; D, *Phœocedus*; E, *Drassodes*; F, *Scotophœus*; G, *Zelotes*. H, Notched trochanter of *Drassodes lapidosus*.

chitinous ridge in *Gnaphosa* (Text-fig. 50, A), see also *Phæocedus* (Text-fig. 55, E)). MAXILLÆ : Variable (Text-fig. 50, B to G) inner margins inclined more or less inwards. LABIUM : Longer than broad, reaching beyond the mid point of maxillæ. LEGS : Rather long, bearing spines on all femora, on tibiæ and metatarsi III and IV and, sometimes, on tibiæ and metatarsi I and II (these last may be used in identification ; the rest are not referred to again in descriptions). The tarsi at least bear scopulæ (often less distinct on III and IV). There are two pectinate tarsal claws and claw tufts.

The GNAPHOSIDÆ are, for the most part, dull coloured or black, living under stones, amongst leaves or the roots of grasses or heather (*Scotophæus* normally occurs only inside houses or out-buildings). Some build silken retreats but no regular web for the capture of prey. Most are nocturnal in habits, but *Micaria* is found running in sunshine.

KEY TO THE GENERA

1. Cheliceræ with a prominent serrated ridge on the inner margin (Text-fig. 50, A). Posterior row of eyes recurved. Maxillæ : Text-fig. 50, B . . . . . (5) **Gnaphosa**

——Cheliceræ with a tooth or teeth on inner margin (except *Phæocedus*), but no serrated ridge. Posterior row of eyes procurved or straight. Maxillæ : (Text-fig. 50, C to G)   2

2. Carapace with no fovea. Anterior spinners close to one another. Maxillæ : Text-fig. 50, C. Small spiders clothed with squamiform hairs . . . . (6) **Micaria**

——Carapace with a fovea. Anterior spinners set well apart from each other. Larger spiders   3

3. Anterior median eyes larger than the laterals. (The medians are circular, the laterals elliptical ; the comparison applies to the minor axis) . . (2) **Scotophæus**

——Anterior median eyes not larger, usually smaller, than the laterals   4

4. Both rows of eyes nearly straight (the anteriors viewed from in front). Sternum long and narrow. Abdomen with a characteristic pattern (see description, p. 106) . . . . (3) **Phæocedus**

——Anterior row of eyes procurved (as viewed from in front). Sternum oval, not so narrow. No characteristic abdominal pattern   5

5. Posterior row of eyes straight, or nearly so, and scarcely longer than the anterior. Carapace markedly attenuated in front. Most species black . . . . (4) **Zelotes**

——Posterior row of eyes procurved, longer than the anterior. Carapace broad, not attenuated, in front (Text-fig. 49) . . . . (1) **Drassodes**

1. Genus **DRASSODES** N. Westring 1851.

CHARACTERS OF GENUS. CARAPACE : Rather flat, broad in front (cf. *Scotophœus*, *Phœocedus* and *Zelotes*), with a fovea (cf. *Micaria*) and covered with fine pubescence (Text-fig. 49). EYES : Anterior row slightly procurved (as seen from in front) ; medians slightly smaller than laterals (cf. *Scotophœus*) and a little closer to the laterals than to each other. Posterior row longer, slightly procurved ; medians oval, slightly larger than laterals and much closer to each other than to adjacent laterals. ABDOMEN : The whole covered with a fine pubescence and with a " mousy " appearance. A faint longitudinal dorsal stripe may be visible on anterior half, followed, in some cases by some light chevrons. Three pairs of faint light spots or impressions usually present about the middle, the central pair being closest to one another and posterior pair the largest. SPINNERS : Typical of the family. STERNUM : Oval and pointed behind. CHELICERÆ : Strong ; ♀, nearly vertical ; ♂, often much longer and projecting forwards. There are normally two teeth on inner margin and two on the outer, with one median, basal to the rest ; but the arrangement of the outer ones in the male is variable. MAXILLÆ and LABIUM : Text-fig. 50, E. LEGS : Tibiæ I and II sometimes bear one ventral spine on the apical half (cf. *Scotophœus*) ; metatarsus I bears 0–2 (at the base) and metatarsus II bears 1–2. Scopulæ consist of closely set, short, blunt little spines, often mixed with slightly longer aculeate spines and bristles, and extend nearly to the base of metatarsi I and II, and to the base of tarsi III and IV.

The six British species fall naturally into two groups :

Group I. *Drassodes lapidosus, D. pubescens.*

Each with a similar appearance and mouse-grey colouration. Tibia IV with two dorsal spines. Trochanters notched (Text-fig. 50, H). Male tibial apophysis small, pointed, directed outwards and forwards. Epigyne small.

Group II. *Drassodes signifer, D. dalmatensis, D. silvestris, D. minor.*

These species are darker and have relatively shorter legs. Tibia IV with no dorsal spine, or one (*D. silvestris*). Trochanters without a notch. Male palpal tibial apophysis blunt and directed forwards. Epigyne large.

Group I.

Drassodes lapidosus (Walckenaer).
(Text-figs. 7, A, B ; 49 ; 50, H ; 51, A, B, E ; 52, A)

Aranea lapidosa C. A. Walckenaer, 1802, p. 222. *Drassus lapidicolens* J. Blackwall, 1861–4, p. 116 ; O. P.-Cambridge, 1879–81, p. 19. *D. lapidicola* C. Chyzer and L. Kulczynski, 1891–7, II, p. 220. *Drassodes lapidosus* E. Simon, 1914, pp. 121, 126, 129 ; E. Reimoser, 1937, p. 13 ; A. Tullgren, 1946, p. 94.

DESCRIPTION. LENGTH : Very variable, from 6 to 24 mm., but usually about 10–15 mm. CARAPACE : Light yellow brown to red brown, covered thickly with very small hairs. Faint streaks radiate

from a fovea ; there is a thin dark borderline. ABDOMEN : Mouse
grey, covered with pubescence as the carapace, with sometimes a
faint dorsal marking to about the mid point. STERNUM : Coloured as
the carapace, darker towards the edges. CHELICERÆ : Strong ;
darker than the carapace. In the male divergent, elongated and

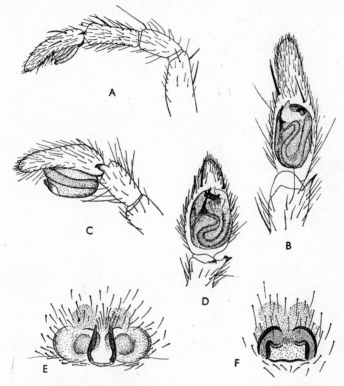

TEXT-FIG. 51.—Male palps : A, *Drassodes lapidosus* (side) ; B, do. (below) ;
C, *D. pubescens* (side) ; D, do. (below).
Epigynes : E, *Drassodes lapidosus;* F, *D. pubescens.*

projecting in front. Teeth in outer row normally as in Text-fig.
52, A (cf. *D. pubescens*). LEGS : Almost the same uniform colour as
carapace, usually lighter on ventral sides. EPIGYNE : Text-fig. 51, E.
MALE PALP : Text-fig. 51, A, B. The tibia is relatively very long compared with the other species of the genus, the apophysis being small
and acute.

OCCURRENCE : This is the commonest species of the genus and is
very widespread ; to be found in most localities, often abundantly,
under stones, tiles, etc., usually occupying a silken cell. Adults can
be taken at all seasons.

VARIETIES.

D. lapidosus is a variable species. The cheliceral teeth and, to some
extent, the tibial apophysis on the male palps, vary somewhat according
to the size of the spider, and allometric growth is almost certainly taking
place here. Different opinions have been expressed as to the status of
the varieties but two, occurring in Britain, have been generally

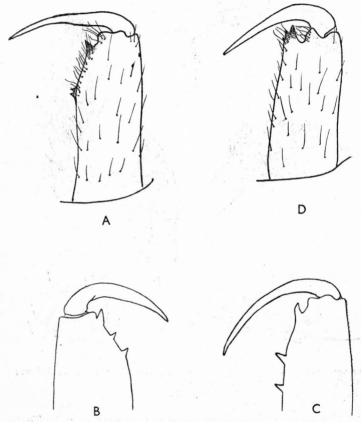

TEXT-FIG. 52.—Male cheliceræ : A, *Drassodes lapidosus;* B, do. var. *macer;*
C, do. var. *cupreus;* D, *Drassodes pubescens.*

recognised : var. *macer* (Thor.) and var. *cupreus* (Bl.). They may be
recognised by the teeth in the outer row of the cheliceræ (Text-Figs.
52, B and C). This different spacing of the teeth does not seem to
depend on the size of the spider and is thus not merely the result of
allometric growth. If females exist corresponding to these male
varieties, they cannot be distinguished with certainty by any constant
characters known at present.

Drassodes lapidosus var. macer (Thorell).
(Text-fig. 52, B)

Drassus lapidicola macer T. Thorell, 1875 (1), p. 94. *Drassus macer* O. P.-Cambridge, 1895, p. 100. *Drassodes lapidosus macer* E. Simon, 1914, p. 126 ; E. Reimoser, 1937, p. 14 ; Tullgren, 1946, p. 94.

OCCURRENCE : Mainly southern in range and not very common.

Drassodes lapidosus var. cupreus (Blackwall).
(Text-fig. 52, C)

Drassus cupreus J. Blackwall, 1834, p. 435, and 1861–4, p. 114. *Drassodes lapidosus cupreus* E. Simon, 1914, p. 127 ; Tullgren, 1946, p. 94.

OCCURRENCE : Extends north into Scotland and is said to be predominant in northern England, Scotland and parts of Eire.

Drassodes pubescens (Thorell).
(Text-figs. 51, C, D, F ; 52, D)

Drassus pubescens T. Thorell, 1856, p. 110 ; O. P.-Cambridge, 1879–81, p. 20 ; C. Chyzer and L. Kulczynski, 1891–7, II, p. 220. *Drassodes pubescens* E. Simon, 1914, pp. 124, 130 ; E. Reimoser, 1937, p. 14 ; Tullgren, 1946, p. 96.

DESCRIPTION. LENGTH : ♀ : about 6·5 mm. ♂ : about 4·5 mm. This species resembles the lighter specimens of *D. lapidosus*, from which it is distinguished by considering the following characters : CARAPACE : Borderline very narrow, often scarcely visible. CHELICERÆ : ♂ : Furnished with a strong trifid process (Text-fig. 52, D) as opposed to the single large tooth of *D. lapidosus*, at the apical end of the outer margin of the fang groove. EPIGYNE : Text-fig. 51, F. This is quite distinct from that of *D. lapidosus*. MALE PALP : Text-fig. 51, C, D. This differs from that of *D. lapidosus* (*a*) in the much shorter tibia (*b*) in the form of the tibial apophysis.

OCCURRENCE : Rather rare but widespread. It has been found in fens, on heaths and in woods, usually under stones or pieces of dried mud or turf.

Group II.

Drassodes signifer (C. L. Koch).
(Text-figs. 53, A, D, G ; 54, A)

Drassus signifer C. L. Koch, 1839 (1), VI, p. 31. *D. clavator* J. Blackwall, 1861–4, p. 109. *D. troglodytes* O. P.-Cambridge, 1879–81, p. 17 ; C. Chyzer and L Kulczynski, 1891–7, II, p. 217. *D. mysticus* O. P.-Cambridge, 1894 (1), p. 104. *Drassodes signifer* E. Simon, 1914, pp. 122, 140 ; B. J. Kaston, 1948, p. 350. *Haplodrassus signifer* E. Reimoser, 1937, p. 17 ; A. Tullgren, 1946, p. 98.

DESCRIPTION. LENGTH : ♀ : 8–8·5 mm. ♂ : 6–8 mm. CARAPACE : Greyish-yellow to red-brown with more or less distinct radiating markings, rather thickly covered with longish hairs. ABDOMEN : Dark brown or nearly black, covered with thick, short pubescence. A darker longitudinal stripe may occur in anterior half, sometimes flanked by two pairs of light spots followed by a pair of oval patches.

Between these and the spinners obscure light chevrons may occur. In living specimens the abdomen frequently has a coppery sheen. LEGS: Tibiæ I and II with no ventral spines. Metatarsus II with one pair of ventral spines near the base; metatarsus I with none (cf.

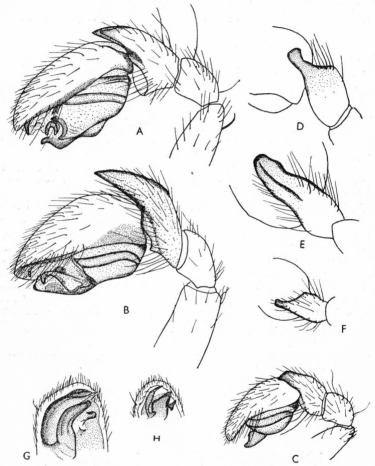

TEXT-FIG. 53.—Male palps (side): A, *Drassodes signifer;* B, *D. silvestris:* C, *D. dalmatensis.*
Male palpal tibiæ (above): D, *Drassodes signifer;* E, *D. silvestris;* F, *D. dalmatensis.*
Tips of palps (below): G, *Drassodes signifer;* H, *D. dalmatensis.*

D. dalmatensis and *D. silvestris).* EPIGYNE: Text-fig. 54, A. This is very distinct and makes the identification of the species an easy matter. MALE PALP: Text-fig. 53, A. The tibial apophysis is quite distinct when seen from above (Text-fig. 53, D) ; the only possible confusion would be with the much smaller *D. dalmatensis* (Text-fig. 53, F) but the tips of the palps viewed from below are different (Text-fig. 53, G, H).

OCCURRENCE : Widespread and fairly frequent on open heaths ; under stones or among roots of heather or grass. Mature in spring and summer.

Drassodes dalmatensis (L. Koch).
(Text-figs. 53, C, F, H ; 54, B)

Drassus dalmatensis L. Koch 1866, p. 89. *D. minisculus* C. Chyzer and L. Kulczynski 1891-7, p. 217. *D. delinquens* O.P.-Cambridge, 1879-81, p. 21 *Drassodes dalmatensis* E. Simon, 1914, p. 137. *Haplodrassus dalmatensis* Tullgren 1946, p. 100.

DESCRIPTION. This species resembles *D. signifer*, but is much smaller. LENGTH : ♀: 5 mm. ♂ : 4·5 mm. It differs also from that species in the following characters : ABDOMEN : Light chevrons usually more distinct and joined by a light median stripe. LEGS : Metatarsi I and II with one ventral spine. EPIGYNE : Text-fig. 54, B. MALE PALP : Text-fig. 53, C, F. The tibial apophysis is not unlike that of *D. signifer* viewed from above, but the tip of the palp seen from below is different (Text-fig. 53, G, H).

OCCURRENCE : A rare species, found amongst heather. Not recorded north of Staffordshire. Mature in April, and probably throughout the summer.

Drassodes silvestris (Blackwall).
(Text-figs. 53, B, E ; 54, D)

Drassus silvestris J. Blackwall, 1833, p. 440, and 1861-4, p. 113 ; C. Chyzer and L. Kulczynski, 1891-7, II, p. 216. *D. criminalis* O. P.-Cambridge, 1875, p. 224, 1879-81, p. 20. *Drassodes silvestris* E. Simon, 1914, p. 135. *Haplodrassus silvestris* E. Reimoser, 1937, p. 15 ; A. Tullgren, 1946, p. 105.

DESCRIPTION. LENGTH : ♀: 8–10 mm. ♂ : 7·5 mm. This spider resembles *D. signifer* in general appearance but differs thus : CARAPACE and LEGS of a more reddish-brown. Metatarsi I and II each have a pair of spines, or a single spine, ventrally. EPIGYNE : Text-fig. 54, D. The characteristic " key-hole " appearance is very distinct. MALE PALP : Text-fig. 53, B. The tibial apophysis has a slightly serrated ridge along its dorsal side and is quite different from that of *D. signifer* seen from above (Text-fig. 53, E).

OCCURRENCE : Widespread but rather rare. Woods, among leaves or under stones. Mature in spring and autumn.

Drassodes minor (O. P.-Cambridge).
(Text-fig. 54, C)

Drassus minor O. P.-Cambridge, 1879, p. 192 ; Chyzer and L. Kulczynski, 1891-7, II, p. 219. *Haplodrassus minor* E. Reimoser, 1937, p. 18.

DESCRIPTION. Like *D. silvestris* in form and general appearance, but is smaller. LENGTH : ♀: 4 mm. EPIGYNE : Text fig. 54, C.

H

OCCURRENCE : A single adult and two immature females were found by O. Pickard-Cambridge at the roots of coarse grass and herbage on the Chesil beach near Portland Station on 6th June, 1879 ; an immature female was found near the same spot on 11th June, 1895.

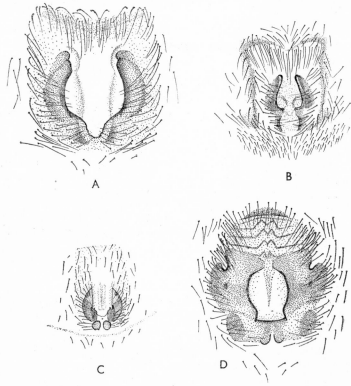

TEXT-FIG. 54.—Epigynes : A, *Drassodes signifer;* B, *D. dalmatensis;* C, *D. minor;* D, *D. silvestris.*

2. Genus **SCOTOPHÆUS** E. Simon 1893.

CHARACTERS OF GENUS. General appearance very like that of *Drassodes*. CARAPACE : Narrower in front than in *Drassodes*. EYES : Anterior medians considerably larger than laterals. Posterior row slightly longer than anterior, very slightly procurved ; eyes equidistant and equal (cf. *Drassodes, Phœocedus, Gnaphosa*). MAXILLÆ and LABIUM : Text-fig. 50, F. There is but a single British species.

Scotophæus blackwalli (Thorell).
(Text-figs. 50, F ; 55, A, C)

Drassus blackwalli T. Thorell, 1873, p. 430 ; O. P.-Cambridge, 1879–81, p. 17. *Drassus sericeus* J. Blackwall, 1861–4, p. 67. *Scotophœus blackwalli* E. Simon, 1914, pp. 147, 150 ; E. Reimoser, 1937, p. 22 ; A. Tullgren, 1946, p. 110.

DESCRIPTION. LENGTH : ♀ : 10–11 mm. ♂ : 8–9 mm. CARAPACE: Narrower in front than in *Drassodes;* light to deep reddish-brown, covered sparsely and evenly with longish black hairs, with some pubescence, especially round the edges. EYES : Anterior row very slightly procurved, as seen from in front, almost straight ; medians

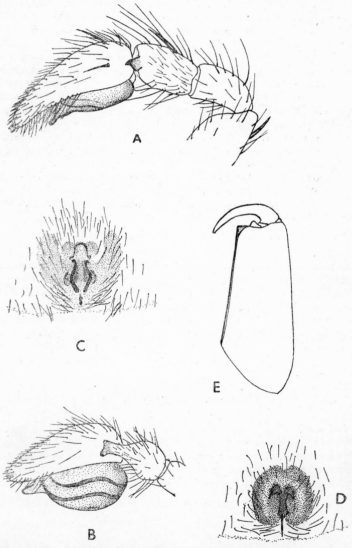

TEXT-FIG. 55.—*Scotophæus blackwalli:* A, male palp ; C, epigyne. *Phæocedus braccatus:* B, male palp ; D, epigyne ; E, chelicera.

considerably larger than the laterals (a distinctive character). Posterior row slightly longer and very slightly procurved ; eyes equidistant and equal (cf. *Drassodes, Phœocedus, Gnaphosa*). ABDOMEN : Uniform light brown to grey, covered thickly with fine pubescence, with a scutum in the male sometimes giving a wrinkled appearance along the sides. STERNUM : Oval, colour of the carapace. CHELICERÆ : Vertical, not as large as in *Drassodes* nor projecting in the male, with a number of long bristles on anterior surface. Outer margin with three teeth, inner with one (cf. *Drassodes*). LEGS : Colour as the carapace. ♂ : Tibiæ I and II with three pairs of ventral spines, metatarsi I and II with one pair. ♀ : Tibiæ I and II with two to three single spines, metatarsi I and II with one spine (cf. *Drassodes*). Scopulæ (consisting of hairs as in *Drassodes*) reach nearly to base of metatarsi I and II and tarsi III and IV. EPIGYNE : Text-fig. 55, C. MALE PALP : Text-fig. 55, A. The spider has a very mouse-like appearance and resembles a *Drassodes* in life, but is easily identified by considering the above characters (especially the eyes) as well as the sexual organs, which are quite distinct.

OCCURRENCE : Widespread. It seems to be confined almost exclusively to houses and out-houses, but in this habitat it is met with frequently and may often be found wandering at night. Mature in summer months.

3. Genus **PHAEOCEDUS** E. Simon 1893.

CHARACTERS OF GENUS. CARAPACE : slightly narrowed in front. EYES : anterior row straight (as seen from in front), eyes equal. Posterior row straight, slightly longer than anterior, medians irregular in shape, very slightly larger than laterals and further from them than from each other (cf. *Scotophœus*). STERNUM : oval and narrow. CHELICERÆ : vertical, noticeably long and narrow, convex at base, bearing no teeth, but with an angular projection apically inside (Text fig. 55, E). MAXILLÆ and LABIUM : Text-fig. 50, D. LEGS : Tibia II sometimes with an apical prolateral spine, but, except on femora, no other spines on I and II.

Phaeocedus braccatus (L. Koch).
(Text-figs. 50, D ; 55, B, D, E)

Drassus braccatus L. Koch, 1866, p. 97.   *D. bulbifer* O. P.-Cambridge, 1874, p. 386, 1879–81, p. 18.   *Phœocedus braccatus* C. Chyzer and L. Kulczynski, 1891–7, II, p. 229 ; E. Simon, 1914, p. 144 ; E. Reimoser, 1937, p. 19 ; T. Tullgren, 1946, p. 127.

DESCRIPTION. LENGTH : ♀ : 4·5–6·5 mm.   ♂ : 4·5 mm. CARAPACE : Brown, often reddish, depth of colour variable, covered sparsely with fine black hairs and having a dark borderline. There are faint radiating markings (two especially run from a little circular mark in front of the fovea to below the lateral eyes). ABDOMEN : Grey to black, covered with fine pubescence. Pattern in lighter specimens very distinct. It consists of a light pair of spots adjacent to the anterior margin, a second pair of oval spots just in front of the mid point, and another similar pair directly behind the mid point and usually smaller. Between the first two pairs is a less distinct longitudinal median oval patch tapering behind. (These marks are obscure in dark specimens). STERNUM : Oval and narrow, bluntly pointed behind ; colour as carapace, becoming darker round edges. LEGS : Femora I and II dark, other segments brown-orange or yellow (metatarsi I and II sometimes a little darker). Tibia II with sometimes an apical prolateral spine. Scopulæ reach nearly to base of metatarsi I and II and of tarsi III and IV. EPIGYNE : Text-fig. 55, D. MALE PALP : Text-fig. 55, B. The tibial apophysis and deep outlines of the palpal coils are noticeable characters.

OCCURRENCE : A rare southern species ; found amongst leaves, in woods, and under stones.

4. Genus **ZELOTES** Gistel 1848.

CHARACTERS OF GENUS. CARAPACE : Oval ; narrowed markedly in front (cf. *Drassodes*, *Gnaphosa*) covered with fine hairs. Pattern, of widening streaks diverging from short fovea, frequent. EYES : Rather closely grouped, posterior row being slightly the longer (cf. *Drassodes*). Anterior row more or less procurved (as seen from in front), laterals larger than medians. Posterior row straight ; medians often irregular in shape, sometimes larger than laterals and further from these than from each other or equally spaced. ABDOMEN : Dark or black (except in *Z. rusticus*) covered with fine hairs. Dorsally there may occur three pairs of lighter spots or impressions. Branchial opercula usually yellow and often conspicuous. STERNUM : Oval, pointed behind. CHELICERÆ : not very strong, vertical, with a number of hairs (spines in *Z. pedestris*) on inner part of anterior surface. Teeth of the inner row 0–2. MAXILLÆ AND LABIUM : Text-fig. 50, G. LEGS : Tibiæ and metatarsi I and II may bear ventral spines. Scopulæ (double rows of short, evenly spaced spines, sometimes aculeate but usually spatulate) reach to between mid point and base of metatarsi I and II and (aculeate spines) to apices of metatarsi III and IV. MALE PALPS : With a large single apophysis outside ; tip of tarsus blunt reaching a relatively short distance beyond anterior edge of alveolus. Most of the British species appear to have a more polished surface when alive than other members of the family.

The nine British species are identified fairly easily by the sexual organs, although the ventral sides of the palpal organs in the males require examination, as well as the sides and the tibial apophyses. Differences in colour, and other characters which also help to separate the species, are summarised in the Table on p. 108.

Zelotes pedestris (C. L. Koch).
(Text-figs. 56, A, B, G)

Melanophora pedestris C. L. Koch, 1839 (1), VI, p. 82. *Prosthesima pedestris* C. Chyzer and L. Kulczynski, 1891–7, II, p. 208. *Zelotes pedestris* E. Simon, 1914, p. 152 ; E. Reimoser, 1937, p. 31 ; A. Tullgren, 1946, p. 118.

	Carapace	Eyes	Colour of legs I and II				Ventral spines	
			Femur	Tibia	M-tarsus	Tarsus	Tibia II	M-tarsus II*
Z. pedestris .	Black	X	Black†	Yellow-orange	Yellow-orange	Yellow-orange	0	None
Z. lutetianus	Dark brown	V	Dark brown	Dark brown	Lighter (yellow-ish)	Lighter (yellow-ish)	0, 1 or 2	1 pr.
Z. pusillus .	Dark brown	V	Dark brown	Dark brown	Lighter brown or orange	Lighter brown or orange	0	1 pr.
Z. rusticus .	Orange or yellow-brown	V	Orange	Orange	Orange	Orange	0	1 pr. and 1 single
Z. præficus .	Black	V	Black	Black	Black	Yellow‡	0, 1 or 2	1 pr.
Z. electus .	Red-brown to orange	X	Yellow	Dark	Orange-brown	Orange-brown	0	2 prs.
Z. latreillei .	Black	X	Black†	Black	Black	Lighter	1	2 prs.
Z. apricorum	,,	X	,, †	,,	,,	,,	0	2 prs.
Z. serotinus.	,.	X	,, †	,,	,,	,,	0	1 pr. and 1 single

X.—Posterior eyes not very different in size, equidistant or nearly so.

V.—Posterior eyes with medians larger than laterals, irregular, contiguous, or nearly so, distant from laterals.

† With a lighter patch on prolateral surface of femur I.

‡ Obscure in fresh specimens.

* The numbers of these spines are not absolutely reliable as characters. Ventral spines may occur also on tibia I and metatarsus I ; the numbers of these are less useful and are omitted here and in the descriptions of species.

DESCRIPTION. LENGTH : ♀ : c. 7 mm. ♂ : 4·5–6 mm. CARAPACE : Black in fresh specimens, becoming reddish-brown on preservation ; often with faint darker radiating marks and veinings. EYES : Posterior row straight ; eyes nearly equidistant, medians slightly irregular, but scarcely larger than laterals. ABDOMEN : Black ; branchial opercula yellow. STERNUM : Coloured as carapace. CHELICERÆ :

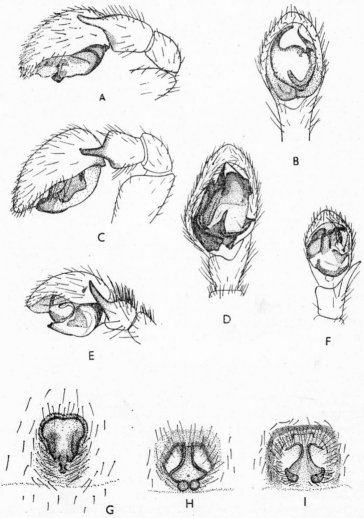

TEXT-FIG. 56.—Male palps : A, *Zelotes pedestris* (side) ; B, do. (below) ; C, *Z. lutetianus* (side) ; D, do. (below) ; E, *Z. pusillus* (side) ; F, do. (below). Epigynes : G, *Zelotes pedestris* ; H, *Z. lutetianus* ; I, *Z. pusillus*.

With a scopula of short, stout, unequal, upright spines on inner part of anterior surface (a distinctive character of this species). LEGS : Femora blackish, with lighter patches dorsally at apical ends. All other segments light yellow (becoming red-brown or orange on keeping). Scopulæ on I and II of small stout spines rather widely spaced (cf. *Z. pusillus* and *Z. lutetianus*). Metatarsus II has no ventral spines (unlike all other species of the genus). EPIGYNE : Text-fig. 56, G. MALE PALP : Text-fig. 56, A, B.

OCCURRENCE : A southern species. Found under stones, especially on chalk. Rather local. Adult in spring and summer.

Zelotes lutetianus (L. Koch).
(Text-fig. 56, C, D, H)

Melanophora lutetiana L. Koch, 1866-7, p. 157. *Prosthesima lutetiana* C. Chyzer and L. Kulczynski, 1891-7, II, p. 202. *Zelotes lutetianus* E. Simon, 1914, pp. 158, 170 ; E. Reimoser, 1937, p. 35.

DESCRIPTION. LENGTH : ♀ : 5–7·5 mm. ♂ : 4–5 mm. CARAPACE : Dark brown with radiating sooty markings, forming a rather striking pattern. EYES : Anterior row rather strongly procurved (as viewed from in front). Posterior medians larger than laterals, triangular in shape and contiguous. ABDOMEN : Dark brown to black ; branchial opercula not so striking as in other species. STERNUM : Coloured as carapace, with, usually, faint dark radiating markings. LEGS : Femora and tibiæ dark, metatarsi and tarsi brown-orange or yellowish (the contrast in colour less marked in III and IV). Tibia II bears 0, 1 or 2 ventral spines ; metatarsi I and II, one pair. Scopulæ on I and II consist of small aculeate spines, scarcely more than hairs. EPIGYNE : Text-fig. 56, H. MALE PALP : Text-fig. 56, C, D. This is distinct, especially when viewed ventrally. The disposition of the parts at the apex varies a good deal with slight changes of view-point ; the thick pointed apophysis often appears further to the right or may be hidden.

OCCURRENCE : Widespread but rare. Usually found among detritus in marshes, also among stones on the sea shore. Adult in early summer.

Zelotes pusillus (C. L. Koch).
(Text-fig. 56, E, F, I)

Melanophora pusilla C. L. Koch, 1833 and (1) 1839, VI, p. 90. *Drassus pusilla* J. Blackwall, 1861-4, p. 107. *Prosthesima pusilla* O. P.-Cambridge, 1879-81, p. 16 ; C. Chyzer and L. Kulczynski, 1891-7, II, p. 202. *Zelotes pusillus* E. Simon, 1914, pp. 152, 176 ; E. Reimoser, 1937, p. 35 ; A. Tullgren, 1946, p. 123.

DESCRIPTION. LENGTH : ♀ : 4–4·5 mm. ♂ : c. 3·5 mm. CARAPACE : Dark brown, very like that of *Z. lutetianus*. EYES : Posterior medians larger than laterals, irregular ; not quite so triangular nor so nearly touching as in *Z. lutetianus*. ABDOMEN : Like *Z. lutetianus*. STERNUM : deep blackish brown. LEGS : Colour as in *Z. lutetianus*, scopulæ on I and II of same small aculeate spines. No ventral spines on tibia II, metatarsus I and II have one pair. EPIGYNE : Text-fig. 56, I. This differs from that of *Z. lutetianus* in that the spermathecæ (visible just in front of the epigastric fold) are almost always further apart and elliptical rather than circular, although both species can vary in this respect. The anterior border is different, being cut away, and the corners of this part are darker and vary somewhat in shape, sometimes appearing as " eyebrows ". The form the epigyne, together with size, is the most reliable character for distinguishing between the females of these two species. MALE PALP : Text-fig. 56, E. F. The tibia bears a number of stout upright spines (in addition to the other hairs usually found). No other British species shares this character.

OCCURRENCE : Widespread but not common. Under stones, among rubbish etc., often in dry situations. Adult in early summer.

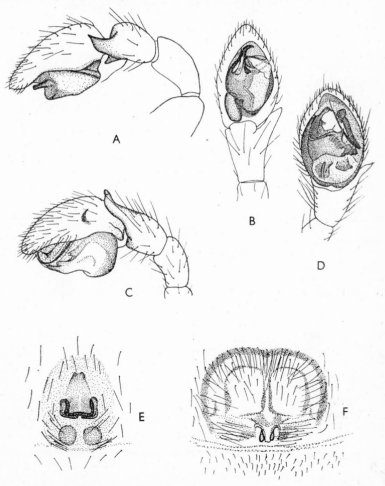

TEXT-FIG. 57.—Male palps : A, *Zelotes rusticus* (side) ; B, do. (below) ; C, *Z. præficus* (side) ; D, do. (below).
Epigynes : E, *Zelotes rusticus;* F, *Z. præficus.*

Zelotes rusticus (L. Koch).
(Text-fig. 57, A, B, E)

Melanophora rustica L. Koch, 1872, p. 309.   *Drassus razoumowskyi* P. Pavesi, 1873,. p. 123.   *Prosthesima rustica* O. P.-Cambridge, 1889, p. 111; 1905, p. 43 ; C. Chyzer and L. Kulczynski, 1891–7, II, p. 207.   *Zelotes rusticus* E. Reimoser, 1937, p. 36. *Z. razoumowskyi* E. Simon, 1914, pp. 156, 167 ; W. S. Bristowe, 1939, p. 20.

DESCRIPTION.   LENGTH :   ♀ :   8·5 mm. (one spec.).   ♂ :   6·5 mm. (one spec.).   CARAPACE :   Yellow-brown to orange, with very faint radiating markings.   EYES :   Posterior medians much larger than laterals, irregular, closer to each other than to adjacent laterals, but not contiguous.   ABDOMEN :   Dull grey or dull clay coloured, with a short reddish yellow-brown wedge-shaped mark anteriorly (which may disappear on preservation) ;   rather thickly clothed with dark hairs. LEGS :   Coloured as carapace.   Metatarsus II with one pair of ventral spines near the base, and may bear another single spine between mid point and apex.   Small spines of scopulæ on I and II of typical spatulate type.   EPIGYNE :   Text-fig. 57, E.   MALE PALP :   Text-fig. 57, A, B. The orange colouring makes this an easy spider to distinguish from the others of the genus.

OCCURRENCE :   Very rare.   Recorded from Salisbury, Wiltshire, under an old board (1886), Epping Forest, Essex (1904 and 1905). Recorded also from Staffordshire and Nottinghamshire.

Zelotes præficus (L. Koch).
(Text-fig. 57, C, D, F)

Melanophora præfica L. Koch, 1867, p. 155.   *Prosthesima latitans* O. P.-Cambridge, 1879–81, p. 420.   *P. præfica* C. Chyzer and L. Kulczynski, 1891–7, II, p. 202., *Zelotes præficus* E. Simon, 1914, pp. 158, 172 ;   E. Reimoser, 1937, p. 32 ;   A. Tullgren 1946, p. 126.

DESCRIPTION.   LENGTH :   ♀ :   5–5·5 mm.   ♂ :   4·5–5 mm.   The whole spider is dull black, except for the branchial opercula (and epigynal area in female) and tarsi, which are yellow.   CARAPACE : With faint radiating markings.   EYES :   Posterior medians larger than laterals, irregular and nearly touching.   LEGS :   Tibia II bears 0, 1 or 2 ventral spines, metatarsi I and II have one pair, near the base. Spines of scopulæ wide but sharp at the ends.   EPIGYNE :   Text-fig. 57, F.   MALE PALP :   Text-fig. 57, C, D.   The species resembles *Z. latreillei, Z. apricorum* and *Z. serotinus* in general appearance, but is generally smaller and differs from them in the posterior median eyes and in the number of spines on metatarsus II.

OCCURRENCE :   Rather rare ;   in southern counties.   Under stones or among loose stones or pieces of chalk.   Adult in early summer.

Zelotes electus (C. L. Koch).
(Text-fig. 58, A, B, C)

Melanophora electa C. L. Koch, 1839 (1), VI, p. 83.   *Drassus pumilus* J. Blackwall, 1861–4, p. 108.   *Prosthesima electa* O. P.-Cambridge, 1879–81, p. 462 ;   C. Chyzer and L. Kulczynski, 1891–7, II, p. 202.   *Zelotes electus* E. Simon, 1914, pp. 162, 173 ; E. Reimoser, 1937, p. 35 ;   A. Tullgren, 1946, p. 116.

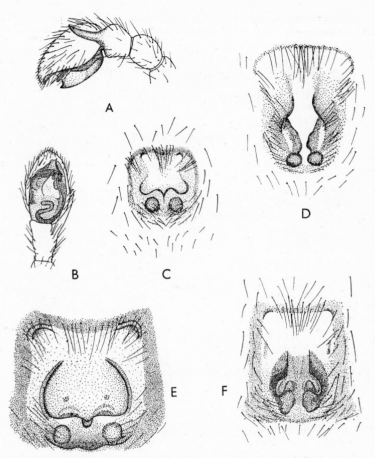

TEXT-FIG. 58.—Male palps: A, *Zelotes electus* (side); B, do. (below).
Epigynes: C, *Z. electus;* D, *Z. latreillei;* E, *Z. apricorum;* F, *Z. serotinus.*

DESCRIPTION. LENGTH: ♀: 4·0–5·5 mm. ♂: 3·5–4·5 mm.
CARAPACE: Reddish-brown to orange, sometimes olive, with sooty
radiating markings and with a darker borderline. EYES: Grouped
together compactly, anterior medians contiguous with laterals.
Posteriors nearly equal; medians a little nearer to laterals than to each
other. ABDOMEN: Brown to black; branchial opercula orange.
LEGS: Femora yellow (with sometimes a dusky patch at apex of I).
Dorsal-apical parts of patellæ darker. Tibiæ I and II dark; metatarsi
and tarsi orange-brown. III and IV have tibiæ and metatarsi dark
(less dark than tibiæ I and II) and tarsi orange. Tibia II bears no
spines, metatarsus I bears one pair and metatarsus II two pairs of
ventral spines. EPIGYNE: Text-fig. 58, C. MALE PALP: Text-fig.
58, A, B.

OCCURRENCE : Widespread but local. Found on sandhills round the coast, sometimes running in the sunshine. Adult spring and summer.

Zelotes latreillei (Simon).
(Text-figs. 58, D ; 59, A, D)

Prosthesima latreillei E. Simon, 1878, IV, p. 62 ; O. P.-Cambridge, 1879–81, p. 421 ; C. Chyzer and L. Kulczynski, 1891–7, II. p. 201. *Zelotes latreillei* E. Simon, 1914, pp. 165, 177 ; E. Reimoser, 1937. p. 32 ; A. Tullgren, 1946, p. 119.

DESCRIPTION. LENGTH : ♀ : 7–8 mm. ♂ : 4·5–7·5 mm. The whole spider is uniform glossy black, but for the orange branchial opercula and tarsi. EYES : Posteriors nearly equal and equally spaced. LEGS : Femur I has a longitudinal yellow patch on the sides. Tibia II with one ventral spine ; metatarsus I with one pair, metatarsus II with two pairs of ventral spines. EPIGYNE : Text-fig. 58, D. MALE PALP : Text-fig. 59, A, D.

OCCURRENCE : Widespread ; perhaps the commonest species of the genus. Usually under stones. Adult in summer.

Zelotes apricorum (L. Koch).
(Text-figs. 58, E ; 59, C, F)

Prosthesima apricorum L. Koch, 1876, p. 307. *Drassus ater* J. Blackwall, 1861–4, p. 106. *Prosthesima petiveri* O. P.-Cambridge, 1879–81, p. 15. *P. apricorum* C. Chyzer and L. Kulczynski. 1891–7, II, p. 200. *Zelotes apricorum* E. Simon, 1914, pp. 165, 179.

DESCRIPTION. LENGTH : ♀ : 6·5–9 mm. ♂ : 5–6 mm. Colour and appearance as in the last species ; there is no ventral spine on tibia II. EPIGYNE : Text-fig. 58, E. MALE PALP : Text-fig. 59, C, F.

OCCURRENCE : Generally distributed. Found under stones and amongst debris, heather, etc., even in mountainous districts.

The species resembles *Z. subterraneus* C. L. Koch. For differences see E. Simon, 1914, pp. 165, 166, 178.

Zelotes serotinus (L. Koch).
(Text-figs. 58, F ; 59, B, E)

Melanophora serotina L. Koch, 1867, p. 185. *Prosthesima longipes* C. Chyzer and L. Kulczynski, 1891–7, II. p. 201 ; British authors. *Zelotes serotinus* E. Simon, 1914, pp. 164, 175 ; E. Reimoser, 1937, p. 34 ; W. S. Bristowe, 1939, p. 19. *Z. longipes* A. Tullgren, 1946, p. 122.

DESCRIPTION. LENGTH : ♀ : 6–8 mm. ♂ : 5–6 mm. Appearance and colour as in the last species, but metatarsus II bears one pair of spines near the base and a single spine about the mid point. EPIGYNE : Text-fig. 58, F. MALE PALP : Text-fig. 59, B, E.

OCCURRENCE : Rare ; generally southern. Amongst moss and heather. Adult in summer.

5. Genus GNAPHOSA P. A. Latreille 1804.

CHARACTERS OF GENUS. CARAPACE : Similar to that of *Zelotes*, but broader in front, not attenuated ; pattern similar. The whole covered sparsely and evenly with black, spine-like hairs. EYES : Anterior

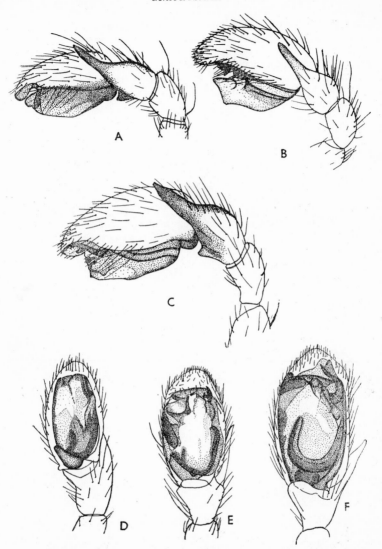

TEXT-FIG. 59.—Male palps (side) : A, *Zelotes latreillei;* B, *Z. serotinus;* C, *Z. apricorum.*
Male palps (below) : D, *Zelotes latreillei;* E, *Z. serotinus;* F, *Z. apricorum.*

row procurved (as seen from in front) occupying one-third to one-half
width of head. Medians smaller than laterals. Posterior row considerably longer than anterior (cf. *Zelotes*) and rather strongly recurved
(distinctive character of this genus) ; medians irregular in outline,
larger than laterals and farther from them than from each other.

ABDOMEN : Black or deep brown, with six faint marks or impressions dorsally as in *Zelotes*. STERNUM : Oval, pointed behind. CHELICERÆ : Not very strong, vertical, bearing numerous long bristles which form a scopula on inner part of apical surface. Inner margin with a prominent chitinous ridge (Text-fig. 50, A) whose edge is concave and serrated (a distinctive character). Outer margin with two teeth. MAXILLÆ and LABIUM : Text-fig. 50, B. LEGS : Colour uniform and as carapace ; more robust than in *Zelotes*. Tibiæ I and II with one

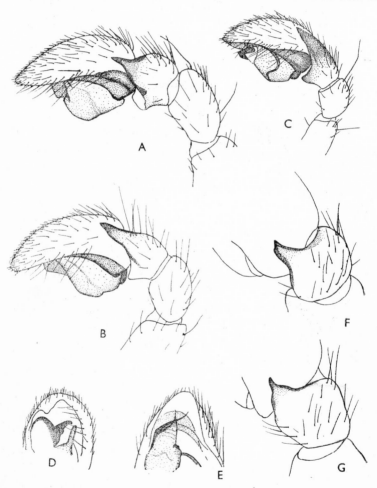

TEXT-FIG. 60.—Male palps (side) : A. *Gnaphosa lugubris;* B, *G. occidentalis;* C, *G. leporina.*
Tips of palps (below) : D, *G. leporina;* E, *G. occidentalis.*
Palpal tibiæ (above) : F, *G. occidentalis;* G, *G. lugubris.*

to two ventral spines ; metatarsi I and II with two to four ventral spines. Scopulæ, of short spatulate hairs set very close, reach to between mid point and base of metatarsi I and II. MALE PALPS : With a strong single tibial apophysis.

The three British species *G. lugubris*, *G. occidentalis* and *G. leporina* are similar in appearance and of a uniform sooty colour, with only the branchial opercula yellow. They can be distinguished by considering the sexual organs ; the following part of the spinal armature is thought to be the most reliable as a check to identification (though exceptions may well be found to occur).

Ventral spines:—	Tibia I		Metatarsus II	
	♀	♂	♀	♂
G. lugubris . .	1	2	2	2
G. occidentalis .	0	1	2	2
G. leporina . .	0	0	4	3

Gnaphosa lugubris (C. L. Koch).
(Text-figs. 60, A, G ; 61, A)

Pythonissa lugubris C. L. Koch, 1839 (1), VI, p. 60. *Gnaphosa lugubris* O. P.-Cambridge, 1879–81, p. 418 ; C. Chyzer and L. Kulczynski, 1891–7, II, p. 187 ; E. Simon, 1914, pp. 197, 200 ; E. Reimoser, 1937, p. 9. *G. nigerrima* A. Tullgren, 1946, p. 88.

DESCRIPTION. LENGTH : ♀: 10–12 mm. ♂ : 9–12 mm. The whole spider is dark brown or sooty black ; only the branchial opercula are yellow. EPIGYNE : Text-fig. 61, A. This is not so broad as in *G. occidentalis*. MALE PALP : Text-fig. 60, A, G. Requires careful comparison with *G. occidentalis*.

OCCURRENCE : A rare southern species, found amongst heather, under stones, and on the sea shore under dried seaweed, sometimes running in sunshine.

Gnaphosa occidentalis Simon.
(Text-figs. 60, B, E, F ; 61, B)

G. occidentalis E. Simon, 1878, IV, p. 177; 1914 (as sub-species of *G. lugubris*), pp. 194, 201 ; A. R. Jackson, 1924, p. 104.

DESCRIPTION. LENGTH : ♀: 10–12 mm. ♂ : ca. 9 mm. The species resembles *G. lugubris* closely. EPIGYNE : Text-fig. 61, B. This is like that of the last species but broader. MALE PALP : Text-fig. 60, B. The tibial apophysis is longer and narrower at the base than in *G. lugubris*, and the point, if looked at from above and a little to the outside, has a different shape, being almost bifid (Text-fig. 60, F).

OCCURRENCE : Kynance and Cadgwith (Cornwall).

Gnaphosa leporina (L. Koch).
(Text-figs. 60, C, D ; 61, C)

Pythonissa leporina L. Koch, 1866, p. 27.   *Drassus lucifugus* J. Blackwall, 1861–4, p. 105.   *Drassus anglicus* O. P.-Cambridge, 1871, p. 410; 1879–81, p. 14.   *Gnaphosa leporina* C. Chyzer and L. Kulczynski, 1891–7, II, p. 186 ; E. Simon, 1914, pp. 197, 203 ; A. Tullgren, 1946, p. 86.

DESCRIPTION. LENGTH : ♀ : 8–9 mm. ♂ : 5·5–7 mm. This species is smaller than the last two but otherwise resembles them closely in colour and appearance. EPIGYNE : Text-fig. 61, C. There is a long process attached to the anterior margin. MALE PALP : Text-fig. 60, C. The tibial apophysis is arched somewhat along the upper surface and the tip of the palp, as seen ventrally, is quite distinct from the other two species (Text-fig. 60, D).

OCCURRENCE : Widespread but rare. Found amongst heather on dry heaths and moors. Adult in summer.

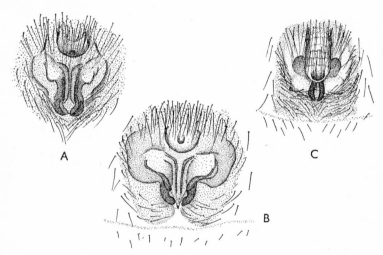

TEXT-FIG. 61.—Epigynes : A, *Gnaphosa lugubris;* B, *G. occidentalis;* C, *G. leporina.*

6. Genus **MICARIA** N. Westring 1851.

CHARACTERS OF GENUS. CARAPACE : Oval, attenuated somewhat in the region of head ; having no fovea (a distinctive character of the genus). More or less covered with small squamiform light hairs, set more thickly along lines radiating from foveal area, (these are often difficult to see in spirit-preserved specimens). EYES : Length of nearly parallel rows about half breadth of head, as seen from above. Anterior row rather strongly procurved (as seen from in front), eyes close ; medians smaller than laterals. Posterior row slightly longer than anterior and procurved ; medians oblong in shape, usually farther

from each other than from adjacent laterals. Medians and laterals
sub-equal. ABDOMEN : Long and narrow. Ground colour usually
black or dark brown, deeper in males, with a metallic sheen in living
specimens. Two or more light transverse bars may be present, sometimes ill-defined. SPINNERS : Anteriors set only a little apart from one
another, about as long as posterior pair ; medians only slightly shorter
though more slender. STERNUM : Oval, pointed behind and projecting
a little between coxæ IV which are set somewhat apart. CHELICERÆ;
Vertical, rather small (stouter in males) with one minute tooth on
inner margin. MAXILLÆ and LABIUM : Text-fig. 50, C. LEGS : Femora,
especially I and II, characteristically thicker and deeper in colour than
other segments, which are long and slender. Scopulæ consist of double
rows of evenly spaced, short spatulate spines extending to mid point or
to base of metatarsus I and II in males, and on to tibiæ in females ;
on III and IV they rarely extend beyond the tarsi (Text-fig. 62, A).
MALE PALPS : Femur with a number of long, ventral, nearly vertical,
spine-like hairs ; in British species there is a single external tibial
apophysis. Tarsus long and narrow ; sexual organs simple.

The genus is in some ways intermediate in its characters between the GNAPHOSIDÆ
and CLUBIONIDÆ and has usually been included the latter family ; the anterior
spinners, for instance, are not separated noticeably as in the other GNAPHOSIDÆ
We include the genus among the GNAPHOSIDÆ for the following reasons : The sexual
organs have more in common with GNAPHOSIDÆ than with CLUBIONIDÆ, as was pointed
out by A. R. Jackson, 1932, p. 4. The posterior median eyes are not circular, but
almost oblong ; such irregularity is common among GNAPHOSIDÆ but not among the
CLUBIONIDÆ. The leg scopulæ consist of little spines which though widely spaced,
are definitely spatulate (Text-fig. 62, A) ; in CLUBIONIDÆ of this size (e.g. *Phrurolithus*) the scopula hairs are aculeate.

The three British species are small and have the dorsal area covered
with small squamiform hairs which, though not striking in spirit-
preserved specimens, yet give the living spiders an iridescent appearance
as they run actively in the sunshine, which they do with a characteristic
up and down movement of the front legs, their movements being
somewhat ant-like.

The characters shown in the Table on p. 120 will help to distinguish
the British species.

Micaria pulicaria (Sundevall).
(Text-figs. 62, B ; 63, A, B, G)

Clubiona pulicaria J. C. Sundevall. 1831, p. 140. *Drassus nitens* and *D. micans*
J. Blackwall, 1861–4, pp. 119, 118. *Micaria pulicaria* C. Chyzer and L. Kulczynski,
1891–7, II, p. 257 ; E. Simon, 1932, p. 953 ; E. Reimoser, 1937, p. 92 ; A. Tullgren,
1946, p. 62.

DESCRIPTION. LENGTH : ♀ : 2·75–4 mm. ♂ : 3–3·5 mm. CARAPACE:
Dark brown or red-brown, with thin pubescence on sides above margin,
becoming thicker above. Lines radiate from foveal area, the Posterior
of these set with thicker white pubescence. EYES : Anterior medians
removed from laterals by not more than half diam. of one lateral.
Posterior medians separated by not more than a length of one of them.

I

Micaria pulicaria	*M. scintillans*	*M. alpina*
EYES		
Distance from edge of clypeus to anterior laterals not greater than diam. of a lateral.	This distance considerably greater than diam. of a lateral.	This distance considerably greater than diam. of a lateral.
Posterior medians separated by not more than length of one of them (Text-fig. 62, B).	Posterior medians separated by more than twice length of one of them (Text-fig. 62, C).	Posterior medians separated by about twice length of one of them.
ABDOMEN		
Two transverse light lines, if present, clearly defined at edges.	Transverse bars less distinct at edges and wider.	Transverse bars even less well defined.
MALE PALPS		
Apex of tarsus with 4 ventral spines (Text-fig. 63, B).	Apex of tarsus with 3 ventral spines (Text-fig. 63, D.)	Apex of tarsus with 3 ventral spines (Text-fig. 63, F).
Tibial apophysis acute but with a broad base (Text-fig. 63, A).	Tibial apophysis not so broad at base, rather more divergent when viewed ventrally, and slightly hooked at extremity. Tibia much longer than in other species (Text-fig. 63, C).	Tibial apophysis much more slender than in the other species (Text-fig. 63, E).
FEMALES		
No spines on tibiæ I and II.	Tibiæ I and II with 2–2 ventral spines, and a single short one apically.	
	This species almost always larger than the others, which are about the same size.	

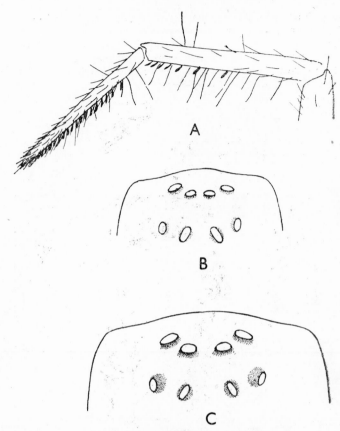

TEXT-FIG. 62.—A, tarsus and metatarsus of *Micaria scintillans*. Arrangement of eyes (above) in: B, *Micaria pulicaria;* C, *M. scintillans*.

ABDOMEN : Dark brown to black, covered with fine pubescence (iridescent in sunlight). A short transverse white line occurs near the anterior margin, which, after a break, is continued round the sides to the epigynal region. Another transverse white line at about the mid point extends to the sides and then stops. There is sometimes a longitudinal row of rather large white spots (three behind the second white line). Ventrally : depth of colour variable ; a slightly darker wedge may occur in females, tapering to spinners. STERNUM : Smooth, usually unicolorous but sometimes with darker blotches, and sometimes darker towards edges. CHELICERÆ : Colour as carapace, with longish spine-like hairs on anterior surface, distributed sparsely and evenly, directed forwards. LEGS : Femora I and II brown-black the rest orange-yellow ; metatarsi may be tinged with brown. EPIGYNE : Text-fig. 63, G. This varies a good deal, but the outlines of the parts

remain constant. MALE PALP : Text-fig. 63, A, B. There are four
ventral spines on the apex of the tarsus ; the hooked central apophysis
of the sexual organs is prominent and placed characteristically. The
tibial apophysis is acute, though wide at the base.

OCCURRENCE : Common and universally distributed. Mature in
spring and summer.

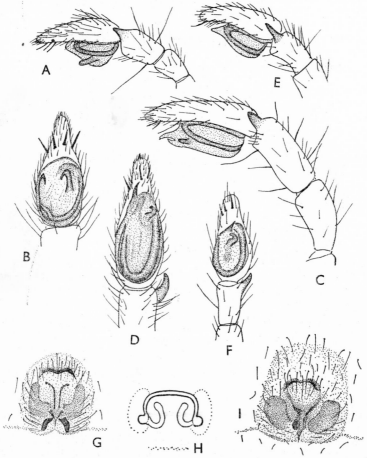

TEXT-FIG. 63.—Male palps : A, *Micaria pulicaria* (side) ; B, do. (below) ;
C, *M. scintillans* (side) ; D, do. (below) ; E, *M. alpina* (side) ; F, do. (below).
Epigynes : G, *Micaria pulicaria;* H, *M. alpina* (in outline) ; I, *M. scintillans*.

Micaria scintillans (O. P.-Cambridge).
(Text-figs. 62, A, C ; 63, C, D, I)

Drassus scintillans O. P.-Cambridge, 1871, p. 412. *Micaria scintillans* O.P.-Cam-
bridge, 1879-81, p. 12, E. Simon, 1932, p. 955.

DESCRIPTION. LENGTH : ♀ : 4·5–5 mm. ♂ : 3·5–4·5mm. This species resembles *M. pulicaria*, from which it differs in the following respects : EYES : Distance between edge of clypeus and anterior laterals considerably greater than diam. of a lateral. Anterior medians removed from adjacent laterals by 2/3–1 diam. of a lateral. Posterior medians separated by more than twice length of one of them. CARAPACE and STERNUM : With a rather thicker pubescence (which however is difficult to see clearly in spirit and which soon becomes knocked off). ABDOMEN : The white spots not apparent, but larger light areas sometimes occur between the bars, and one may occur a little in front of the spinners. Ventrally : darker wedge, (sometimes present in females of *M. pulicaria*) absent. LEGS : Somewhat darker in colour Tibiæ I and II with two pairs of ventral spines and a single short apical spine in females. EPIGYNE : Text-fig. 63, I. This is somewhat irregular and variable. MALE PALP : Text-fig. 63, C, D. There are three ventral spines on the tarsus. The tibia is much longer, relatively, than in either of the other species.

OCCURRENCE : Frequent locally in warm sunny situations on or near the south coast. Adult in the summer months.

Micaria alpina L. Koch.
(Text-fig. 63, E, F, H)

Micaria alpina L. Koch, 1872, p. 363. *M. breviscula* R. de Lessert, 1907, p. 120 ; A. R. Jackson, 1916, p. 356. *M. alpina* E. Simon, 1932, p. 955 ; A. Tullgren, 1946, p. 68.

DESCRIPTION. LENGTH : ♂ : 3·3 mm. This species resembles *M. pulicaria*, but differs from it in the following respects : CARAPACE : Radiant lines of light hairs much less distinct, pubescence clothes the whole area. EYES : Distance between edge of clypeus and anterior laterals considerably greater than diam. of a lateral. Anterior row less strongly procurved (as seen from in front) ; medians removed from adjacent laterals by 1–2/3 diam. of a lateral (cf. also *M. scintillans*). Posterior medians separated by about twice the length of one of them : ABDOMEN : The white transverse marks in the same positions as in the other species, but less well defined and sometimes not visible. Ventral side a uniform dark brown. STERNUM : The whole surface finely shagreened. LEGS : Colouration in this species : Femora brown, especially I and II. Patella and base of tibia I and II light yellow with brown streaks ; metatarsi and tarsi browner (tips of tarsi yellow). III almost unicolorous, yellow tinged with brown. IV similar, except for deep brown metatarsus. EPIGYNE : Text-fig. 63, H. (Shown in outline only after Simon and Tullgren). MALE PALP : Text-fig. 63, E, F. There are three ventral spines on the tarsus. The tibial apophysis is much more slender than in the other species. The female has not yet been taken in Britain.

OCCURRENCE : Glyder Fawr (Carnarvon), above 3,000 ft. Cader Idris (Merioneth). Adult in May and June.

10. Family CLUBIONIDÆ

CHARACTERS OF FAMILY. The spiders of this Family, especially of the genus *Clubiona*, resemble the GNAPHOSIDÆ closely, having leg scopulæ and two tarsal claws with claw tufts (except in *Agroeca*). The most constant difference lies in the anterior spinners, which in CLUBIONIDÆ are contiguous or set closely together. The trochanters are notched, though often not deeply.

KEY TO THE GENERA.

1. Labium much longer than broad, passing mid point of maxillæ, which are cut away at their outsides and narrower in middle than at apices (Text-fig. 64, A). Foot claws with 6–20 teeth 2

——Labium not, or scarcely, longer than broad ; not reaching, or not passing, mid point of maxillæ, which, though rounded outside, are not noticeably dilated at apical ends (Text-fig. 64, B, C). Foot claws with three to five teeth (none in *Phrurolithus*) 3

2. Carapace with median fovea. Posterior row of eyes notably longer than anterior. Legs : IV longer than I. Femora I and II with dorsal spines ; tibia III with one to three ventral spines . . . . . (1) **Clubiona**

——Carapace with no fovea. Posterior row of eyes scarcely longer than anterior. Legs : I longer than IV. Femora I and II with no dorsal spines (but some stout hairs) ; no ventral spines on tibia III . . . (2) **Cheiracanthium**

3. Cheliceræ each with a single long spine in front near inner margin and pointing slightly inwards. Sternum produced backwards a little between coxæ IV which are spaced rather widely (Text-fig. 64, C). Spiders with appearance of *Micaria*. . . . (8) **Phrurolithus**

——Cheliceræ without a single projecting spine in front (though other shorter spines may be present). Sternum not produced backwards between coxæ IV 4

4. Posterior row of eyes strongly recurved, as in LYCOSIDÆ (Text-fig. 4, B) . . . . (7) **Zora**

——Posterior row of eyes slightly recurved, or procurved . . 5

5. Posterior row of eyes slightly recurved. Tibia I and II with four pairs of ventral spines, metatarsi I and II with one pair . . . . (6) **Liocranum**

——Posterior row of eyes procurved. Tibia I with either two pairs or seven to ten pairs of ventral spines . . . 6

6. Tibia I with seven to ten pairs (six to seven in ♂) of ventral spines. Median posterior eyes slightly further from each other than from adjacent laterals . . . (5) **Scotina**

——Tibia I with two pairs of ventral spines. Posterior eyes nearly equidistant 7

7. Metatarsi I and II with two pairs of long ventral spines (no apical spines) (Text-fig. 77, F). Male tibial apophysis long and slender . . . . (4) **Agräecina**
———Metatarsi I and II with three pairs of ventral spines (the sub-apical pair are short and more lateral) (Text-fig. 77, E) . . . . (3) **Agroeca**

1. Genus **CLUBIONA** P. A. Latreille, 1804.

CHARACTERS OF GENUS. General appearance, Text-fig. 2. CARAPACE : Rather long, somewhat narrowed in front and slightly convex ; covered with fine, sometimes silky, hairs, with a few large hairs on anterior part. Fovea usually short ; faint radiating striæ sometimes originate from it and occasionally form a pattern of darker veinings. EYES : Rows parallel, nearly straight or very slightly procurved ; posterior row markedly the longest. Anterior medians closer together than posterior medians. ABDOMEN : Patterns and depth of colouring very varied (often between different specimens of the same species), but all conforming to a fundamental design, of which different aspects are emphasised or suppressed (Text-fig. 2, p. 20). Sides varying in colour owing to curved, parallel, often punctate, lighter lines on darker ground colour. Ventrally : a field lighter, or darker, than the sides, bounded by two converging rows of light spots, having two further rows within it, sometimes broken or quite suppressed. (The colour and markings of the abdomen are frequently much changed by immersion in spirit owing to the presence of a clothing of small hairs, which, in larger species especially, give the spiders a typical mouse-like appearance. Descriptions will apply to spiders as seen under the spirit.) SPINNERS : Posteriors as long as anteriors and more slender (Text-fig. 12, E, p. 38). STERNUM : Attenuated in front and behind, and pointed behind. CHELICERÆ : Robust and convex and usually nearly vertical ; more cylindrical sometimes in males and narrower, occasionally projecting forwards. Two rows of teeth ; inner margin in females with two to six teeth (of which two are usually larger than the others), often reduced in size and number in males. MAXILLÆ and LABIUM : Text-fig. 64, A. LEGS : Order of length IV, I, II, III ; unicolourous and bearing scopulæ (reaching in I and II some way along tibiæ ; less well defined in males and reduced to single row of hairs in smaller species). All bear spines, the following being of use in identification : Femora I and II with dorsal spines (cf. *Cheiracanthium*). Tibia III with one to three ventral spines (cf. *Cheiracanthium*). Tibia I with two pairs of ventral spines or single spines (cf. *Liocranum* and *Scotina*). Metatarsus I with one pair of sub-basal spines (cf. *Agroeca* and *Agroecina*). MALE PALPS : Tibia about same size as patella, with an apophysis, very variable in shape and size, on its outside. Tarsus rather narrow ; bulb, with sexual organs, nearly reaching the end, which is blunt as seen from above.

The 18 species of the genus are divided naturally into the following groups, primarily according to the forms of the sexual organs.

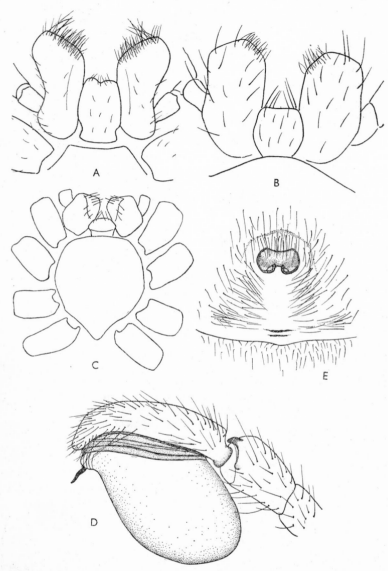

TEXT-FIG. 64.—Maxillæ and labium, etc.: A, *Clubiona;* B, *Agroeca;* C, *Phrurolithus.*
D, male palp of *Clubiona corticalis.* E, epigyne of *C. corticalis.*

Group I. *Clubiona corticalis.*

DISTINCTIVE CHARACTERS. ABDOMEN : Black-brown pattern on yellow-white ground, very marked and recognisable in the field. CHELICERÆ : Inner row with two teeth. LEGS : Tibia III with three ventral spines. EPIGYNE : Lies far forward of the epigastric fold (Text-fig. 64, E). MALE PALP : Tibial apophysis very small ; bulb containing sexual organs very large and, seen from the side, appears to reach nearly to patella (Text-fig. 64, D).

Group II.

DISTINCTIVE CHARACTERS. CHELICERÆ : Inner row with usually five teeth. LEGS : Tibia III with two ventral spines. EPIGYNE : Not provided with a small median depression (as in those of Group III). MALE PALP : With tibial apophysis branched.

The Group is divided into two sections :

Group II(a). *Clubiona reclusa, C. subsultans, C. stagnatilis, C. norvegica.* These four species are very alike in colour and appearance. The inferior branch of the tibial apophysis on the male palps has a characteristic barbed appearance. The epigynes are rather alike, the skin covering the seminal sacs having convergent wrinkles (also found in *C. pallidula* of Group II(b)).

The males are easy enough to identify by their palps ; the females present more difficulty, but can be distinguished by a careful study of their epigynes.

Group II(b). *Clubiona coerulescens, C. pallidula, C. phragmitis, C. terrestris, C. neglecta, C. lutescens.* In these species the tibial apophysis of the male palp, although branched, has not a barbed extension. The females of the last three species are alike and require care in identification.

Group III. *Clubiona compta, C. brevipes, C. trivialis, C. juvenis, C. genevensis, C. diversa, C. subtilis.*

DISTINCTIVE CHARACTERS. CHELICERÆ : Inner row with two to six teeth. LEGS : Tibia III with one or two ventral spines. EPIGYNE : With a small median depression anteriorly.* MALE PALP : Tibial apophysis single not branched.†

The first two species are quite distinct, both sexes being identifiable by the sexual organs ; *C. compta* can usually be recognised in the field by its clear abdominal pattern. The remaining species are alike in general appearance, except that *C. genevensis* has a fairly distinct abdominal pattern ; the epigynes are rather similar, although they still constitute the most reliable characters for identification. The following additional characters serve to subdivide the group further.

---

* This character is not strictly true of *C. brevipes.*

† This character is not strictly true of *C. compta.*

(The numbers of cheliceral teeth refer to the females. The males are in any case identifiable by their tibial apophyses).

With two ventral spines on Tibia III* :

C. trivialis. Small (4–4·5 mm.). Inner cheliceral teeth : three.

C. juvenis. Larger (5–6 mm.). Inner cheliceral teeth : four. (It has a slender, elongated appearance, the hairs being fine and silky. The outline of the carapace, seen from above, appears almost oblong.)

With one ventral spine on Tibia III :—

C. genevensis. Abdominal pattern distinct and recognisable in the field. Median depression of epigyne characteristically heart-shaped (with the point forward) Inner cheliceral teeth : three.

C. diversa. Length : 4–5 mm. Inner cheliceral teeth : four to six. Body rather broad.

C. subtilis. Length : 3–4·5 mm. Inner cheliceral teeth : four to five. Body more elongated. Dark veinings sometimes present just around the fovea.

GROUP I
Clubiona corticalis (Walckenaer).
(Text-fig. 64, D, E)

Aranea corticalis C. A. Walckenaer. 1802, p. 429. *Clubiona corticalis* J. Blackwall, 1861–4, p. 126 ; O. P.-Cambridge, 1879–81, p. 26 ; C. Chyzer and L. Kulczynski, 1891–7, II, p. 225 ; E. Simon, 1932. p. 905 ; E. Reimoser, 1937, p. 60 ; A. Tullgren, 1946, p. 33.

DESCRIPTION. LENGTH : ♀ : 7–9 mm. ♂ : 6–10 mm. CARAPACE : Reddish-brown with a darker borderline ; head sometimes a little darker. ABDOMEN : Pattern very clear and striking. Dorsal stripe almost black on a light yellow-white field, extending about half way to spinners and followed by four to five light chevrons alternating with dark bars, which become nearly merged towards spinners. Colouration similar in the male, but abdomen narrower. STERNUM : Orange, with red-brown border. CHELICERÆ : Slightly darker brown than head. Each margin with two teeth, with one median basal tooth. LEGS : Coloured as carapace, sometimes yellowish. EPIGYNE : Text-fig. 64, E. MALE PALP : Text-fig 64, D. The spider is easy to identify for, apart from the sexual organs, which are very distinctive, the abdominal pattern is more pronounced than in any other species of the genus (although variation in colouring does occur and one specimen was observed with the dorsal side of the abdomen uniformly black).

OCCURRENCE : Under loose bark, stones etc. Fairly common, as far north as Yorkshire. Adult May to July.

GROUP II(a)
Clubiona reclusa O. P.-Cambridge.
(Text-figs. 65, A ; 66, A)

Clubiona reclusa O. P.-Cambridge, 1863, p. 8567 ; 1879–81, p. 24 ; C. Chyzer and L. Kulczynski, 1891–7, II, p. 226 ; E. Simon, 1932, p. 910, 915 ; E. Reimoser, 1937, p. 69 ; A. Tullgren, 1946, p. 25. *C. grisea* L. Koch, 1867, p. 319.

---

* This character is not constant in *C. juvenis.*

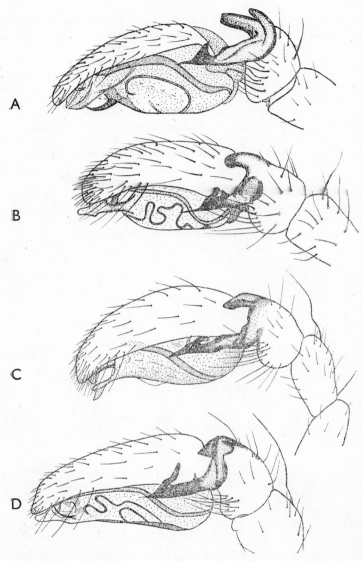

TEXT-FIG. 65.—Male palps: A, *Clubiona reclusa;* B, *C. stagnatilis;* C, *C. subsultans;* D, *C. norvegica.*

DESCRIPTION. LENGTH : ♀ : 6–8·5 mm. ♂ : 5–6 mm. CARAPACE : Light or reddish-brown with a darker borderline. Faint purplish veinings radiate from fovea, sometimes indiscernible in males (cf. *C. pallidula*). ABDOMEN : Brown, often dark. Dorsal stripe to half way, visible on lighter specimens, sometimes flanked and succeeded by pairs of lighter spots. Light chevrons sometimes visible on posterior half terminating in these spots. STERNUM : Often deep brown, but sometimes not darker than carapace. CHELICERÆ : Usually deep brown, but sometimes not darker than carapace. Brown to light yellow in the male. LEGS : Yellow to red brown, often much lighter in the male. EPIGYNE : Text fig. 66, A. The chitinised parts vary considerably in appearance, the posterior border being constant in outline. The skin covering the seminal sacs has convergent wrinkles. MALE PALP : Text-fig. 65, A. The female resembles C. pallidula (q.v.) while the male tibial apophysis is not unlike that of C. stagnatilis at first glance, the shapes of the barbed parts are however different.

OCCURRENCE : Widespread and not uncommon, usually in marshy places, amongst grass and herbage and also in woods ; sometimes found in curled leaves, where the females place their egg cocoons. Males adult in April, May and June ; females often throughout the year.

Clubiona subsultans Thorell.
(Text-figs. 65, C ; 66. C)

Clubiona subsultans T. Thorell, 1875 (3), p. 90.   C. erratica C. L. Koch, 1836 (1), X, p. 131 (not C. A. Walckenaer).   C.subsultans C. Chyzer and L. Kulczynski, 1891–7, II, p. 226 ; A. R. Jackson, 1914, p. 125 ; O. P.-Cambridge, 1914, p. 122 ; E. Simon, 1932, pp. 908, 918 ; E. Reimoser, 1937, p. 70 ; A. Tullgren, 1946, p. 29.

DESCRIPTION. LENGTH : ♀ : 5–7 mm. ♂ : 5–7 mm. CARAPACE : Light yellowish-brown with faint greyish radiating striations. ABDOMEN : Red-brown. Dorsal stripe dark chocolate colour, extending as a fine line in posterior half to spinners. Several light chevrons occur on posterior half, variable in distinctness. Ventrally : two faint, rather wide, convergent brown bands enclose a lighter field in most specimens (cf. C. stagnatilis). These marks are just within the line usually occupied, in the genus, by lines of white spots (which are not always present in this species). Markings of the male similar. STERNUM: Brownish yellow, sometimes with an interrupted brown border. CHELICERÆ : Deeper brown than carapace, variable in depth of colour and lighter in the male. LEGS : Light yellow. The general colouring of the male is very like that of the female. The description applies to Scottish specimens, continental specimens seem to be a good deal darker. EPIGYNE : Text-fig. 66, C. (viewed somewhat from behind, to compare with C. stagnatilis), the skin covering the seminal sacs may have convergent wrinkles. MALE PALP : Text-fig. 65, C. This is not unlike that of C. reclusa and C. stagnatilis.

The female is difficult to distinguish from that of C. stagnatilis. The following differences taken together should be reliable, but as yet only three females have been taken in Britain and there may well be some variation.

(a) Epigynes, viewed from behind (Text-fig. 66, C, D) ; the shapes of the dark regions at either side are distinct in spite of other variation. (in a cleared specimen the seminal ducts of C. subsultans are looped repeatedly, but not in C. stagnatilis.

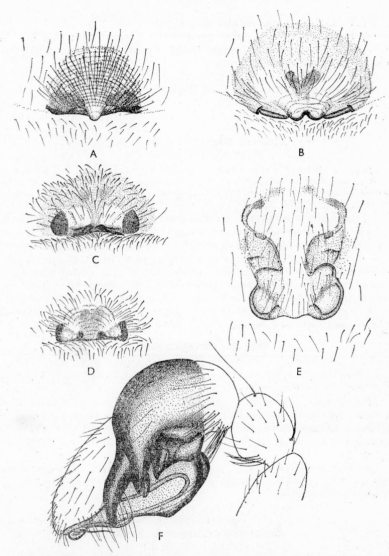

TEXT-FIG. 66.—Epigynes: A, *Clubiona reclusa ;* B, *C. norvegica ;* C, *C. subsultans ;* D, *C. stagnatilis ;* E, *C. coerulescens.* F, Male palp of *C. coerulescens.*

(*b*) Anterior median eyes distinctly smaller than anterior laterals and slightly smaller than posterior medians in *C. subsultans.* In *C. stagnatilis :* anterior medians nearly equal to anterior laterals and equal to or slightly larger than posterior medians.

(c) Ventral markings on abdomen (q.v.).

(d) Dorsal abdominal stripe reaches the spinners as a thin line in
C. *subsultans*, but rarely beyond the mid point in C. *stagnatilis* (this
character is not absolutely reliable).

(e) Chelicerae darker in C. *stagnatilis*.

OCCURRENCE : Black Wood of Rannoch, Perthshire (1914). Abernethy Forest, Inverness (1945). It should be looked for on and under
bark of conifers and amongst pine needles. Adult early summer.

Clubiona stagnatilis Kulczynski.
(Text-figs. 65, B ; 66, D)

Clubiona stagnatilis C. Chyzer and L. Kulczynski, 1891–7, II, p. 226.　C. *holosericea*
J. Blackwall, 1861–4, p. 122.　C. *grisea* O. P.-Cambridge, 1879–81, p. 22.　C. *stagnatilis* E. Simon, 1932, pp. 909, 917 ; E. Reimoser, 1937, p. 69 ; A. Tullgren, 1946,
p. 28.

DESCRIPTION. LENGTH : ♀ : 6–8 mm.　♂ : 5–6 mm. This species
closely resembles the last, under which the main differences are listed.
In addition the ventral side of the abdomen is here almost uniform in
colour, as the sides. Two converging lines of white spots are usually
distinct (there may be four lines in the male). The dorsal lanceolate
stripe rarely reaches beyond the mid point. EPIGYNE : Text-fig.
66, D (as seen from a little behind). MALE PALP : Text-fig. 65, B.

OCCURRENCE : Widespread and quite common. Damp marshy
places, on plants and bushes and in moss.

Clubiona norvegica Strand.
(Text-figs. 65, D ; 66, B)

Clubiona norvegica E. Strand, 1900, p. 30.　C. *humida* A. R. Jackson, 1915, p. 188.
C. *norvegica* A. Tullgren, 1946, p. 31.

DESCRIPTION. LENGTH : ♀ : 5–7·5 mm.　♂ : 4–4·5 mm. The
resemblance to C. *stagnatilis* is very close, although the sexual organs
afford a reliable distinction. EPIGYNE : Text-fig. 66, B. (This is
distinctly broader than that of C. *stagnatilis*). MALE PALP : Text-
fig. 65, D.

OCCURRENCE : Delamere Forest, Cheshire, where it is frequent in
one spot (Abbot's Moss) among moss and sphagnum. Rosedale Abbey,
Yorkshire (1948).

GROUP II(b)
Clubiona coerulescens L. Koch.
(Text-fig. 66, E, F)

Clubiona coerulescens L. Koch, 1867, pp. 294, 342.　C. *voluta* O. P.-Cambridge,
1873 (3), p. 533.　C. *coerulescens* O. P.-Cambridge, 1879–81, p. 29 ; C. Chyzer and L.
Kulczynski, 1891–7, II, p. 226 ; E. Simon, 1932, p. 907 ; E. Reimoser, 1937, p. 70 ;
A. Tullgren, 1946, p. 32.

DESCRIPTION. LENGTH : ♀ : 6–9 mm.　♂ : 5·5–7 mm. CARAPACE :
Uniform yellow-brown (no margin). ABDOMEN : Covered with rather
long silky hairs, visible in living specimens. Darkish brown (lighter
that in C. *phragmitis* and C. *pallidula*) ; dorsal stripe not very distinct

but may reach the spinners ; spots and chevrons usually distinct. STERNUM : Yellow : slightly darkened at edges. CHELICERÆ : Brown, not very dark ; rather lighter in males. LEGS : Very light brownish-yellow (continental specimens seem to be darker). EPIGYNE : Text-fig. 66, E. The great length of the seminal ducts, parts of which can be seen beneath the skin, and the form of the epigyne, which projects from the surface of the abdomen, are quite unique and the species is not difficult to identify. The sexual organs and colour distinguish it from *C. pallidula*, to which it bears a superficial resemblance. MALE PALP : Text-fig. 66, F. Confusion of the male with any other species is impossible owing to the enormous tibial apophysis.

OCCURRENCE : Very rare. It occurs on low plants amongst under-wood. Mature males occur in May in the south, but may be found until September in some places.

Clubiona pallidula (Clerck).
(=*C. holosericea* (Linnaeus))
(Text-fig. 67, A, B)

Araneus pallidulus C. Clerck, 1757, p. 81. *A. holosericea* Linnaeus, 1758, p. 622. *Clubiona epimelas* J. Blackwall, 1861-4, p. 124. *C. pallidula* British authors and E. Simon, 1932, pp. 911, 915. *C. holosericea* E. Reimoser, 1937, p. 67 ; W. S. Bristowe, 1939, p. 22 ; A. Tullgren, 1946, p. 17.

DESCRIPTION. LENGTH : ♀ : 7·5–11 mm. ♂ : 6–8 mm. CARAPACE : Yellow-brown, darkening towards the head, with a narrow dark border line. Ramified veinings originate from fovea, similar to those in *C. reclusa*, but sometimes very faint, more distinct near margin (they may be absent in males). ABDOMEN : Almost uniform dark brown, dorsal stripe very obscure or absent, sometimes with a lighter centre. Light chevrons and spots can sometimes be made out on posterior half. STERNUM : Deep brown. CHELICERÆ : Black-brown (darker than in *C. reclusa*) ; lighter in males. LEGS : Pale yellowish-brown (in *C. reclusa* they are more reddish). EPIGYNE : Text-fig. 67, B. MALE PALP : Text-fig. 67, A.

This species resembles *C. phragmitis* in colouring but is larger and the sexual organs are very different. The female can be distinguished from *C. reclusa* by size, colour of legs and cheliceræ and sternum, as well as the sexual organs.

The tibial apophysis, seen from the side, is not unlike that of *C. neglecta* (Text-fig. 69, C), but otherwise the spiders are not very alike.

OCCURRENCE : Distributed over the British Isles, frequent in many localities. On bushes, plants and under bark. Adult in summer.

Clubiona phragmitis C. L. Koch.
(Text-fig. 67, C, D)

Clubiona phragmitis C. L. Koch, 1843 (1) X, p. 134. *C. holosericea* Degeer, 1778, p. 266 ; and British authors. *C. phragmitis* C. Chyzer and L. Kulczynski, 1891-7, II, p. 228 ; E. Simon, 1932, pp. 910, 916 ; E. Reimoser, 1937, p. 68 ; A. Tullgren, 1946, p. 17 ; W. S. Bristowe, 1947, pl. 11.

DESCRIPTION. LENGTH : ♀ : 7·5–11 mm. ♂ : 5–10 mm. CARA-
PACE : Pale to reddish-brown, darker on head. Hairs here and on
abdomen noticeably silky. ABDOMEN : Usually almost uniform,
rather dark brown, but very variable in depth of colour and sometimes

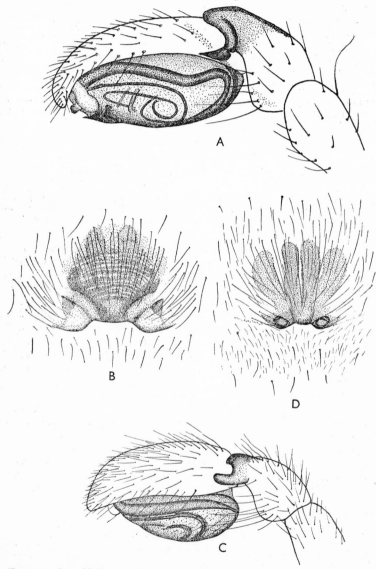

TEXT-FIG. 67.—*Clubiona pallidula:* A, male palp ; B, epigyne.
Clubiona phragmitis: C, male palp ; D, epigyne.

reddish. Dorsal stripe visible on lighter specimens sometimes with light centre. Traces of light spots and chevrons sometimes discernible on posterior half. STERNUM : Yellow-brown sometimes with a darker broken borderline. CHELICERÆ : Black-brown and markedly swollen in front at the base, and visible thus from above. (This is less marked in the male.) LEGS : Pale yellowish-brown. EPIGYNE : Text-fig. 67, D. The seminal sacs usually appear as four finger-like processes, but the outer pair is sometimes not visible. MALE PALP : Text-fig. 67, C.

OCCURRENCE : Locally abundant in marshy places. It can usually be found by beating sedges and reeds near the water's edge. Adult from April onwards.

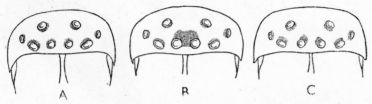

TEXT-FIG. 68.—Eyes (from in front) : A, *Clubiona terrestris;* B, *C. neglecta;* C, *C. lutescens.*

Clubiona terrestris Westring.
(Text-figs. 68, A ; 69, A ; 70, A)

Clubiona terrestris N. Westring, 1862, p. 395. *C. amarantha* J. Blackwall, 1861–4, p. 123. *C. terrestris* O. P.-Cambridge, 1877–81, p. 33 ; C. Chyzer and L. Kulczynski, 1891–7, II, p. 227 ; E. Simon, 1932, pp. 904, 906 ; E. Reimoser, 1937, p. 65 ; A. Tullgren, 1946, p. 18.

DESCRIPTION. LENGTH : ♀ : 6–6·5 mm. ♂ : 5–6 mm. CARAPACE ; Uniform light yellowish-brown. ABDOMEN : Lighter than in the other species, varying from yellow to purplish-brown. Dorsal stripe reddish-brown, usually, but not always, well defined and sometimes continuing in posterior half as a thin line to spinners. Light chevrons and spots sometimes visible on posterior half. EYES : Anterior laterals noticeably larger than anterior medians (cf. *C. neglecta* and *C. lutescens*). Posteriors nearly equidistant (Text-fig. 68, A). STERNUM : Yellow, sometimes with a slight intermittent brown border. CHELICERÆ : Brown to black, usually lighter in the male and more slender. LEGS : Pale yellow. EPIGYNE : Text-fig. 70, A. Two angular marks (part of the seminal ducts) are visible on the anterior half of the region, outside the seminal sacs, and are very characteristic. MALE PALP : Text-fig. 69, A. The tibial apophysis has a certain resemblance to that of *C. lutescens,* but the tarsus and palpal organs are very different.

The female closely resembles *C. neglecta* and *C. lutescens,* from which it can be distinguished by the epigyne and the eyes.

OCCURRENCE : Perhaps the commonest species of the genus. On trees, shrubs, and bushes and under stones and bark. Males are adult from May onwards.

K

Clubiona neglecta O. P.-Cambridge.
(Text-figs. 68, B ; 69, D ; 70, C)

Clubiona neglecta O. P.-Cambridge, 1862, p. 7955, and 1879–81, p. 25 ; C. Chyzer and L. Kulczynski, 1891–7, p. 227 ; E. Simon, 1932, pp. 913, 918 ; E. Reimoser, 1937, p. 66 ; A. Tullgren, 1946, p. 24.

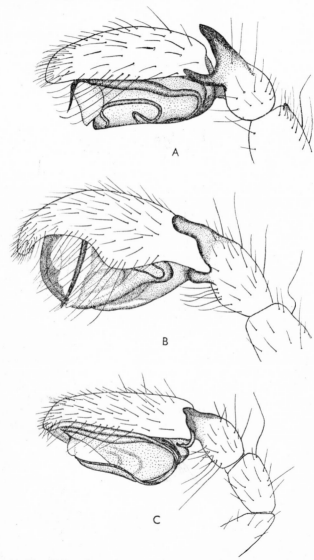

TEXT-FIG. 69.—Male palps: A *Clubiona terrestris;* B *C, lutescens;* C, *C. neglecta.*

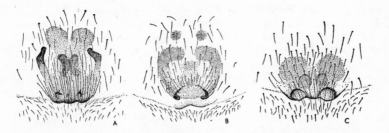

TEXT-FIG. 70.—Epigynes : A, *Clubiona terrestris;* B, *C. lutescens;* C, *C. neglecta.*

DESCRIPTION. LENGTH : ♀ : 6–8 mm.   ♂ : c. 4·5 mm.   CARAPACE: Like *C. terrestris,* but usually rather darker (especially on head in male).   EYES : Text-fig. 68, B.   Anteriors nearly equal in size (cf. *C. terrestris*) ; medians a little closer to each other than diameter of one of them and dark pigmented areas round them confluent (cf. *C. lutescens*).   ABDOMEN : Almost uniform brown.   Dorsal stripe visible on fresh specimens ; chevrons and spots on posterior half obscure and often scarcely visible.   STERNUM : Like *C. terrestris.*   CHELICERÆ : Darkish-brown ; narrower in the male.   LEGS : Pale yellowish-brown. EPIGYNE : Text-fig. 70, C.   The seminal ducts, if their outlines are dark, occasionally present a superficial resemblance to the elbow-shaped ducts of *C. lutescens,* but the epigyne is different and the disposition of the seminal sacs ; also the openings to the ducts are close to the epigastric fold.   MALE PALP : Text-fig. 69, C.   The tibial apophysis is rather like that of *C. pallidula* (seen from the side), but the sexual organs and rest of the palp are quite different.

The female needs to be distinguished carefully from *C. lutescens;* the epigyne is the best character, while the pigment round the anterior median eyes is almost always reliable.

OCCURRENCE : Widespread ; not very common.   Beneath stones, especially in moist places, and also on sandhills round the coast. Adult from May onwards.

Clubiona lutescens Westring.
(Text-figs. 68, C ; 69, B ; 70, B)

Clubiona lutescens N. Westring, 1851 and 1862, p. 394 ; O. P.-Cambridge, 1879–81, p. 24 ; C. Chyzer and L. Kulczynski, 1891–7, II, p. 227 ; E. Simon, 1932, pp. 912, 921 ; E. Reimoser, 1937, p. 65 ; A. Tullgren, 1946, p. 19.

DESCRIPTION. LENGTH : ♀ : 6–8 mm.   ♂ : 4·5–6 mm.   CARAPACE : Like *C. neglecta* except that two faint lines, enclosing a very faint darker line, usually run from fovea to median eyes in females.   EYES : Text-fig. 68, C.   Anteriors equally spaced and nearly equal (cf. *C. terrestris*) ; medians separated by more than a diameter of one of them (cf. *C. neglecta*).   Pigmented areas round anterior medians rarely confluent (though fresh specimens may have them so), nor so marked as in *C.*

neglecta. ABDOMEN : Like *C. neglecta*. STERNUM, CHELICERÆ and
LEGS : Like *C. terrestris*. EPIGYNE : Text-fig. 70, B. The elbow-
shaped seminal ducts, when visible, are characteristic and the form of
the epigyne is distinctive. There is a greater distance between the
opening to the ducts and the epigastric fold than in *C. neglecta*. MALE
PALP : Text-fig. 69, B. In some positions the appearance of the tibial
apophysis is very like that of *C. terrestris*, but the sexual organs are
quite different.

The female needs to be distinguished carefully from *C. neglecta* and
sometimes resembles *C. terrestris* closely.

OCCURRENCE : Widespread and fairly common. Moist places,
grasses and bushes and trees in woods. Adult in May and June and
probably later in many places.

GROUP III.

Clubiona compta C. L. Koch.
(Text-fig. 71, C, E)

Clubiona compta C. L. Koch, 1839 (1) VI,, p. 16 ; J. Blackwall, 1861–4, p. 128 ;
O. P.-Cambridge, 1879–81, p. 29 ; C. Chyzer and L. Kulczynski, 1891–7, II, p. 228 ;
E. Simon, 1932, pp. 922, 927 ; E. Reimoser, 1937, p. 63 ; A. Tullgren, 1946, p. 14.

DESCRIPTION. LENGTH : ♀ : 3·5–6 mm. ♂ : 3·5–4·5 mm. CARA-
PACE : ♀ : Light brown, sometimes with a dark borderline. ♂ :
Darkish brown, usually a little deeper on head, but sometimes lighter ;
borderline broader. ABDOMEN : Pattern usually very distinct and
recognisable in the field, but sometimes faint in specimens freshly
moulted. Fore part of the reddish dorsal stripe flanked by two wide
lighter patches. There follow five white chevrons which break the
stripe between mid point and spinners and which alternate with reddish
bars ; they may extend round sides. STERNUM : Yellow with brown
border which projects inwards between coxæ. CHELICERÆ : Colour as
carapace ; in males more attenuated and brown or dark brown. LEGS :
Colour as carapace. Tibia III with one ventral spine. EPIGYNE : Text-
fig. 71, E. MALE PALP : Text-fig. 71, C.

OCCURRENCE : Widespread and common, on trees and bushes.
Adult April to July, but females may be found occasionally throughout
the year.

Clubiona brevipes Blackwall.
(Text-fig. 71, A, B, D)

Clubiona brevipes J. Blackwall, 1841, p. 603, and 1861–4, p. 127 ; O. P.-Cambridge,
1879–81, p. 28 ; C. Chyzer and L. Kulczynski, 1891–7, II, p. 228 ; E. Simon, 1932,
p. 921 ; E. Reimoser, 1937, p. 63 ; A. Tullgren, 1946, p. 12.

DESCRIPTION. LENGTH : ♀ : 5–7 mm. ♂ : 4·5–5·5 mm. CARA-
PACE : Darkish-brown with a thin dark borderline and radiating
veinings (sometimes faint). Head often darker. ABDOMEN : Dull
brown, usually much darker in males. Dorsal stripe very indistinct
and may run whole length. STERNUM : Usually deep brown.

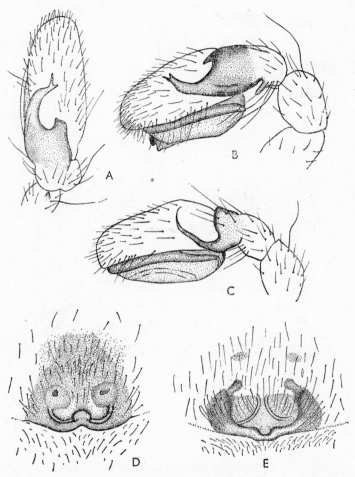

TEXT-FIG. 71.—Male palps : A, *Clubiona brevipes* (above) ; B, do. (side) ; C, *Clubiona compta.*
Epigynes : D, *Clubiona brevipes;* E, *C. compta.*

CHELICERÆ : Brown, as head, projecting in front slightly at base in female. LEGS : Brownish-yellow, usually much lighter than carapace, EPIGYNE : Text-fig. 71, D. The chitinisation and depth of colour of the different parts can vary appreciably, but the main lines are un-mistakable. MALE PALP : Text-fig. 71, A, B.

OCCURRENCE : Common and widespread. It can be beaten from trees and shrubs (especially oaks) in early summer, often in great abundance. Also found under bark of trees. Males are adult from April to early June.

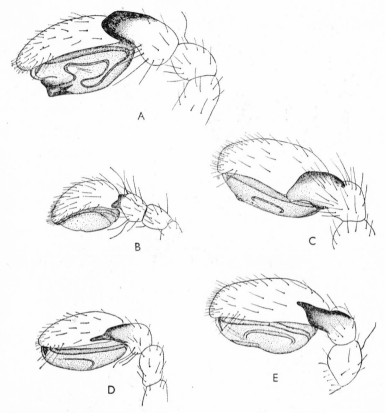

Text-fig. 72.—Male palps: A, *Clubiona trivialis;* B, *C. genevensis;* C, *C. juvenis;* D, *C. subtilis;* E, *C. diversa.*

Clubiona trivialis C. L. Koch.
(Text-figs. 72, A ; 73, A)

Clubiona trivialis C. L. Koch, 1841 (1), X, p. 132 ; O. P.-Cambridge, 1879–81, p. 30 ; C. Chyzer and L. Kulczynski, 1891–7, II, p. 229 ; E. Simon, 1932, pp. 924, 926 ; E. Reimoser, 1937, p. 64 ; A. Tullgren, 1946, p. 8 ; W. S. Bristowe, 1947, pl. 10.

DESCRIPTION. LENGTH : ♀ : 4–4·5 mm. ♂ : 3·5–4 mm. CARAPACE : Uniform yellow-brown, tending to reddish in darker specimens and somewhat darker in males. EYES : Anterior about equal in size (cf. *C. juvenis*). ABDOMEN : Almost uniform reddish-brown. Dorsal stripe sometimes visible; light spots, forming rough chevrons may flank and follow it. Darker in males. STERNUM : Lemon-yellow to reddish-orange. CHELICERÆ : Rarely darker than carapace in either sex. LEGS : Whitish-yellow ; light-brown in males. Tibia III with two ventral spines. (cf. *C. diversa* and *C. subtilis*). EPIGYNE : Text-fig.

73, A. MALE PALP : Text-fig. 72, A. The species resembles *C. diversa* and *C. subtilis*. As a rule it has a characteristic reddish colour.

OCCURRENCE : Widespread. Frequent locally in mountainous and heathery places, especially in the North of Britain. Found on gorse, low plants, heather etc., and under stones. Adult in May and June, and until September in the north.

Clubiona juvenis Simon.
(Text-figs. 72, C ; 73, B)

Clubiona juvenis E. Simon, 1878, IV, p. 227 ; A. R. Jackson, 1913 (1), p. 205 ; O. P.-Cambridge, 1914, p. 122 ; E. Simon, 1932, pp. 924, 926.

DESCRIPTION. LENGTH : ♀: 5–6 mm. ♂: 5 mm. CARAPACE : Like *C. trivialis* in colour (darker in the male), but differs noticeably

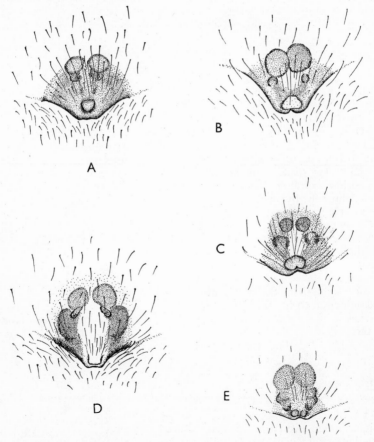

TEXT-FIG. 73.—Epigynes : A, *Clubiona trivialis;* B, *C. juvenis;* C, *C. genevensis;* D, *C. diversa;* E, *C. subtilis.*

in outline as seen from above, giving a somewhat oblong appearance
EYES : Anterior medians much larger than laterals (cf. *C. trivialis*).
ABDOMEN : Whitish-yellow. Dorsal stripe sometimes well marked and
reddish-purple, but may be absent. Abdomen of male dark brown-
grey. STERNUM : Yellow-orange with brown border of varying width.
CHELICERÆ : Hardly darker than carapace (A. R. Jackson and Pack
Beresford (1913) describe them as " usually deep brown ". The
colour must fade in spirit) ; rather long and narrow. Dark brown in
male. LEGS : Whitish-yellow, only slightly darker in male ; clothed
with fine silky hairs ; the usual leg scopulæ not recognisable. Tibia II
usually with two ventral spines. EPIGYNE : Text-fig. 73, B. MALE
PALP : Text-fig. 72, C. The spider is quite easily distinguished from the
others of the Group by the shape of the carapace, the median anterior
eyes and its fine silky hairs. It has an elongated delicate appearance
which is quite distinct.

OCCURRENCE : Wicklow (Eire), on sandhills.

Clubiona genevensis L. Koch.
(Text-figs. 72, B ; 73, C)

Clubiona genevensis L. Koch, 1867, p. 294. *C. decora* C. Chyzer and L. Kulczynski,
1891–7, II. p. 229 ; C. Warburton, 1892, p. 223. *C. genevensis* E. Simon, 1932,
pp. 925, 930 ; E. Reimoser, 1937, p. 61 ; (*C. genevensis* W. S. Bristowe, 1939, p. 170
only, = *C. leucaspis* Simon) ; Tullgren, 1946, p. 9.

DESCRIPTION. LENGTH : ♀ : 3·5–4·5 mm. ♂ : 3·5 mm. CARAPACE :
Like *C. trivialis*. EYES : Anteriors of about equal size. (cf. *C. juvenis*).
ABDOMEN : Usually with a rusty-red mark on anterior margin. Pattern
usually very distinct (rather like *C. compta*). Dorsal stripe rusty-red,
sometimes broken, flanked by wide light patches and, in posterior
half, broken by wide light chevrons radiating from the middle.
STERNUM : Yellow, with no border. CHELICERÆ : Brown, darker
than carapace. LEGS : As carapace, or lighter. Tibia III normally
with one ventral spine. EPIGYNE : Text-fig. 73, C. The heart-shaped
mediam depression is characteristic. MALE PALP : Text-fig. 72, B. The
spider is readily recognisable by the sexual organs and abdominal
pattern.

OCCURRENCE : Scilly, Ramsey and Skokholm Islands, Channel
Islands, Lulworth and Ringstead (Dorset). Under stones, where it
makes a silken cocoon or amongst berbage. Adult in April and probably
later.

Clubiona diversa O. P.-Cambridge.
(Text-figs. 72, E ; 73, D)

Clubiona diversa O. P.-Cambridge, 1862, p. 7959. *C. pallens* O. P.-Cambridge, 1871,
p. 413 and 1879–81, p. 31. *C. diversa* C. Chyzer and L. Kulczynski, 1891–7, II, p. 229,
E. Simon, 1932, pp. 924, 927 ; E. Reimoser, 1937, p. 62 ; A. Tullgren, 1946, p. 11.

DESCRIPTION. LENGTH : ♀ : 4–4·5 mm. ♂ : 3–4 mm. CARAPACE :
Light yellow-brown, a little darker in the male. EYES : Anterior
medians slightly nearer to adjacent laterals than to each other and
very slightly smaller than laterals (cf. *C. subtilis*). ABDOMEN : Rather

lighter usually than *C. trivialis*. Dorsal stripe usually not discernible ; male resembles female (cf. *C. subtilis*). STERNUM : Yellow. CHELICERÆ : Light brown, only a little darker than carapace. LEGS : Coloured as carapace. Tibia III with one ventral spine normally (though two have been observed). EPIGYNE : Text-fig. 73, D. MALE PALP : Text fig. 72, E. This spider resembles *C. subtilis* (q.v.).

OCCURRENCE : Widespread, but not common except locally. Low plants in damp places, heather roots, sometimes in moss or under stones ; it has been beaten from bushes.

Clubiona subtilis L. Koch.
(Text-figs. 72, D ; 73, E)

Clubiona subtilis L. Koch, 1867, p. 351. *C. pallens* J. Blackwall (not Hahn), 1861–4, p. 130. *C. subtilis* O. P.-Cambridge, 1879–81, p. 31 ; C. Chyzer and L. Kulczynski, 1891–7, II, p. 229 ; E. Simon, 1932, pp. 924, 927 ; E. Reimoser, 1937, p. 62 ; A. Tullgren, 1946, p. 11.

DESCRIPTION. LENGTH : ♀ : 3–4·5 mm. ♂ : 2·5–3 mm. CARAPACE: Light yellow-brown, often a little darker on head. Traces of veinings sometimes occur round fovea. Male : sometimes considerably darker and with a darker borderline. EYES : Anteriors of equal size ; medians slightly nearer to each other than to adjacent laterals. (cf. *C. diversa*). ABDOMEN : Similar in colour to the last species. Dorsal stripe usually visible, sometimes flanked by two light spots followed by the usual rows of spots ; chevrons scarcely discernible. Darker in the male, with pattern often distinct. (cf. *C. diversa*). STERNUM : Lemon-yellow to orange. CHELICERÆ : Light brown, only a little darker than carapace. LEGS : Female, yellow ; male, light brown. Tibia III with one ventral spine. EPIGYNE : Text-fig. 73, E. MALE PALP : Text-fig. 72, D. The female resembles *C. diversa*, from which it is distinguished by the epigyne, the anterior eyes and its more elongated general appearance.

OCCURRENCE : Low plants and moss on swampy ground. Sand-hills round the coast. A southern species. Adult males are found from early summer until August or even later.

2. Genus CHEIRACANTHIUM C. L. Koch 1839.

CHARACTERS OF GENUS. The spiders of this genus resemble those of *Clubiona* in general appearance but differ from them in the following particulars. CARAPACE : No clearly defined fovea in the British species. EYES : Smaller, relative to the distances between them. Posterior row scarcely longer than anterior. Trapezium formed by four median eyes not, relatively, so narrow in front as in *Clubiona*. Eyes of lateral pairs very close. ABDOMEN : Chevrons succeeding the dorsal stripe, where they occur, narrower and closer together, giving the appearance of a continual longitudinal stripe. STERNUM : Broader, not attenuated in front. CHELICERÆ : Somewhat attenuated apically, markedly so in males. Inner row with two teeth far removed from the fang. LEGS : Longer relatively, and more slender, I being longer than IV. No dorsal spines on femora I and II ; no ventral spines on tibia III. Scopulæ on I and II consist of more widely spaced finer hairs (and are in fact difficult to make out) extending on I nearly to metatarsus and on II to apical end of metatarsus. More pronounced on tarsus and apical end of metatarsus of III and IV. EPIGYNE : Very much alike and different from any of the *Clubiona* species ; characterised by a large median cavity surrounded by a chitinised arch. Anterior to this, dark or black bands appear, whose disposition varies somewhat and which are part of the seminal ducts lying near the surface of the cuticle. MALE PALPS : Tibia noticeably longer and more slender. Bulb with sexual organs not reaching the end of the tarsus, at the basal end of which is a long spur extending back over the tibia.

There are three British species : *Cheiracanthium erraticum* (Walck.), *C. pennyi* Camb. and *C. virescens* (Sund.).

Cheiracanthium erraticum (Walckenaer).

(Text-fig. 74, A, D)

Aranea erratica C. A. Walckenaer, 1802, p. 219. *Clubiona nutrix* and *C. erratica* J. Blackwall, 1861–4, pp. 134, 135. *Cheiracanthium erroneum* and *C. carnifex* O. P.-Cambridge, 1873 (2), pp. 520, 532. *C. carnifex* O. P.-Cambridge, 1879–81, p. 32. *C. erraticum* C. Chyzer and L. Kulczynski, 1891–7, II, p. 233 ; E. Simon, 1932, p. 902 ; E. Reimoser, 1937, p. 73 ; A. Tullgren, 1946, p. 29.

DESCRIPTION. LENGTH : ♀ : 7–7·5 mm. ♂ : 5–5·5 mm. CARA-PACE : Light brown. Wide, sooty streaks (which become ill-defined on keeping) radiate from foveal area, not visible on lighter specimens (cf. *C. virescens*); two nearly parallel lines reach median posterior eyes. ABDOMEN : A carmine dorsal stripe flanked by narrow lighter green-yellow patches in the anterior half and succeeded by seven short contiguous chevrons, of nearly the same (carmine) colour, which reach the spinners. The stripe and chevrons, especially before the spider has been put in spirit, may form one continuous stripe, which is very easily recognised in the field. STERNUM : Brown, or deep brown ; darker round edges and between coxæ. In fresh specimens, dark grey-green with a yellow stripe down middle, but this colour not permanent. CHELICERÆ : Somewhat attenuated apically, markedly so in males. Apical ends and margins deep brown to black. LEGS : Light yellow-white to brown (becoming brown on preservation). EPIGYNE : Text-fig. 74, D. MALE PALP : Text-fig. 74, A. This is the commonest species. It resembles *C. pennyi* (q.v.) closely and long-preserved specimens are not unlike *C. virescens*.

OCCURRENCE : Widespread. Fairly common on low plants in early summer. The females build their cocoons in June and July amongst several leaves which are woven together. Males adult from April onwards.

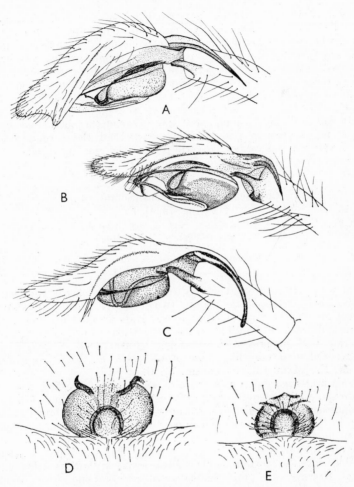

TEXT-FIG. 74.—Male palps : A, *Cheiracanthium erraticum;* B, *C. virescens;* C, *C. pennyi.*
Epigynes : D, *C. erraticum;* E, *C. virescens.*

Cheiracanthium pennyi O.P.-Cambridge.
(Text-fig. 74, C)

Cheiracanthium pennyi O. P.-Cambridge, 1873 (2), p. 533, and 1879–81, p. 464 ; C. Chyzer and L. Kulczynski, 1891–7, II, p. 233 ; E. Simon ,1932, p. 904 ; E. Reimoser, 1937, p. 72.

DESCRIPTION. This species resembles *C. erraticum* very closely. The type specimens are very old and bleached, but the following characters serve to distinguish it : FEMALE : Probably the only reliable character is the chitinous arch in the centre of the epigyne. This is not circular but slightly, though quite definitely, broader than long, whereas in *C. erraticum* it is nearly circular. MALE : The tarsal spur of palp not aculeate at its tip, but tapering more gradually through-out its length. Projection between apical end of alveolus and tip of tarsus (characteristic in *C. erraticum*, Text-fig. 74, A) here negligible. Whole tarsus narrower than in *C. erraticum*. MALE PALP : Text-fig. 74, C.

(It will probably be found that the colour of the abdominal dorsal stripe is browner in this species, rather than the carmine of *C. erraticum*, but this cannot be verified from the existing specimens.)

OCCURRENCE : Wokingham, Berkshire, 1872. The only record.

Cheiracanthium virescens (Sundevall).
(Text-fig. 74, B, E)

Clubiona virescens J. C. Sundevall, 1833, p. 267. *Chiracanthium nutrix* O. P.-Cambridge, 1873 (2), p. 531, and 1879–81, p. 33. *C. lapidicolens* C. Chyzer and L. Kulczynski, 1891–7, II, p. 234 ; W. Bosenberg, 1901–3, p. 282. *C. virescens* E. Simon, 1932, pp. 899, 901 ; E. Reimoser, 1937, p. 76. *C. nutrix* A. Tullgren, 1946, p. 38.

DESCRIPTION. LENGTH : ♀ : 5–7 mm. ♂ : 5–6 mm. CARAPACE : Light yellow to brown. Veinings from foveal area clearly and beauti-fully marked (less so in the male) ; two of these lines run parallel from foveal area to posterior median eyes. ABDOMEN : Grey-green. No marked dorsal stripe visible on fresh specimens, but a faint mark on anterior half in preserved specimens. CHELICERÆ, STERNUM and LEGS : Coloured very like those of *C. erraticum*. EPIGYNE : Text-fig. 74, E. MALE PALP : Text-fig. 74, B.

Long-preserved specimens require to be distinguished from *C. erraticum*. In the female of *C. virescens* the dark region (indicating the seminal sacs) round the chitinized arch of the epigyne is much smaller than in *C. erraticum*. The markings of the carapace are also useful as a confirmation (but not in the male). The males differ in the direction taken by the tarsal spur of the palp, but this character is not altogether reliable, since the apparent angle changes so quickly with position of the palp. However, the projection between the apical end of the alveolus and tip of the tarsus is not pronounced in this species, as it is in *C. erraticum*, and the tip of the tarsus is rather more slender.

OCCURRENCE : Widespread but rather rare. Dry and sandy places. Males adult in May.

3. Genus **AGROECA** N. Westring 1861.

CHARACTERS OF GENUS. CARAPACE : Oval, narrowed in front. Fovea rather long ; streaks radiate from this and, widening out and sometimes forming loops, make a pattern which is more or less characteristic. There are usually clear or lighter, submarginal lateral bands, sometimes invaded by the pattern. EYES : In a compact group, both rows procurved. Anterior medians usually smaller than laterals (except in *A. lusatica* and *A. proxima*). Posteriors nearly equidistant (cf. *Scotina*). ABDOMEN : General dorsal pattern consists of central lighter region (on fore part, on which may be a darker stripe) branching laterally into a series of curved bars. The central stripe may reach the spinners (*A. lusatica*) and is flanked by a series of six pairs of lighter spots (which may be obscure or represented by depressions). STERNUM : Almost circular, pointed behind. CHELICERÆ : Moderately robust and short. Two rows of teeth ; inner row with two teeth. MAXILLÆ and LABIUM : Text-fig. 64, B. LEGS : Order of length : IV, I, II, III. Tibia I with two pairs of ventral spines (cf. *Scotina*). Metatarsi I and II with three pairs of ventral spines, the apical ones being shorter and more lateral (Text-fig. 77, E) (cf. *Clubiona* and *Agraecina*). Scopulæ, not well defined in smaller species, present on tarsi and extend sometimes to metatarsi.

The five species, *Agroeca brunnea* (Bl.), *A. proxima* (Camb.), *A. inopina* Camb., *A. lusatica* (L. Koch) and *A. cuprea* Menge, are similar at first sight in colouration but are not difficult to distinguish by the sexual organs.

Agroeca brunnea (Blackwall).
(Text-fig. 75, A, B, D)

Agelena brunnea J. Blackwall, 1833, p. 351, and 1861–4, p. 159. *Agroeca brunnea* O. P.-Cambridge, 1879–81, p. 35 ; C. Chyzer and L. Kulczynski, 1891–7, II, p. 244 ; W. Bosenberg, 1901–3, p. 261 ; E. Simon, 1932, pp. 940, 944 ; E. Reimoser, 1937, p. 81 ; A. Tullgren, 1946, p. 48.

DESCRIPTION. LENGTH : ♀ : 7–8 mm. ♂ : 6–7 mm. CARAPACE : Light brown. Red-brown streaks run out radially from fovea and sometimes stop short leaving a wide, clear margin, but sometimes invade this area, which is anyhow not well defined. There is a thin, dark borderline. Head sometimes darker than the rest. EYES : Anterior medians smaller than adjacent laterals. ABDOMEN : Reddish-brown, pattern typical but very faint. A darker dorsal stripe anteriorly is followed by a lighter region and branches from this alternate with darker patches. STERNUM : Red-brown, darker than coxæ and darker in males, sometimes with darker blotches coming in from the edges. CHELICERÆ : Colour as carapace. LEGS : Reddish-brown, femora a little lighter. EPIGYNE : Text-fig. 75, D. MALE PALP : Text-fig. 75, A, B. The colouring of the male is usually darker than in the female but is otherwise similar.

OCCURRENCE : Widespread, but not common, except locally. Woods.

Agroeca proxima (O. P.-Cambridge).
(Text-figs. 76, A, B ; 77, A)

Agelena proxima O. P.-Cambridge, 1871, p. 415. *Agroeca proxima* O. P.-Cambridge, 1886, p. 2 (Figs. 4, a and 4, b=*A. proxima* and *A. brunnea* respectively, and not *vice versa*, as stated) ; 1879–81, p. 36 ; W. Bosenberg, 1901–3, p. 262 ; F. P. Smith, 1904, p. 59 ; E. Simon, 1932, pp. 942, 943 ; E. Reimoser, 1947, p. 83 ; A. Tullgren, 1946, p. 52 ; W. S. Bristowe, 1947, pl. 12.

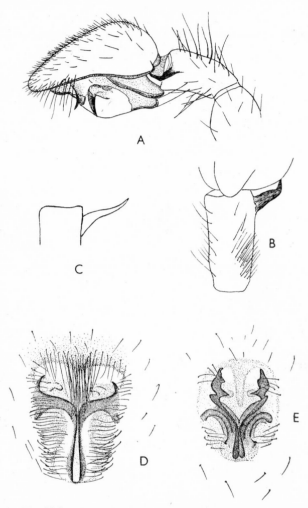

TEXT-FIG. 75.—Male palps: A, *Agroeca brunnea* (side); B, do. (tibia from below); C, *Agroeca lusatica* (tibial apophysis from below in outline). Epigynes: D, *Agroeca brunnea;* E, *A. lusatica.*

DESCRIPTION. LENGTH: ♀: 5·5–7·5 mm. ♂: 4–5 mm. CARAPACE: Similar to *A. brunnea* but the red-brown veinings often extend to margin (less well defined in males). A borderline sometimes present. EYES: Anterior medians same size as laterals (or only very slightly smaller) and equal to, or very slightly larger than posterior medians (cf. *A. cuprea*). ABDOMEN: Typical pattern extremely faint A dark central band with a lighter centre is followed by series of very obscure dark bars. STERNUM: Variable; brown, reddish-yellow or

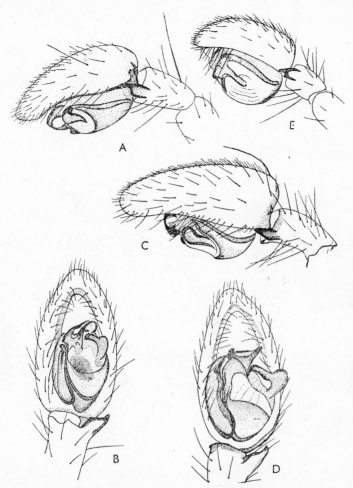

TEXT-FIG. 76.—Male palps: A, *Agroeca proxima* (side); B, do. (below).
C, *A. inopina* (side); D, do. (below); E, *Agroeca cuprea* (side).

light yellow, coloured as coxæ. Some specimens have a darker
borderline. CHELICERÆ: Colour as carapace, with faint sooty longitudinal marks. LEGS: Uniform reddish-yellow to red-brown; no
annulations (cf. *A. inopina*). EPIGYNE: Text-fig. 77, A. MALE
PALP: Text-fig. 76, A, B. This species resembles *A. inopina* (q.v. for
differences), but its general colouration is much more reddish than the
" mousy " brown of the latter species. The males are like the females
but lighter.

OCCURRENCE: Widespread and common locally. Woods and dry
sandy places. Adult summer and autumn, possibly most of the year.

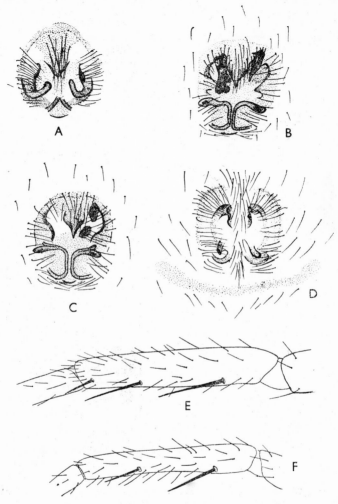

TEXT-FIG. 77.—Epigynes: A, *Agroeca proxima;* B, C, *A. inopina;* D, *A. cuprea;* E, Metatarsus I, of *Agroeca;* F, do. *Agraecina.*

Agroeca inopina O.P.-Cambridge.
(Text-figs. 76, C, D ; 77, B, C)

Agroeca inopina O. P.-Cambridge, 1886, p. 2.   *A. proxima* L. Kulczynski, 1898, p. 97.   *A. inopina* E. Simon, 1932, pp. 942, 943.

DESCRIPTION. LENGTH :   ♀: 4·5–7·5 mm.   ♂: 3·5–4·5 mm. CARAPACE : There are two wide light lateral bands and a median light band, the region between them occupied by sooty radiating streaks which widen at their lower ends.   There is a dark borderline.   EYES :

Anterior medians smaller than laterals, and equal in size to posterior medians (cf. *A. cuprea*). ABDOMEN : Central lighter region, on which is a thin darker streak, reaches to half way, followed by alternate light and dark bars, often well defined, but sometimes whole pattern obscure and dark. Markings sooty on dark brown to red-brown ground. STERNUM : As coxæ, grey-brown, often slightly darker at edges. CHELICERÆ : Colour as carapace, with a very faint sooty blotch on front of each. LEGS : Brown, with very faint wide annulations (cf. *A. proxima*). EPIGYNE : Text-fig. 77, B, C. This often presents an irregular and unsymmetrical appearance. MALE PALP : Text-fig. 76, C, D. The species resembles *A. proxima* in general appearance. It may be distinguished, as well as by the sexual organs, (*a*) by the very faint annulations of the legs, (*b*) by the absence of a wedge-shaped ventral mark on the abdomen, which often occurs on *A. proxima*.

OCCURRENCE : A southern species ; frequent locally on coastal sand-hills. Also found in woods.

Agroeca lusatica (L. Koch).
(Text-fig. 75, C, E)

Liocranum lusaticum L. Koch, 1875, p. 6. *Agroeca thorelli* C. Chyzer and L. Kulczynski, 1891–7, II, p. 244. *A. lusatica* E. Simon, 1932, pp. 941, 944 ; E. Reimoser, 1937, p. 82 ; W. S. Bristowe, 1939, p. 25 ; A. Tullgren, 1946, p. 50.

DESCRIPTION. LENGTH : ♀ : 6–6·5 mm. CARAPACE : Typical and like *A. inopina*, with a dark borderline. EYES : Anterior medians almost same size as laterals, not smaller (cf. *A. brunnea*). ABDOMEN : A light brown central band reaches to spinners, flanked by six pairs of angular darker bars ; sides with blotches of this same colour. STERNUM : Brown, slightly darker towards edges. CHELICERÆ : Uniform brown. LEGS : Brown with femora and patellæ considerably lighter. EPIGYNE : Text-fig. 75, E. This is very distinct and the female is not likely to be confused with any other species. The male is not recorded in Britain and specimens are not available. It could be distinguished from *A. brunnea* by the appearance of the palpal tibial apophysis as seen from below (Text-fig. 75, C, after Reimoser and Simon).

OCCURRENCE : Sandwich (Kent), 1938, on sandhills.

Agroeca cuprea Menge.
(Text-figs. 76, E ; 77, D)

Agroeca cuprea A. Menge, 1866–77, Abt. VI, p. 339. *A. pullata* T. Thorell, 1875 (1), p. 83. *A. chrysea* C. Chyzer and L. Kulczynski, 1891–7, II, p. 244. *A. notata* O. P.-Cambridge, 1902 (1), p. 30. *A. pullata* E. Simon, 1932, pp. 941, 942 ; E. Reimoser, 1937, p. 83. *A. cuprea* A. Tullgren, 1946, p. 51.

DESCRIPTION. LENGTH : ♀ : 4·5 mm. ♂ : 4 mm. CARAPACE : Markings as in *A. inopina;* colour of lighter bands brown, with edges and darker streaks more diffuse than in that species. There is a thin black borderline. EYES : Anterior medians smaller than laterals and considerably smaller than posterior medians (cf. *A. proxima* and *A. inopina*). ABDOMEN : Brown with very faint darker markings, no clear pattern in female. In the male darker in front with three to four chevrons on posterior half. Sides with darker streaks. STERNUM : Yellow-brown ; lighter in the male. CHELICERÆ : Coloured as light bands of carapace with a faint sooty mark on inner margin in female. LEGS : Uniform yellow-brown, lighter in the male. EPIGYNE : Text-fig. 77, D. MALE PALP : Text-fig. 76, E. The male is readily identified by the great convexity of the tarsal bulb, together with the shape of the tibial apophysis, which has a dark border. The female is distinguished from *A. proxima* and *A. inopina* by the epigyne and by the anterior median eyes being a good deal smaller than the posterior medians.

OCCURRENCE : Folkestone and St. Margaret's Bay (Kent), 1902.

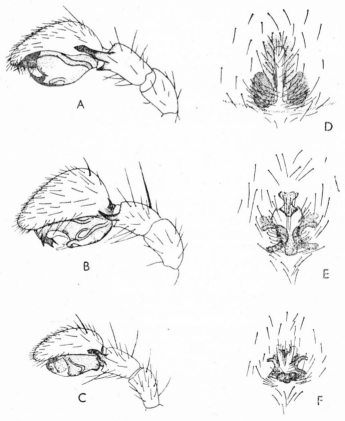

TEXT-FIG. 78.—Male palps : A, *Agraecina striata;* B, *Scotina celans;* C, *S. gracilipes.*
Epigynes : D, *Agraecina striata;* E, *Scotina celans;* F, *S. gracilipes.*

4. Genus **AGRAECINA** E. Simon 1932.

CHARACTERS OF GENUS. The only differences between this and *Agroeca* are that metatarsus I possesses two ventral spines (instead of three) (Text-fig. 77, F) and that the tibial apophysis of the male palp is long and slender.

Agraecina striata (Kulczynski).
(Text-figs. 77, F ; 78, A, D)

Agroeca striata L. Kulczynski, 1882, p. 31, and 1891-7, II, p. 244. *Agroeca littoralis* O. P.-Cambridge, 1895, p. 26. *Agraecina striata* E. Simon, 1932, p. 940 ; E. Reimoser, 1937, p. 79 ; A. Tullgren, 1946, p. 46.

DESCRIPTION. LENGTH : ♀ : 4·5–5·5 mm. ♂ : c. 3·5 mm. CARAPACE : ♀ : light yellow without a borderline. ♂ : Brown with, sometimes, a greyish-black borderline. Pattern, as in *Agroeca,* of greyish-black widening striations, which stop short leaving clear lateral sub-marginal stripes. (These markings sometimes very faint in females.) EYES : Both rows procurved. Anterior medians slightly smaller than laterals. ABDOMEN : Depth of colour very variable. Dusky grey with a yellow lighter central band reaching nearly to spinners and flanked by six pairs of light spots diminishing in size, disposed as in *Agroeca.* Outside this again may be two further longitudinal yellow stripes. STERNUM : Almost circular and light yellow. CHELICERÆ : Colour as carapace. LEGS : Yellow-brown ; tibiæ and metatarsi I and II sometimes sooty grey or faintly annulated. EPIGYNE : Text-fig. 78, D. MALE PALP : Text-fig. 78, A.

OCCURRENCE : A rare southern species. Marshy places. Adult in May and June.

5. Genus **SCOTINA** A. Menge 1873.

CHARACTERS OF GENUS. The genus resembles *Agroeca* very closely. The following are the points of difference :

(*a*) Posterior median eyes noticeably further from each other than from the laterals. (*b*) Tibia I has seven to ten pairs of ventral spines (sometimes six in the male). Metatarsus I has five to seven pairs (three in the male).

There are two British species : *Scotina celans* (Bl.) and *S. gracilipes* (Bl.).

Scotina celans (Blackwall).
(Text-fig. 78, B, E)

Agelena celans J. Blackwall, 1841, p. 624, and 1861-4, p. 161. *Agroeca celans* C. Chyzer and L. Kulczynski, 1891-7, II, p. 245. *Liocranum celans* O. P.-Cambridge, 1879-81, p. 41. *Scotina celans* E. Simon, 1932, p. 945 ; E. Reimoser, 1937, p. 84 ; A. Tullgren, 1946, p. 55.

DESCRIPTION. LENGTH : ♀ : 4–4·5 mm. ♂ : 2·5–3 mm. CARAPACE : ♂ : A light yellow central band runs whole length from behind eyes ; there are two similarly coloured lateral bands. Intermediate region grey-brown with dark widening streaks of same pattern as in

Agroeca inopina. No borderline. ♀: Similar but edges of light bands not so well defined. EYES: Both rows procurved. Anterior medians much smaller than laterals (cf. *S. gracilipes*). ABDOMEN: ♂: A light central stripe on anterior half followed by five to six chevrons; these and the spots disposed as in *Agroeca.* ♀: Similar, but markings much more obscure and difficult to make out. STERNUM: Uniform yellow. CHELICERÆ: Colour as light bands of carapace, with faint sooty streaks. LEGS: ♀: Coxæ yellow, femora and tarsi slightly darker. Tibiæ and metatarsi all brown. ♂: Coxæ and femora yellow. Tibiæ and tarsi I and II darker brown, yellow in III and IV. Ventral spines (pairs) on legs I and II:

	Female		Male	
Leg	Tibia	Metatarsus	Tibia	Metatarsus
I	10	7	7	3
II	7–9	5–6	6–7	3

EPIGYNE: Text-fig. 78, E. MALE PALP: Text-fig. 78, B.

OCCURRENCE: A rather rare southern species, found in heather or in woods. Adult in August and September.

Scotina gracilipes (Blackwall).
(Text-fig. 78, C, F)

Agelena gracilipes J. Blackwall, 1859, p. 97, and 1861–4, p. 162 (♂). *Drassus prælongipes* O. P.-Cambridge, 1861, p. 428. *Liocranum prælongipes* O. P.-Cambridge, 1871, p. 440 (in part). *L. gracilipes* O. P.-Cambridge, 1879–81, p. 39. *Agroeca gracilipes* C. Chyzer and L. Kulczynski, 1891–7, p. 245. *Scotina gracilipes* E. Simon, 1932, p. 945; A. Tullgren, 1946, p. 53. (E. Reimoser, 1937, confuses this species with *S. palliardi* L. Koch.)

DESCRIPTION. LENGTH: ♀: 2–3·5 mm. ♂: 2·5–3·5 mm. CARAPACE: Dark sooty-brown pattern as in *Agroeca inopina,* but no light central or lateral band (cf. *S. celans*). There is a thin black borderline. EYES: Anterior medians only slightly smaller than laterals (cf. *S. celans*). ABDOMEN: Dark brown-black, with a yellow V on fore part, its apex pointing backwards, followed by five W marks (alternating with light marks of similar shape) which are distinct. Sides dark and mottled. STERNUM: Brown. CHELICERÆ: Ground colour of carapace. LEGS: ♀: Femora yellow, tibiæ and metatarsi I, II and III dark brown (this is striking in fresh specimens, especially in the male), not so deep in IV, which are almost uniform. ♂: I and II similar; III and IV not such deep brown, with patellæ yellow.

Ventral spines (pairs) on legs I and II.

Leg	Female		Male	
	Tibia	Metatarsus	Tibia	Metatarsus
I	7	5	6	3
II	7	3	5	3

EPIGYNE : Text-fig. 78, F. MALE PALP : Text-fig. 78, C.
OCCURRENCE : Widespread but rare. Heathery places. Adult in August.

6. Genus **LIOCRANUM** L. Koch 1866.

CHARACTERS OF GENUS. CARAPACE : Broad in front (cf. *Agroeca*) ; fovea long. EYES : Anterior row straight (as seen from in front), eyes equal in size and equidistant. Posterior row longer, very slightly recurved, almost straight (cf. *Agroeca*) ; medians further from each other than from adjacent laterals, than which they are smaller. ABDOMEN : Pattern distinct on the sole British species. Median spinners compressed laterally (not always easy to see). STERNUM : Heart-shaped, pointed behind. Slightly longer than *Agroeca*. CHELI-CERÆ : Somewhat like *Clubiona* in shape, attenuated in the male. Teeth : Outer row with three, inner with two (the apical one in the male being larger). MAXILLÆ : Broadest at base ; tips directed a little outwards, but not dilated as in *Clubiona*. LABIUM : As broad as long ; narrowed suddenly at base. LEGS : Tibiae I and II with four pairs of ventral spines ; metatarsi I and II with one pair. Scopulæ extend to some way along tibiæ in I and II, to apical end of metatarsi in III and IV.

There is but one British species.

Liocranum rupicola (Walckenaer).
(Text-fig. 79, A, B)

Clubiona rupicola C. A. Walckenaer, 1825, p. 126. *C. domestica* Wider, 1834, p. 208 ; J. Blackwall, 1861-4, p. 132. *Liocranum domestica* O. P.-Cambridge and other British authors. *L. rupicola* C. Chyzer and L. Kulczynski, 1891-7, II, pl. 240 ; E. Simon, 1932, p. 938 ; E. Reimoser, 1937, p. 78 ; W. S. Bristowe, 1947, pl. 13 ; A. Tullgren, 1946, p. 45.

DESCRIPTION. LENGTH : ♀: 6·5–7·5 mm. ♂ : 5·5–6 mm. CARA-PACE : Pattern sooty brown, similar to that in *Agroeca;* with a light central region, a light yellow-brown sub-marginal band and a dark borderline. ABDOMEN : Pattern, sooty black on a yellow-brown field, very distinct. A single median bar on anterior half is followed by a pair of spots or bars (sometimes joining them) and then, in posterior half, by a series of sinuous bars of diminishing size, roughly of the form of a W. Sides black with lighter spots. STERNUM : Yellow, sometimes with a darker border. CHELICERÆ : Red-brown, colour as head. LEGS : Yellow-brown, sometimes with very faint annulations, especially on IV. EPIGYNE : Text-fig. 79, B. MALE PALP : Text-fig. 79, A.

OCCURRENCE : A southern species ; rather rare. Under stones, tiles, etc., in dry places. Adult autumn and spring, and probably at other times.

7. Genus **ZORA** C. L. Koch 1848.

CHARACTERS OF GENUS. CARAPACE : In shape and pattern rather like *Agroeca*, strongly attenuated in front (Text-fig. 4, B, p. 22). EYES : Anterior row nearly straight (as seen from in front) ; posterior row very strongly recurved. (The eyes are thus disposed very much as in the LYCOSIDÆ). Anterior medians usually a little larger than laterals. ABDOMEN : Pattern, when discernible, of same general plan as in *Agroeca*, though usually reduced to isolated spots. STERNUM : Nearly circular, pointed behind. CHELICERÆ : Rather weak and almost vertical, with three teeth in outer, and two in inner row. LABIUM : Broader than long. MAXILLÆ : Similar to *Agroeca*, but a little broader at base. LEGS : Order of length : IV, I, II, III. Tibiæ I and II with six to eight pairs of strong ventral spines, metatarsi I and II with three pairs. Scopulæ present on tarsi.

Three species occur in Britain : *Zora spinimana* (Sund.), *Z. armillata* Sim. and *Z. nemoralis* (Bl.).

Zora spinimana (Sundevall).
(Text-figs. 4, B ; 79, C ; 80, B, D, F)

Lycæna spinimana C. J. Sundevall, 1833, p. 266. *Hecœrge spinimana* J. Blackwall, 1861–4, p. 41. *H. maculata* O. P.-Cambridge, 1879–81, p. 43. *Zora spinimana* C. Chyzer and L. Kulczynski, 1891–7, II, p. 250 ; W. Falconer, 1912, p. 312 ; F. and M. Dahl, 1927, p. 5 ; E. Simon, 1932, p. 933 ; A. Tullgren, 1946, p. 71.

DESCRIPTION. LENGTH : ♀ : 5–6·5 mm. ♂ : c. 4·5 mm. CARAPACE : Text-fig. 4, B, p. 22. The ground light yellow, markings chocolate brown ; light bands wider than the dark ones (cf. *Z. nemoralis*). ABDOMEN : Yellow-white. Two longitudinal red-brown stripes (usually somewhat broken or merged into mottling of sides) enclose a light field. On fore part of this are two parallel rows of three spots, sometimes elongated and joined, especially in males. In posterior half is a single row of spots of diminishing size. Sides mottled with transverse rows of spots of same rusty colour. STERNUM : Light yellow with rusty brown spots between coxæ and at posterior tip. CHELICERÆ : Each with a hollow stripe in front terminating in a blunt point, sometimes only the outlines visible. LEGS : ♀ : Femora light yellow with darker stripes, one dorsal, two retrolateral, often broken or partly missing, especially on III and IV. Patellæ and tibiæ I, II and III brown, variable in depth ; metatarsi usually brown only at apical ends.

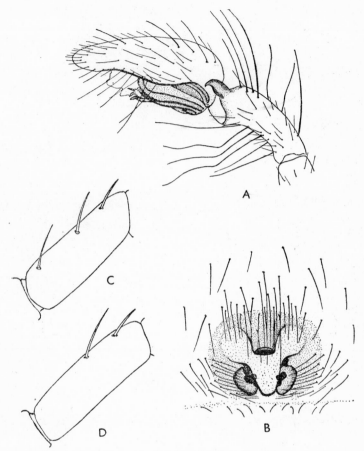

TEXT-FIG. 79.—*Liocranum rupicola:* A, male palp ; B, epigyne.
Male palpal femora : C, *Zora spinimana;* D, *Z. armillata.*

(Patella has a lighter dorsal surface, on which is a thin dark pointed
streak.) IV similar but metatarsus brown along its whole length.
♂ : Colouring similar, but patellæ and tibiæ sometimes only light
brown, femoral stripes very broken, faint or absent. Tibiæ I and II
with at least eight pairs of ventral spines ; metatarsi with three pairs.
In males coxæ IV partly covered with short hairs forming a kind of
brush. EPIGYNE : Text-fig. 80, F. MALE PALP : Text-fig. 80, B, D.
Palpal femur has *three* dorsal spines (Text-fig. 79, C). The species
resembles the others of the genus fairly closely ; the differences will be
found under their respective names.

OCCURRENCE : A widespread and common species. Found among
leaves in woods, grass, moss, heather and in hedgerows.

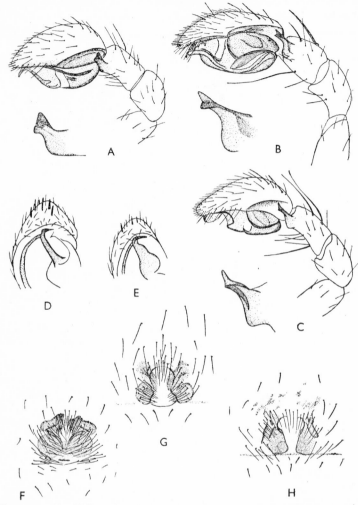

TEXT-FIG. 80.—Male palps : A, *Zora nemoralis;* B, *Z. spinimana;* C, *Z. armillata.*
Tips of palps (from below) : D, *Z. spinimana;* E, *Z. armillata.*
Epigynes : F, *Zora spinimana;* G, *Z. armillata;* H, *Z. nemoralis.*

Zora armillata Simon.
(Text-figs. 4, B; 79, D ; 80, C, E, G)

Zora armillata E. Simon, 1878, IV, p. 320.   *Z. letifera* W. Falconer, 1912, p. 317 ;
O. P.-Cambridge, 1913, p. 111.   *Z. armillata* E. Simon, 1932, pp. 933, 934 ; A. Tullgren,
1946, p. 72.

DESCRIPTION.   LENGTH : ♀ : 4–6·5 mm.   ♂: c. 4 mm.   The species
resembles *Z. spinimana,* from which it differs in the following respects :

CARAPACE : The dark margin somewhat diffused inwards. ABDOMEN : Colouration like that of lighter specimens of *Z. spinimana*, the spots tending to be smaller. LEGS : Yellow-brown, with only apical ends of metatarsi coloured deep brown. Femoral stripes and punctuations absent. Male tibiæ wholly or almost wholly suffused with dark brown in fresh specimens, but this colour liable to fade in spirit. Tibiæ I and II usually with seven pairs ventral spines, but the number may vary. Coxæ IV of male have hairs, but less dense and finer than in *Z. spinimana*. EPIGYNE : Text-fig. 80, G. MALE PALP : Text-fig. 80, C. The tibia is thinner, while the tibial apophysis differs appreciably in shape from that of *Z. spinimana*, but the appearance of these varies much with position and a useful check is to look at the ventral side of the tip of the palp (Text-fig. 80, E). There are only two dorsal spines on the femur (Text-fig. 79, D). In the female the lack of markings on the legs is a useful check.

OCCURRENCE : Wicken and Edmund Fens, Cambridgeshire, where it is found to the exclusion of *Z. spinimana*.

Zora nemoralis (Blackwall).
(Text-fig. 80, A, H)

Hecæge nemoralis J. Blackwall, 1861, p. 441 ; O. P.-Cambridge 1873 (1), p. 433 and 1879–81, p . 43. *Zora nemoralis* F. and M. Dahl, 1927, p. 5 ; E. Simon, 1932, pp. 932, 934 ; A. T ullgren, 1946, p. 73.

DESCRIPTION. LENGTH : ♀ : 3·5–5 mm. ♂ : c. 3·5 mm. This species resembles *Z. spinimana* in size and general appearance, though the colouring is darker. It differs from the latter species in the following particulars : CARAPACE : Light median and lateral bands narrower than the dark bands (cf. Text-fig. 4, B, p. 22). Marginal line widened to form a dark band. ABDOMEN : Mottled, dorsally and on sides, with the same rusty-brown colour, but the mottling here forms a rather badly-defined pattern of the kind found in *Agroeca inopina* ; darker and more clearly defined in the male. STERNUM : Sometimes as in *Z. spinimana*, but often with a median line or with white spots enlarged into diffuse marks ; darker in the male. CHELICERÆ : Dark marks usually deeper in colour and better defined. LEGS : Marking on femora and patellæ usually more diffuse. Patellæ, tibiæ and metatarsi brown, often deep brown ; metatarsi sometimes darkened at tip in male. Tibiæ I and II with six pairs of ventral spines (but the number may well vary). Coxæ IV in the male with no brush of short hairs. EPIGYNE : Text-fig. 80, H. MALE PALP : Text-fig. 80, A. The male is readily distinguishable from the other species by (*a*) the shape of the tibial apophysis (Text-fig. 80, A), (*b*) the fact that the patella of the palp is enlarged apically, especially on the outside (which is not the case with the other two species), (*c*) by the absence of the brush of hairs on coxæ IV. Both sexes are also recognisable by the colouration, especially of the carapace.

OCCURRENCE : A rather rare species, occurring more frequently in the north of Britain. In woods and heather.

8. Genus **PHRUROLITHUS** C. L. Koch 1839.

CHARACTERS OF GENUS. CARAPACE : Oval; fovea short. Radiating streaks, when present, widen towards the margin. EYES : Anterior row procurved (as seen from in front). Posterior row straight, only slightly longer than anterior. Anterior medians smaller than laterals and nearer to them than to each other. Posteriors about equidistant and about equal in size to anterior laterals. ABDOMEN : Elongated, about equal in width in front and behind. STERNUM : Heart-shaped.

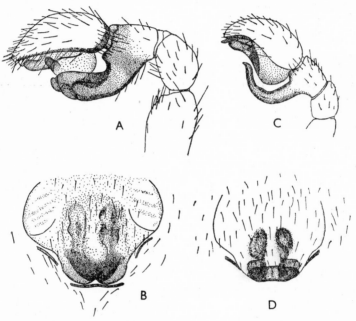

TEXT-FIG. 81.—*Phrurolithus festivus:* A, male palp ; B, epigyne.
  P. minimus: C, male palp ; D, epigyne.

Coxæ IV spaced widely apart so that posterior point of sternum projects somewhat between them (Text-fig. 64, C). CHELICERÆ : Vertical and not very strong ; each bears a spine near the inner margin, pointing slightly inwards (a character unique in this family). Two teeth on inner row (only), almost in contact, far removed from fang. MAXILLÆ and LABIUM : Text-fig. 64, C. LEGS : Order of length : IV, I, II, III. Tibiæ I and II with four to five pairs of ventral spines, metatarsi with two to three pairs. (The tarsi are usually said to have no scopulæ. Nevertheless the hairs on the ventral side of the tarsi and apical ends of the metatarsi are a little stronger than the others and are arranged more regularly ; they would thus appear to form at least the vestiges of a scopula.) There are tufts of spatulate hairs under the claws.

MALE PALP : Femur dilated ventrally ; tibia with a large and characteristic apophysis.

The two British species *Phrurolithus festivus* (C. L. K.) and *P. minimus* C. L. K. are small spiders somewhat resembling *Micaria*.

Phrurolithus festivus (C. L. Koch).
(Text-fig. 81, A, B)

Micaria festiva C. L. Koch, 1835, 129.15. *Drassus propinquus* J. Blackwall, 1854, p. 175, and 1861–4, p. 120. *Phrurolithus festivus* O. P.-Cambridge, 1879–81, p. 44 : C. Chyzer and L. Kulczynski, 1891–7, II, p. 247 ; E. Simon, 1932, p. 947 ; E. Reimoser, 1937, p. 85 ; A. Tullgren, 1946, p. 57.

DESCRIPTION. LENGTH : ♀ : 2·5–3 mm. ♂ : 2·5–3 mm. CARAPACE : Brown with sooty radiating streaks (rather similar to those in *Agroeca*), reaching to edge, which is marked by a thin borderline. ABDOMEN : Dark grey, iridescent in sunshine, almost encircled by two whitish bands, very characteristic and visible in the field. Dorsally the front band appears on the anterior extremity, being broken in the middle ; the second forms a wide V, its apex forward, about half way along and is followed by seven very narrow chevrons, there being a light patch between the fourth and fifth. Ventrally, the anterior light band, sometimes unbroken, passes immediately behind epigyne in female. Bands and dorsal markings obscure in males. STERNUM : Yellow-brown suffused with greyish-black round edges. Usually with a hollow stripe anteriorly, from which widening streaks radiate to points between coxæ. CHELICERÆ : Coloured as carapace, with a dark line along inner and outer margins and an almost oval dark loop on apical half. LEGS : Yellow-brown. Femora I and II with brown streaks ; patellæ often brown ventrally. EPIGYNE : Text-fig. 81, B. The region of the sexual organs is very wide, the posterior median part of the epigyne usually very dark. The disposition of the seminal sacs appears variable and sometimes they are scarcely visible. MALE PALP : Text-fig. 81, A.

OCCURRENCE : Widespread and usually fairly common. It is often found running in sunshine, or under stones, dead leaves, etc., in both dry and wet places. Adult in early summer.

Phrurolithus minimus C. L. Koch.
(Text-fig. 81, C, D)

Phrurolithus minimus C. L. Koch, 1839 (1), VI, p. 111. *Micariosoma minima* O. P.-Cambridge, 1912, p. 72. *Phrurolithus minimus* C. Chyzer and L. Kulczynski, 1891–7, II, p. 249 ; A. R. Jackson, 1911, p. 385 ; E. Simon, 1932, p. 947 ; E. Reimoser, 1937, p. 86 ; A. Tullgren, 1946, p. 58.

DESCRIPTION. LENGTH : ♀ : 2·5–3·5 mm. ♂ : 2–2·5 mm. CARAPACE : Reddish-brown to yellow ; radiating streaks very obscure and faint. No borderline. ABDOMEN : Red-brown to yellow, sometimes quite uniform, sometimes with very indistinct markings. These consist of two light patches at either side of fore extremity and, sometimes, a faint light median stripe in anterior half, flanked by two darker spots almost at mid point. STERNUM : Uniform light yellow. CHELICERÆ : Uniform reddish-brown as carapace. LEGS : Light yellow. EPIGYNE : Text-fig. 81, D. This is distinct from that of *P. festivus;* the seminal sacs shown are not visible at all in some specimens, and the chitinisation of the darker parts is variable. MALE PALP : Text-fig. 81, C. The tibial apophysis is pointed, not wide, at its extremity (cf. *P. festivus*).

OCCURRENCE : Box Hill, Surrey, amongst stones and broken chalk. Parkhurst Forest, and Firestone Copse, near Wootton, Isle of Wight. They run about in sunshine, vanishing periodically into cracks and interstices between stones or among grass roots. Adult May to July.

11. Family ANYPHÆNIDÆ.

CHARACTERS OF FAMILY. Very similar to the CLUBIONIDÆ, in which Family it has been included by some authors. The chief differences lie (*a*) in the position of the tracheal spiracle, which lies almost in the middle of the ventral side of the abdomen, far removed from the spinners (Text-fig. 83, C), (*b*) in the hairs of the claw tufts (Text-fig. 83, D), which are clavate to a greater extent than in the CLUBIONIDÆ.

Genus **ANYPHÆNA** J. C. Sundevall 1833.

CHARACTERS OF GENUS. CARAPACE : Text-fig. 82. EYES : Anterior row recurved (as seen from in front) or straight ; medians a little smaller than laterals. Posterior row slightly procurved or straight ; Eyes nearly equal and equally spaced. Trapezium formed by four median eyes, longer than broad and narrower in front than behind. CHELICERÆ : Moderately strong with three teeth in the outer and up to six teeth in the inner row. LABIUM : Much longer than broad, reaching further than mid-point of maxillæ. LEGS : Scopulæ on tarsi and apical half of metatarsi I and II. Trochanters notched. There is but one British species.

Anyphæna accentuata (Walckenaer).
(Text-figs. 82, 83)

Aranea accentuata C. A. Walckenaer, 1802, p. 226. *Clubiona accentuata* J. Blackwall, 1861–4, p. 131. *Anyphæna accentuata* O. P.-Cambridge, 1879–81, p. 34 ; C. Chyzer and L. Kulczynski, 1891–7, II, p. 260 ; E. Simon, 1932, p. 895 ; E. Reimoser, 1937, p. 43 ; A. Tullgren, 1946, p. 41.

DESCRIPTION. LENGTH : ♀ : 4·5–7·5 mm. ♂ : 4–6·5 mm. CARAPACE : Text-fig. 82. ABDOMEN : The dark mark in the centre very characteristic (Text-fig. 82). Ventrally a dark line runs from epigastric fold to tracheal spiracle (Text-fig. 83, C) sometimes enlarged and covering a wider area. STERNUM : Brown, usually darker towards margin. Depth of colour very variable ; usually darker in males. CHELICERÆ : Moderately robust ; more attenuated and streaked with darker brown in males. Outer margin with three, inner with six teeth (the basal three being close and smaller). LEGS : Coloured as carapace ; annulations on femora and sometimes on other segments, but variable. EPIGYNE : Text-fig. 83, B. MALE PALP : Text-fig. 83, A.

The general appearance of the species is shown in Text-fig. 82. Colouration is very variable. The ground colour is cream or light brown, the markings brown, grey or a sooty black, usually darker and more distinct in the male. A melanic form has been taken which is almost uniformly black, the black pigment having invaded the normally light area. The pattern is very distinct on the living spider and can be recognised in the field.

OCCURRENCE : Distributed all over the British Isles. It is beaten out of trees and bushes, often in great abundance. Adult in early summer.

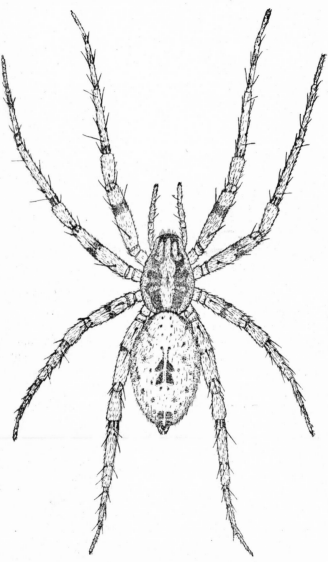

TEXT-FIG. 82.—*Anyphœna accentuata* ♀ (ANYPHÆNIDÆ).

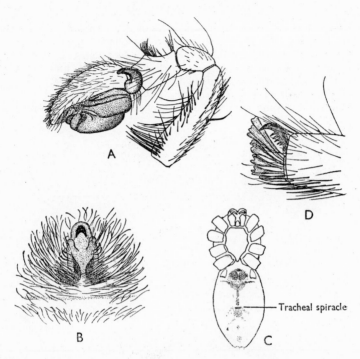

TEXT-FIG. 83.—*Anyphœna accentuata:* A, male palp; B, epigyne; C, body, ventral side; D, foot.

12. Family SPARASSIDÆ.

CHARACTERS OF FAMILY. The spiders of this family are very similar to the CLUBIONIDÆ, with which they have been included by some authorities. They have well-developed leg scopulæ, two tarsal claws with claw tufts, the trochanters are lightly notched, and the apical ends of the metatarsi are furnished with a soft membrane. The only British species is bright green in the female and green and scarlet in he male, and cannot be mistaken for any other (see description below).

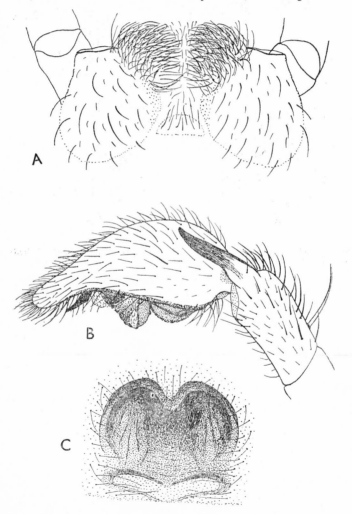

TEXT-FIG. 84.—*Micrommata virescens:* A, maxillæ with scopulæ and labium ; B, male palp (side) ; C, epigyne.

Genus **MICROMMATA** P. A. Latreille 1804.

CHARACTERS OF GENUS. CARAPACE : Longer than broad, considerably narrowed in front. EYES : Anterior row recurved, posterior row slightly procurved ; anterior laterals slightly greater than anterior medians ; posterior medians closer to laterals than to each other. LABIUM : Short and practically semicircular (Text-fig. 84, A). MAXILLÆ : Not inclined towards the labium, rounded at the apices and armed with a dense scopula (Text-fig. 84, A). LEGS : Not greatly unequal, but legs IV longest ; not obviously laterigrade.

Micrommata virescens (Clerck).
(=*M. viridissima* (Degeer))
(Text-fig. 84)

Araneus virescens and *A. roseus* C. Clerck, 1757, p. 137–8. *Aranea viridissima* C. Degeer, 1778, p. 252. *A. smaragdula* J. C. Fabricius, 1793, p. 412. *Sparassus smaragdulus* J. Blackwall, 1861–4, p. 102. *Micrommata virescens* O. P.-Cambridge, 1879–81, p. 341 ; C. Chyzer and L. Kulczynski, 1891–7, I, p. 79. *M. roseum* E. Simon, 1932, p. 892.

DESCRIPTION. LENGTH : ♀: ca. 12 mm. ♂: ca. 8 mm. This spider is bright emerald green in the ♀ and in young individuals of both sexes, while the ♂ is yellowish-green with the abdomen decorated with three longitudinal vivid scarlet bands. CHELICERÆ : Inner margin armed with two strong teeth and one small one ; well-defined cheliceral scopula present. LEGS : Tarsi not much longer than one-third of the metatarsi ; tarsal and metatarsal scopulæ composed of long hairs ; foot-claws with numerous teeth. EPIGYNE : Text-fig. 84, C. MALE PALP : Text-fig. 84, B.

OCCURRENCE : On long herbage, bushes and young trees, particularly young oaks, in the summer months. It is more frequent in the south than in the north. Adult in May-June, but adult males are rare.

M

13. Family THOMISIDÆ.

CHARACTERS OF FAMILY. The typical members of this family have
a very crab-like appearance (Text-figs. 85, 86). CARAPACE and
ABDOMEN : Usually short and broad, but more elongate in the genera
Tibellus and *Thanatus*. EYES : Small, particularly the posteriors,
usually circled with black, both rows being recurved. LEGS of the
first two pairs are long, stout and laterigrade in typical members, which
frequently move sideways like a crab ; the legs are less obviously
laterigrade in the genera *Philodromus* and *Thanatus*, and not at all in
Tibellus. The legs bear ventrally a variable number of paired spines
on the tibiæ and metatarsi ; there are two tarsal claws. CHELICERÆ :
Small, bearing either no teeth or one small tooth on the outer edge.
The members of the genus *Oxyptila* have the integument furnished with
some characteristic clavate hairs (Text-fig. 89, B), but in the other
genera the hairs are normal or somewhat plumose.

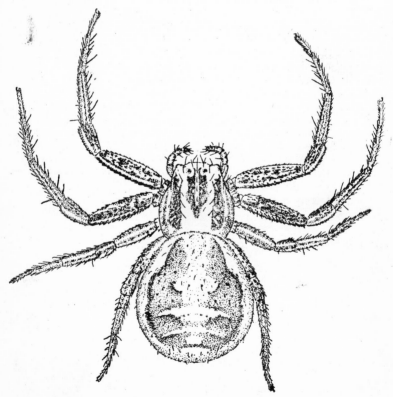

TEXT-FIG. 85.—*Xysticus ulmi* ♀ (THOMISIDÆ).

The spiders of this family build no snare, but in general catch their prey by lying in wait or hunting for it. They live at ground level or in low vegetation.

The British species fall into two sub-families, **Misumeninæ** and **Philodrominæ,** separated as follows :

Misumeninæ : Legs I and II much longer than legs III and IV ; true claw tufts and scopulæ absent ; cheliceræ with no teeth ; palpal tarsus of ♂ usually broad and discoid ; very crab-like in appearance.

Philodrominæ : Legs approximately equal in length ; true claw tufts and scopulæ present on legs I and II (less strongly developed in the males) ; cheliceræ with one tooth on anterior margin ; palpal tarsus of ♂ usually longer and more acuminate, rarely discoid ; less crab-like in appearance.

KEY TO MISUMENINOID GENERA.

1. Lateral eyes on strong conical protuberances ; abdomen widened and truncated behind, where at either corner of dorsal side is a short blunt conical protuberance (Text-fig. 86) . . . . (1) **Thomisus**
——Lateral eyes on shallow tubercles ; abdomen broadened and truncated behind . . . . (4) **Pistius**
——Lateral eyes on shallow tubercles (Text-fig. 89, A, B) ; abdomen not truncated behind (Text-fig. 85)   2
2. Median ocular trapezium longer than broad   3
——Median ocular trapezium square or broader than long . .   4
3. Integument clothed with some clavate hairs (much reduced in some males, but always present on the clypeus) ; tibia I armed ventrally with two pairs of spines ; posterior central eyes closer to one another than to laterals . . . . (6) **Oxyptila**
——Integument clothed with normal setaceous (not clavate) spines ; tibia I with three to six pairs of spines ventrally ; posterior eyes equidistant . . . . . (2) **Diæa**
4. Anterior median eyes (as seen from in front) approximately equal in size to anterior laterals ; anterior eyes practically equidistant ; width of clypeus approximately equal to distance apart of anterior medians ; few spines on carapace . . . . (3) **Misumena**
——Anterior median eyes (as seen from in front) approximately one-half diameter of anterior laterals ; anterior medians closer to the laterals than to each other ; width of clypeus usually considerably less than the distance apart of anterior medians ; many spines on carapace . . . (5) **Xysticus**

KEY TO PHILODROMINOID GENERA.

1. Posterior eyes slightly recurved, the medians further from each other than from the laterals (Text-fig. 89, C) . . . . (7) **Philodromus**

——Posterior eyes strongly recurved, the medians equidistant
or nearer to each other than to the laterals (Text-fig.
89, D, E)   2

2. Posterior median eyes much nearer to one another than to
laterals (Text-fig. 89, E) ; abdomen long and narrow,
almost cylindrical (Text-fig. 101, C) ; carapace much
longer than wide . . . .   (9) **Tibellus**

——Posterior median eyes slightly nearer to one another than
to laterals or equidistant (Text-fig. 89, D) ; abdomen
oval and fairly wide ; carapace scarcely longer than
wide . . . .   (8) **Thanatus**

The *palpal organs* of the males are best observed from their
ventral aspect, and all drawings have been made from this viewpoint
(except for *Tibellus*).

1. Genus **THOMISUS** C. A. Walckenaer 1805.

CHARACTERS OF GENUS. CARAPACE : Truncated in front, with the
upper fore-corners strongly and conically protuberant and divergent,
bearing the lateral eyes (Text-figs. 86, 87, A). EYES : Very small.
ABDOMEN : Narrow and truncated in front (Text-fig. 86), enlarging to
a considerable width behind, where at either corner of the dorsal side
is a short blunt conical protuberance. LEGS : Long, relatively much
longer in ♂ than in ♀, with legs I and II much longer than legs III and
IV.

Thomisus onustus Walckenaer.
(Text-figs. 86 ; 87, A, B ; 88, E)

Thomisus onustus C. A. Walckenaer, 1806. *T. abbreviatus* J. Blackwall, 1861–4,
p. 90. *T. albus* C. Chyzer and L. Kulczynski, 1891–7, I, p. 82. *T. onustus* O. P.-
Cambridge, 1879–81, p. 288 ; E. Simon, 1932, p. 788 ; A. Tullgren, 1944, p. 65.

DESCRIPTION. LENGTH : ♀ : 6–7 mm. ♂ : ca. 3 mm. With its
characteristic shape and eye tubercles, this spider cannot be mistaken
for any other. CARAPACE : Centrally whitish-yellow (♀) or yellow-
brown (♂), with sides brown (♀) or dark brown (♂), armed (♀) with
numerous very short, rather clavate, hairs and (♂) thickly covered with
minute granulations each bearing a small blunt spine, and thickly
margined similarly. ABDOMEN : Shape as in generic description ;
♀ : whitish-yellow, sometimes (particularly when found on pink
flowers) suffused with pink ; ♂ : yellow-brown ; armed in each sex
with a number of short, blunt hairs. CLYPEUS : With no spines.
LEGS : ♀ : Tibia I and metatarsus I armed with a few short in-
significant spines ; ♂ : Legs spineless. EPIGYNE : Text-fig. 88, E,
rather indistinct, with central septum. MALE PALP : Text-fig. 87, B :
tibia armed below and to lateral side with a row of small black tubercles
each carrying a long bristle.

OCCURRENCE : This species is rare, occurring only in the southern
counties, usually on sunny heaths on heather and other plants, where
it waits amongst the blooms for its prey. It is adult in May to July.

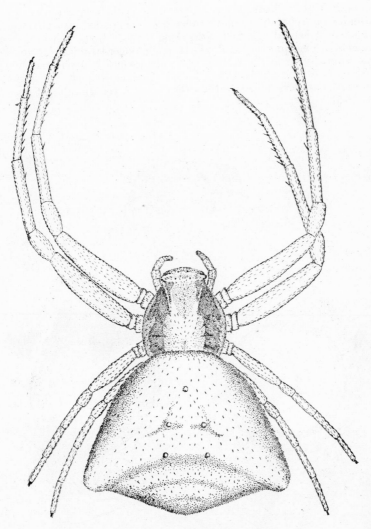

Text-fig. 86.—*Thomisus onustus* ♀.

2. Genus **DIÆA** T. Thorell 1869.

CHARACTERS OF GENUS. CARAPACE : Armed with a number of long spines. EYES : Medians form a rectangle slightly longer than wide ; laterals on separate shallow tubercles. ABDOMEN : Oval, slightly broadened behind, clothed with long hairs. LEGS : Armed with numerous long spines ; legs I and II much longer than legs III and IV, exceptionally so in the male. The only species is green and brown in colour (especially so in the ♀), and this fact coupled with the disproportionate length of legs I and II render it recognisable at once in the field.

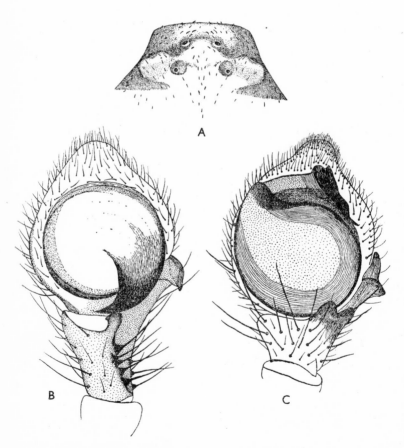

TEXT-FIG. 87.—A, *Thomisus onustus* ♂ eyes from above.
Male palps (below) : B, *T. onustus*; C, *Pistius truncatus*.

Diæa dorsata (Fabricius).
(Text-fig. 88, A, C)

Aranea dorsata J. C. Fabricius, 1777, p. 249. *Thomisus floricolens* J. Blackwall, 1861–4, p. 76. *Diæa devoniensis* O. P.-Cambridge, 1879–81, p. 535. *D. dorsata* idem, 1879–81, p. 293 ; C. Chyzer and L. Kulczynski, 1891–7, I, p. 86 ; E. Simon, 1932, p. 793 ; A. Tullgren, 1944, p. 69.

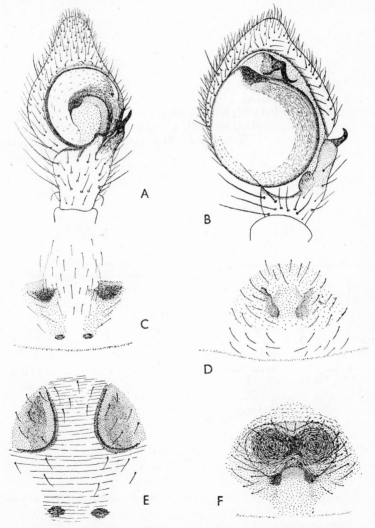

TEXT-FIG. 88.—Male palps (below) : A, *Diæa dorsata;* B, *Misumena vatia.* Epigynes : C, *Diæa dorsata;* D, *Misumena vatia;* E, *Thomisus onustus;* F, *Pistius truncatus.*

DESCRIPTION. LENGTH : ♀: 5–6 mm. ♂: 3–4 mm.

♀: CARAPACE, CHELICERÆ, STERNUM and PALPS : Emerald green when freshly caught. LEGS : Emerald green with tarsi and metatarsi usually suffused with pale brown ; tibia I and metatarsus I with usually six pairs each of long spines ventrally. ABDOMEN : Oval, slightly dilated behind, pale yellowish-green with the dorsal area to the spinners practically filled by a brown to dark brown folium with indented margins. EPIGYNE : Text-fig. 88, C, inconspicuous, clothed with some practically colourless hairs. Some specimens are less green than others.

♂: CARAPACE : Reddish-brown with a few darker spots each carrying a long bristle. ABDOMEN : With a pronounced dark brown folium dorsally, and with more brown markings than in the ♀. LEGS : Yellow-brown annulated with darker brown, but with the femora often greenish spotted with brown ; tibia I and metatarsus I with three to four pairs of long spines ventrally ; numerous spines dorsally on all femora. MALE PALP : Text-fig. 88, A : tarsus somewhat elongate, with simple palpal organs.

Immature specimens of either sex possess a striking colour of emerald green and brown ; the green colour fades rapidly in spirit.

OCCURRENCE : This spider occurs on trees and bushes, particularly on box, and is common in many parts of Britain, though not recorded north of Yorkshire. It is adult usually in May and June, but immature specimens may be found during most of the year, on the shrubs or in the undergrowth beneath.

3. Genus **MISUMENA** P. A. Latreille 1804.

CHARACTERS OF GENUS. CARAPACE : Armed with a few only very short fine spines. EYES : Small, medians forming practically a square ; lateral eyes on one shallow tubercle ; anterior eyes subequal. ABDOMEN: Dilated and rounded behind in ♀, much less so in ♂. LEGS : I and II much longer than III and IV, armed (♀) ventrally on tibia I with six or more pairs, on metatarsus I with seven or more pairs of robust spines ; in ♂ these spines are absent or scarcely distinguishable from hairs.

Misumena vatia (Clerck).
(=*M. calycina* (Linnaeus))
(Text-fig. 88, B, D)

Araneus vatius C. Clerck, 1757, p. 128. *A. calycina* Linnaeus, 1758, p. 620; *Thomisus citreus* J. Blackwall, 1861–4, p. 88. *Misumena vatia* O. P.-Cambridge, 1879–81, p. 290 ; C. Chyzer and L. Kulczynski, 1891–7, I, p. 83 ; E. Simon, 1932, p, 790. *Misumena calycina* W. S. Bristowe, 1939, p. 27; A. Tullgren, 1944, p. 68 ; B. J. Kaston, 1948, p. 411.

DESCRIPTION. LENGTH : ♀: up to 10–11 mm. ♂: 3–4 mm.

♀: CARAPACE : With whitish central band edged on either side with olive green or brown. ABDOMEN : Pale green or whitish, but a variety is common in which the prevailing colour is yellow bearing dorsally two longitudinal crimson lines. EPIGYNE : Text-fig. 88, D. Is small and very simple. This sex, with its abdomen widened and rounded behind, and its general colour of pale green, yellow or whitish, cannot well be mistaken for any other species.

♂ : CARAPACE : Dark brownish on sides with ocular area and central band whitish green. EYES: Laterals on distinct prominences. ABDOMEN : Greenish-white with two dark brown to black longitudinal bands and some dark spots. LEGS : Very long (particularly I and II) with no spines ; femora and patellæ of I and II dark reddish-brown with remaining segments greenish-yellow with tibiæ, metatarsi and tarsi of I and II red-brown at apices. MALE PALP : Text-fig. 88, B, has two tibial apophyses and a small curved stylus at tip of palpal organs. This sex differs considerably in appearance and size from the ♀.

OCCURRENCE : This is a common species in the southern part of the country, being found on flowers and low plants and bushes (e.g. furze). It appears to use its colour as a means of concealment, but is sometimes conspicuous to the human eye, for example when the yellow and red variety is seen on green leaves. It is adult in May-July.

4. Genus PISTIUS E. Simon 1875.

CHARACTERS OF GENUS. Very similar to *Misumena*, but the abdomen is much widened and truncated behind, particularly in the ♀. The only species is fairly large and brown in colour.

Pistius truncatus (Pallas).
(Text-figs. 87, C ; 88, F)

Aranea truncata P. S. Pallas, 1772, p. 47. *Pistius truncatus* O. P.-Cambridge, 1879-81, p. 534 ; C. Chyzer and L. Kulczynski, 1891-7, I, p. 83 ; E. Simon, 1932, p. 794 ; A. Tullgren, 1944, p. 67.

DESCRIPTION. LENGTH : ♀ : up to 8–9 mm. ♂ : 4–5 mm. This species, with its abdomen widened and sharply truncated behind, and its general colour of mottled brown, is readily identified. CARAPACE : Brown, mottled with yellow or yellow-brown, clothed with a number of very short, fine hairs. ABDOMEN : Brown, with whitish ill-defined chevrons. LEGS : Brown mottled with yellow, and with some darker brown annulations. STERNUM : Brown with numerous clear yellow flecks. EPIGYNE : Text-fig. 88, F. MALE PALP : Text-fig. 87, C, very similar in form to *Misumena*.

OCCURRENCE : This species has been found in one locality only, near Brockenhurst in the New Forest ; the exact locality is no longer known. The spider is probably adult in May and June, but immature examples would be readily recognisable.

5. Genus XYSTICUS C. L. Koch 1835.

CHARACTERS OF GENUS. CARAPACE : Rather square-fronted (Text-fig. 89, A), bearing a pattern, rather similar in type in all British species, composed of a broad central longitudinal pale band containing a darker marking, wedge or spade shaped, beginning close behind the posterior eyes and with the point directed backwards ; carapace armed with numerous spines. CLYPEUS : Vertical, armed with seven or more long stout spines directed forwards. EYES : Median ocular trapezium is square or slightly broader than long ; anterior laterals much larger than the remainder ; lateral eye tubercles fairly large and well separated (Text-fig. 89, A). ABDOMEN : Much wider behind than in front, usually bearing a dentated band (folium) on its dorsal surface (Text-fig. 85). LEGS : Comparatively short, stout and very spiny ; four or more pairs

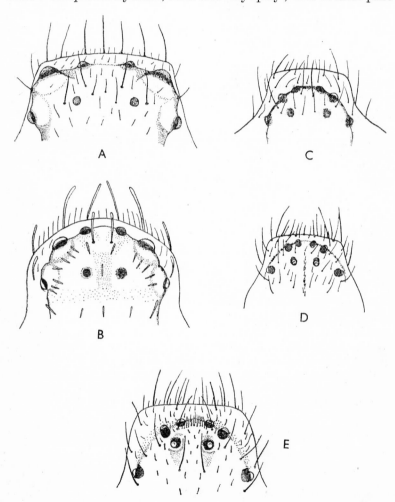

TEXT-FIG. 89.—Arrangements of eyes : A, *Xysticus ;* B, *Oxyptila ;* C, *Philodromus ;* D, *Thanatus ;* E, *Tibellus.*

of spines ventrally on tibia I. MALE PALPS : The palpal organs of some species have strongly chitinised apophyses, clearly seen when the palp is viewed from the ventral aspect ; these apophyses when present are very valuable for separating the males ; the palpal tibia is usually armed with two apophyses, one ventral and one retrolateral, but occasionally (e.g. in X. robustus in our fauna) a third apophysis is inserted between these two. EPIGYNES : In general consist of an orifice with or without a median septum.

The spiders of this genus are medium-sized and very crab-like in general appearance. The females are usually sober coloured, but the males show more vivid tints, several being very striking. They occur in undergrowth, under stones, on bushes and low herbage, etc. The British species can be split up for convenience into two groups :

A. Male palpal organs with two apophyses (described as median and basal) ; female genital opening usually with a septum or thickened anteriorly : Xysticus cristatus, audax, lanio, ulmi, kochi, erraticus, bifasciatus, luctator.

B. Male palpal organs without apophyses ; female genital opening without septum ; dark coloured species : Xysticus sabulosus, luctuosus, robustus.

The genitalia form the best and safest method of identifying the species.

Xysticus cristatus (Clerck).
(=X. viaticus (Linnaeus))
(Text-figs. 90, A ; 91, B)

Araneus cristatus C. Clerck, 1757, p. 136. A. viatica Linnaeus, 1758, p. 623. Thomisus cristatus J. Blackwall, 1861–4, p. 68. Xysticus cristatus O. P.-Cambridge, 1879–81, p. 298 ; C. Chyzer and L. Kulczynski, 1891–7, I, p. 92 ; E. Simon, 1932, pp. 816 and 828. X. viaticus W. S. Bristowe, 1939, p. 28 ; A. Tullgren, 1944, p. 87.

DESCRIPTION. LENGTH : ♀ : 6–7 mm. ♂ : 4–5 mm.

♀ : CARAPACE : Mottled fawn-brown on sides, with central whitish-yellow band enclosing a fawn wedge-shaped marking ending in a slightly darker well-defined sharp point situated behind the posterior eyes at a distance equal to about three times the distance between the posterior median eyes (cf. X. audax). ABDOMEN : Pale fawn, with pale brown folium. LEGS : Whitish-yellow, marbled with pale brown ; tibia I usually armed ventrally with four pairs of spines. EPIGYNE : Text-fig. 91, B.

♂ : CARAPACE : Brown to dark brown on sides, with central whitish-yellow band enclosing a brown wedge-shaped marking ending in a slightly darker well-defined point as in ♀. ABDOMEN : Yellowish-white with darkish brown folium. LEGS : Yellow-white, marbled with brown particularly on femora and patellæ ; tibia I armed ventrally with four pairs of spines. MALE PALP : Text-fig. 90, A ; median T-shaped apophysis with one arm of T much longer than other, the longer arm being very curved ; tooth on basal apophysis rather small.

This species is closely similar to *X. audax* (q.v.).

OCCURRENCE : This is the most widespread species of the genus, being found commonly all over Britain, in undergrowth, and by sweeping and beating low herbage.   The male is adult in spring and early summer, while the female is to be found adult during most of the summer.

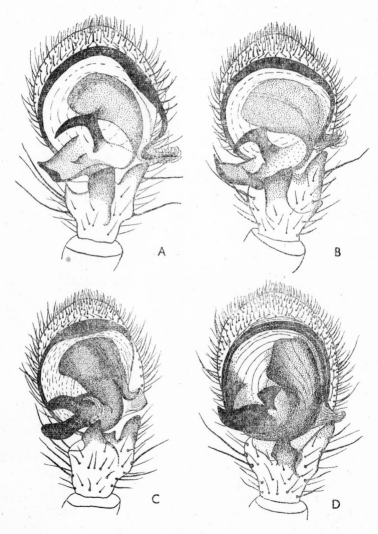

TEXT-FIG. 90.—Male palps (below): A, *Xysticus cristatus;* B, *X. audax;* C, *X. kochi;* D, *X. erraticus.*

Xysticus audax (Schrank).
(Text-fig. 90, B)

Aranea audax F. von P. Schrank, 1803, p. 235; *Thomisus audax* J. Blackwall, 1861–4, p. 70. *Xysticus pini* C. Chyzer and L. Kulczynski, 1891–7, I, p. 93; O. P.-Cambridge, 1879–81, p. 299. *X. audax* E. Simon, 1932, pp. 816, 828; A. Tullgren, 1944, p. 89.

DESCRIPTION. LENGTH: ♀: 5–8 mm. ♂: 3–5 mm.

♀: CARAPACE: Very dark brown at sides, with central band pale whitish-yellow; central wedge-shaped marking indistinct, mottled

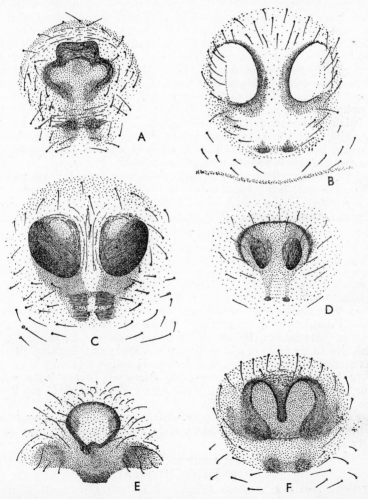

TEXT-FIG. 91.—Epigynes: A, *Xysticus erraticus;* B, *X. cristatus;* C, *X. lanio;* D, *X. Ulmi;* E, *X. bifasciatus;* F, *X. kochi.*

pink (or absent), when present ending not pointed but rounded, and situated behind the posterior eyes at a distance equal to about twice the distance between the posterior eyes. ABDOMEN : Whitish, with edges of folium dark brown and pronounced. LEGS : Pale yellow, marbled and sometimes also annulated distinctly on upper sides with dark reddish-brown. EPIGYNE : Closely similar to *X. cristatus*, and not definitely distinguishable from that species.

♂ : CARAPACE : Very dark mahogany-brown with prominent yellow-ish-white markings near the lateral edges ; central area filled behind posterior central eyes with dark reddish-brown or brown marking (sometimes mottled with much white) with posterior ending rounded as in ♀. ABDOMEN : White, with a very pronounced folium, practically black in colour. LEGS : Yellowish, annulated and marked with dark brown spots, with femora, patellæ and bases of tibiæ I and II very dark brown, marbled with white. MALE PALP : Text-fig. 90, B, median apophysis with arm of T more at right angles to upright, and length of arms of T not so different as in *X. cristatus;* tooth on basal apophysis larger.

This species can usually be distinguished from *X. cristatus* by its colouring and the shape and length of the central wedge-shaped marking behind the eyes. The ♂ palpal organs are distinguishable, but the ♀ epigynes are not with any certainty.

OCCURRENCE : This species occurs mainly on furze bushes, and is quite frequent, being found adult in spring and early summer. It is commoner in the south than in the north, and appreciably less common than *X. cristatus*.

Xysticus kochi Thorell.
(Text-figs. 90, C ; 91, F)

Xysticus viaticus C. L. Koch (1), 1845, XII, p. 70. *X. kochi* T. Thorell, 1872, pp. 233–7 ; C. Chyzer and L. Kulczynski, 1891–7, I, p. 92 ; E. Simon, 1932, pp. 821, 824 ; A. Tullgren, 1944, p. 90. *X. viaticus* O. P.-Cambridge, 1879–81, p. 296.

DESCRIPTION. LENGTH : ♀ : 6–8 mm. ♂ : 4–5 mm.

♀ : Very similar in colour and pattern to *X. cristatus*, but usually a slightly darker brown. CARAPACE : Has large number of short, black bristles. ABDOMEN : Folium not very pronounced. LEGS : Tibia I with five to six pairs of spines ventrally. EPIGYNE : Text-fig. 91, F, has narrow tongue projecting from the anterior edge.

♂ : Usually similar in colour to *X. cristatus*. LEGS : Tibiæ with four pairs of spines ventrally. MALE PALP : Text-fig. 90, C, has both apophyses large and projecting.

OCCURRENCE : This species occurs fairly commonly throughout the country on bushes and in undergrowth, and is adult in spring and early summer.

Xysticus erraticus (Blackwall).
(Text-figs. 90, D ; 91, A)

Thomisus erraticus J. Blackwall, 1834, p. 408, and 1861–4, p. 71 (♀). *Xysticus erraticus* O. P.-Cambridge, 1879–81, p. 309 ; C. Chyzer and L. Kulczynski, 1891–7, I, p. 93 ; E. Simon, 1932, pp. 817, 822 ; A. Tullgren, 1944, p. 92.

Description. Length : ♀ : 6–8 mm. ♂ : ca. 4 mm.

♀ : Carapace : Brown at sides, with central pale band fairly broad with its dark marginal stripes usually distinctly defined ; central wedge-shaped marking faint or lacking, its borders being marked by clear white margins. Abdomen : Sides whitish with fairly well pronounced brown or grey folium, at times reduced to spots. Legs : Brown to yellow-brown, marked with only a very few brown spots ; tibia I armed ventrally with four or five pairs of stout spines. Epigyne : Text-fig. 91, A.

♂ : Carapace : Like ♀, but sides a rich, dark brown, the white margins of the central wedge-shaped marking very sharply defined. Abdomen : White with sharply-defined dark brown irregular folium. Legs : Coxæ, femora and patellæ I and II very dark brown, with remaining segments pale yellow. Male palp : Text-fig. 90, D.

Occurrence : This spider is found in undergrowth and under stones, etc., but not on herbage as a general rule. It is widespread but uncommon, and is adult during the spring and summer months.

Xysticus lanio C. L. Koch.
(Text-figs. 91, C ; 92, A)

Xysticus lanio C. L. Koch, 1824, p. 23, and (1) 1845, XII, p. 77 ; O. P.-Cambridge, 1879–81, p. 303 ; E. Simon, 1932, pp. 818, 822 ; A. Tullgren, 1944, p. 95 ; W. S. Bristowe, 1947, pls. 2, 3. *X. lateralis* C. Chyzer and L. Kulczynski, 1891–7, I, p. 93.

Description. Length : ♀ : 6–7 mm. ♂ : 5 mm.

♀ : Carapace : Sides red-brown with pale yellow central band containing ill-defined wedge-shaped marking. Abdomen : Broad and smoothly rounded behind ; reddish with faint folium. Legs : Reddish, mottled and faintly annulated with brown ; tibia I with five pairs of spines ventrally. Epigyne : Text-fig. 91, C, has two prominent large red or reddish-brown oval chitinised bodies protruding from the central faintly defined septum.

♂ : Carapace : Sides deep reddish-brown, with pale yellow central band and ill-defined dark reddish wedge-shaped marking. Abdomen : Whitish, with well defined dark reddish folium, and dark reddish sides. Legs : Femora I deep reddish, armed dorsally with numerous stout black spines ; the remaining legs are reddish, mottled with whitish-yellow. Sternum : Dark red. Male palp : Text-fig. 92, A, yellow-brown, marked considerably with red.

Occurrence : This spider occurs quite commonly on low trees and bushes in woods, particularly on young oaks. It is adult in May, June and July, and is commoner in the south than in the north. Its obvious reddish colour makes its identification in the field an easy matter.

Xysticus ulmi (Hahn).
(Text-figs. 91, D ; 92, B ; frontispiece)

Thomisus ulmi C. W. Hahn, 1831, p. 38. *Xysticus ulmi* O. P.-Cambridge, 1879–81, p. 310 ; C. Chyzer and L. Kulczynski, 1891–7, I, p. 93 ; E. Simon, 1932, pp. 820–1 ; A. Tullgren, 1944, p. 93.

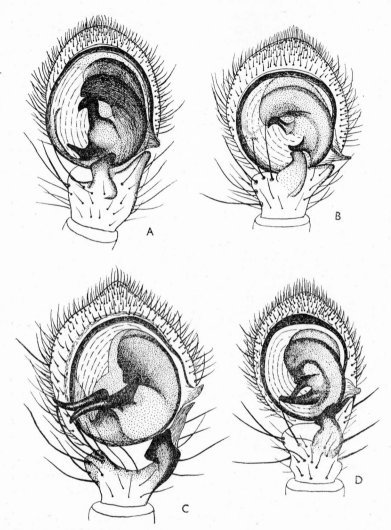

TEXT-FIG. 92.—Male palps (below): A, *Xysticus lanio;* B, *X. ulmi;* C, *X. bifasciatus;* D, *X. luctator.*

DESCRIPTION. LENGTH: ♀: 5–7 mm. ♂ 4 mm. This species resembles *X. cristatus* and *X. kochi* fairly closely in colour and markings. LEGS: Streaked and mottled with much white. EPIGYNE: Text-fig. 91, D, has two small reddish-brown oval chitinised bodies projecting from it, smaller than in *X. lanio.* MALE PALP: Text-fig. 92, B, is similar to *X. lanio* but the anterior hook is more slender and directed more inwards.

OCCURRENCE : This spider is rather rare, but widespread, and is found only in swampy or damp situations, amongst grass, rushes, etc. It is adult in May–July. At Wicken Fen, Cambridgeshire, the ♀ spins a cocoon in the heads of reeds and is found with its egg-sac in such positions in June and July.

Xysticus bifasciatus C. L. Koch.
(Text-figs. 91, E ; 92, C)

Xysticus bifasciatus C. L. Koch 1837, (2), I, p. 26. *Thomisus bifasciatus* J. Blackwall, 1861–4, p. 79. *Xysticus bifasciatus* O. P.-Cambridge, 1879–81, p. 312 ; C. Chyzer and L. Kulczynski, 1891–7. I, p. 92 ; E. Simon, 1932, pp. 817, 822 ; A. Tullgren, 1944, p. 82.

DESCRIPTION. LENGTH : ♀ : up to 9–10 mm. ♂ : 6–7 mm. This spider has a squat, robust form.

♀ : CARAPACE : Sides brown, with a paler central band and a pale spade-shaped marking with a well-defined white margin ; armed with numerous bristles. ABDOMEN : Pale brown with a brown folium. LEGS : Pale brown streaked and spotted with brown. EPIGYNE : Text-fig. 91, E.

♂ : CARAPACE : Sides rich brown, central band yellow with central spade-shaped marking red-brown with well-defined white margin. ABDOMEN : Reddish-brown to brown folium with a few oblique pale yellow bars and pale yellow sides. LEGS : Red-brown with yellow longitudinal stripes and spots ; tarsi and metatarsi rather paler. STERNUM : Yellowish, with red-brown spots. PALP : Text-fig. 92, C, brown, spotted and marked with yellow ; palpal apophyses long and tapering.

OCCURRENCE : This species is fairly widely distributed, but rare. It is found in short grass, under stones, etc., on sunny heaths, and is adult in spring and early summer. Its large size and handsome markings make it a striking and easily identified spider.

Xysticus luctator L. Koch.
(Text-fig. 92, D)

Xysticus luctator L. Koch, 1870, p. 29 ; O. P.-Cambridge, 1879–81, p. 313. *X. cambridgei* E. Simon, 1932, pp. 817, 823 ; A. Tullgren, 1944, p. 85. (J. Blackwall's *Thomisus cambridgei*, 1858, p. 426, and 1861–4, p. 81 (♀), is *X. sabulosus*, so *X. luctator* is the correct name).

DESCRIPTION. LENGTH : ♂ : 6–7 mm. This is rather similar in appearance to *Xysticus bifasciatus*, but even more handsome in the male. The ♀ does not appear to have been taken in this country.

♂ : CARAPACE : Sides a rich brown with two dark brown blotches posteriorly ; central band yellow, with spade-shaped marking pale brown fringed with golden yellow. ABDOMEN : Clear whitish-yellow at sides, with very distinct reddish-brown folium carrying several yellow spots and transverse lines ; sides clear pale yellow. LEGS : Femora dark brown, the anteriors marked with irregular clear golden-yellow blotches and stripes ; the remaining segments yellow, suffused with

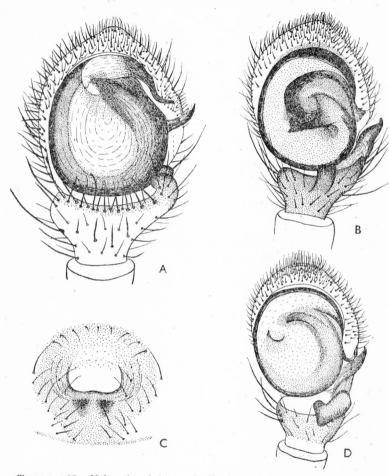

Text-fig. 93.—Male palps (below): A, *Xysticus sabulosus;* B, *X. robustus;*
D, *X. luctuosus.*
Epigyne: C, *X. sabulosus.*

more or less brown and clear golden-yellow. STERNUM: Reddish-
brown. PALP: Text-fig. 92, D, dark reddish-brown spotted with
yellow.

OCCURRENCE: On Bloxworth Heath (Dorset) and Beaulieu Heath
(Hampshire) amongst heather; extremely rare. Adult in summer.

Xysticus sabulosus (Hahn).
(Text-fig. 93, A, C)

Thomisus sabulosus C. W. Hahn, 1831, p. 28. *T. cambridgei* J. Blackwall, 1858, p. 426, and 1861–4, p. 81. *Xysticus cambridgei* O. P.-Cambridge, 1879–81, p. 308. *X. sabulosus* J. Blackwall, 1861–4, p. 72 ; O. P.-Cambridge, 1879–81, p. 310 ; C. Chyzer and L. Kulczynski, 1891–7, I, p. 93 ; E. Simon, 1932, pp. 830, 835 ; A. Tullgren, 1944, p. 101.

DESCRIPTION. LENGTH : ♀ : 8–9 mm. ♂ : ca. 6 mm. CARAPACE : Sides dark brown, almost black posteriorly, with the central marking whitish, and wedge-shaped marking greyish-brown ; thickly armed with a number of short stout bristles ; ♂ slightly darker with few bristles. ABDOMEN : Greyish, with the folium greyish-brown with a number of black lateral bars and spots ; ♂ slightly darker. LEGS : ♀ : Armed with very stout spines ; femora whitish, marked with dark brown blotches and spots ; the remaining segments brown to dark brown marked with some white spots, except for tarsi and metatarsi which are brown. ♂ : Femora white, marked and spotted with dark brown, with remaining segments white with dark brown blotches and markings ; tibiæ, metatarsi and tarsi I and II clothed thickly with short, very fine white hairs in addition to the normal spines and hairs. EPIGYNE : Text-fig. 93, C. MALE PALP : Text-fig. 93, A, devoid of palpal apophyses.

OCCURRENCE : This spider occurs on sandy and gravelly heaths, where its colour renders it inconspicuous ; in the field it appears to be almost black at times. It is widespread but not common, even in the southern counties, and is adult at the end of summer and beginning of autumn.

Xysticus luctuosus (Blackwall).
(Text-figs. 93, D ; 94, A)

Thomisus luctuosus J. Blackwall, 1836, p. 489, and 1861–4, p. 78. *Xysticus luctuosus* O. P.-Cambridge, 1879–81, p. 305 ; C. Chyzer and L. Kulczynski, 1891–7, I, p. 96 ; E. Simon, 1932, pp. 832–3 ; A. Tullgren, 1944, p. 100.

DESCRIPTION. LENGTH : ♀ : 7–8 mm. ♂ : 5 mm.

♀ : CARAPACE : Sides dark rich brown mottled with whitish-yellow ; the central wedge-shaped marking is brown mottled with yellow ; clear whitish-yellow behind, and armed fairly thickly with bristles, particularly on the head. ABDOMEN : Brownish-grey with ill-defined lighter lateral lines but no obvious folium. LEGS : Yellowish-brown, much mottled and streaked with dark red-brown ; tarsi and metatarsi clear yellow ; armed with stout spines. PALP : Clear pale yellow, mottled and streaked more or less with brown. EPIGYNE : Text-fig. 94, A.

♂ : The whole spider is a rich, deep blackish-brown, with few markings. LEGS : Femora I and II deep brown, with patellæ and tibiæ slightly paler and marked with whitish-yellow ; legs III and IV

yellow-brown, marked with dark brown. MALE PALP : Text-fig.
93, D, has a small cusp on inner side but no apophyses.

OCCURRENCE : This species occurs amongst low plants, on bushes,
etc., in woods, particularly in the south, and is rather rare. It is
adult in May-July.

Xysticus robustus (Hahn).
(Text-figs. 93, B ; 94, B)

Thomisus robustus C. W. Hahn, 1831, p. 50.   *Xysticus robustus* O. P.-Cambridge,
1879–81, p. 306 ; C. Chyzer and L. Kulczynski, 1891–7, I, p. 96 ; E. Simon, 1932,
pp. 837, 839 ; A. Tullgren, 1944, p. 96.

DESCRIPTION. LENGTH : ♀ : 7–9 mm.   ♂ : 5–6 mm. This spider
has a stout, broad, squat form, and is very dark in colour. The ♂ is
almost uniformly a rich deep black-brown in colour, with only a few

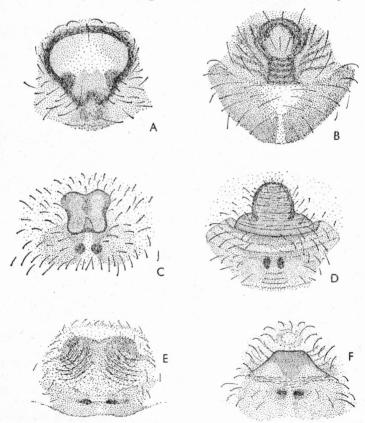

TEXT-FIG. 94.—Epigynes : A, *Xysticusluctuosus;* B, *X. robustus;* C, *Oxyptila
blackwalli;* D, *O. nigrita;* E, *O. sanctuaria;* F, *O.scabricula.*

faint paler markings, and ♀ is almost as dark. CARAPACE : Head very strongly spinose in ♀, much less so in ♂. EPIGYNE : Text-fig. 94, B ; highly pigmented, rendering the detail obscure. MALE PALP : Text-fig. 93, B, has three tibial apophyses.

OCCURRENCE : This spider has been captured on a number of occasions on Bloxworth Heath (Dorset) and Beaulieu Heath (Hampshire). It is rare in these localities, and occurs on the ground amongst heather, under turves, etc., and is adult in May-June.

6. Genus **OXYPTILA** E. Simon 1864.

CHARACTERS OF GENUS. The spiders of this genus are smaller and squatter than those in the genus *Xysticus*. Clothed with some clavate or spatulate hairs (Text-fig. 89, B) on abdomen, carapace and legs ; clypeus with a row of clavate hairs. (The number of clavate hairs varies somewhat from species to species but is not a very reliable character as the hairs are broken off readily.) CARAPACE : Usually with a pale central band, but lacking the wedge-shaped marking of *Xysticus*. EYES : Median ocular trapezium longer than broad ; posterior medians closer to one another than to laterals (Text-fig. 89, B). ABDOMEN : Lacks dorsal folium of *Xysticus*, having instead a variable pattern composed of pale and dark bars and spots. LEGS : Tibiæ I and II armed ventrally with two pairs of spines ; metatarsi I and II with two ventral pairs and a smaller pair apically ; posterior legs with no ventral spines. The species are best distinguished by their genitalia, their colouration and the relative abundance of the clavate hairs. The ♂ palpal organs differ considerably one from another, rendering identification clear and unambiguous. The female epigynes are sometimes poorly pigmented and not so sharply differentiated in some species as the ♂ palpal organs.

Oxyptila blackwalli Simon.
(Text-figs. 94, C ; 95, D)

Thomisus claveatus J. Blackwall, 1861–4, p. 87. *Oxyptila blackwalli* E. Simon, 1875, p. 231, and 1932, pp. 798, 806 ; O. P.-Cambridge, 1879–81, p. 318 ; C. Chyzer and L. Kulczynski, 1891–7, I, p. 100.

DESCRIPTION. LENGTH : ♀ : 3–4 mm. ♂ : 2–3 mm. This species is clothed with a large number of clavate hairs. CARAPACE : Deep brown at the sides with a paler central band. ABDOMEN : Greyish-brown with many black spots and bars. LEGS : Brown, spotted with darker brown ; the dorsal surface of femur I bears three small clavate hairs (the remaining species have two or fewer), and there are numerous clavate hairs on the legs. STERNUM : Clothed with numerous clavate hairs. EPIGYNE: Text-fig. 94, C, contains a large reddish chitinised area, rather M- or H-shaped in outline. MALE PALP : Text-fig. 95, D, has a long outward-projecting apophysis on the tibia, which is quite characteristic.

OCCURRENCE : This species is rather rare and is found only in the southern counties, where it seems to occur more frequently in coastal areas. Found under stones, etc., and in undergrowth. Adult in spring and summer.

Oxyptila scabricula (Westring).
(Text-figs. 94, F ; 95, B)

Thomisus scabriculus N. Westring, 1851, and 1861, p. 441. *Oxyptila scabricula*
C. Chyzer and L. Kulczynski, 1891–7, I, p. 100 ; O. P.-Cambridge, 1907, p. 145 ;
E. Simon, 1932, pp. 798, 807 ; A. Tullgren, 1944, p. 76.

DESCRIPTION. LENGTH : ♀: 3 mm. ♂: 2–3 mm. This species
also is clothed with large numbers of clavate hairs. It is very dark in
colour in both sexes, and when captured is usually coated with particles

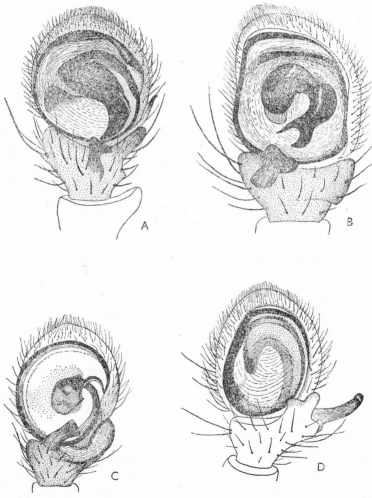

TEXT-FIG. 95.—Male palps (below): A, *Oxyptila nigrita;* B, *O. scabricula;*
C, *O. sanctuaria;* D, *O. blackwalli.*

of dirt or sand which obscure both the vague markings and the spinal armature. CARAPACE : Dark brown (♀) to almost black(♂), with very little trace of a paler central band. ABDOMEN : Dorsally greyish with black markings (♀), almost black(♂). LEGS : Brown with darker markings on femora (♀) ; very dark, with femora almost black dorsally (♂). STERNUM : Dark, clothed with spatulate hairs. EPIGYNE : Text-fig. 94, F, does not have a strongly chitinised area. MALE PALP : Text-fig. 95, B ; the palpal organs have a large, black chitinised claw-like apophysis.

OCCURRENCE : This spider is very rare, occurring on sandy heaths in a few southern counties ; it has been taken in company with ants. Adult May to July.

Oxyptila nigrita (Thorell).
(Text-figs. 94, D ; 95, A)

Xysticus nigritus T. Thorell, 1875, p. 104. *Oxyptila nigrita* C. Chyzer and L. Kulczynski, 1891–7, I, p. 100 ; O. P.-Cambridge, 1908, p. 181, and 1914, p. 138 ; E. Simon, 1932, pp. 797, 806 ; A. Tullgren, 1944, p. 77.

DESCRIPTION. LENGTH : ♀ : 3 mm. ♂ : 2–2·5 mm. This species is also clothed with very numerous clavate hairs. Both sexes are dark in colour, the ♂ appearing almost completely black. CARAPACE : With dark margins and a paler reddish-brown central band (♀) ; very dark brown with central band only faintly visible (♂). ABDOMEN : Greyish with black markings (♀), or almost black (♂). LEGS : Brown, with darker brown spots (♀) ; in ♂, femora I and II are black, femora III and IV are dark brown, and all the remaining segments are brown ; dorsal surface of femur I with two small clavate spines. STERNUM : Clothed with spatulate hairs. EPIGYNE : Text-fig. 94, D, contains a large red chitinised area. MALE PALP : Text-fig. 95, A ; the patella is greatly enlarged apically ; the palpal organs have a large, heavily chitinised black, curved, tooth-shaped apophysis.

OCCURRENCE : This species is rare, very few specimens having been taken ; it seems to be most frequent near the coast, and has occurred in Dorset, Isle of Wight, Kent, Surrey and Channel Isles. Adult in May and June.

Oxyptila sanctuaria (O. P.-Cambridge).
(Text-figs. 94, E ; 95, C)

Thomisus sanctuarius O. P.-Cambridge, 1871, p. 405. *Oxyptila sanctuaria* idem, 1879–81, p. 319 ; E. Simon, 1932, pp. 798, 809 (not *Oxyptila sanctuaria* C. Chyzer and L. Kulczynski, 1891–7, I, p. 100).

DESCRIPTION. LENGTH : ♀ : 3–4 mm. ♂ : 2–2·5 mm. This species, and the remaining British species, are not clothed quite so heavily as the three foregoing species with clavate hairs.

♀ : CARAPACE : Dark brown on edges, lighter centrally. ABDOMEN : Greyish-brown with several black, broken chevrons and a few black spots. LEGS : Yellow-brown, clothed dorsally with a number of clavate hairs. PALPS : Pale yellow with numerous rather spatulate hairs.

STERNUM : Pale yellow, with no clavate or spatulate hairs ; sometimes marked with vague brown spots opposite each femur. EPIGYNE : Text-fig. 94, E.

♂ : CARAPACE : Very dark brown with central pale yellow marking posteriorly ; fewer clavate hairs than ♀. ABDOMEN : Blackish with a few paler spots. LEGS : Femora I and II very dark brown, nearly black ; the remaining segments are dark brown, with the metatarsi and tarsi paler ; there are a few small clavate hairs dorsally. STERNUM : Brown, with slightly darker blotches opposite each leg. MALE PALP : Text-fig. 95, C ; dark brown, with no apophyses.

OCCURRENCE : This species is rare ; in undergrowth, etc., in the more southern counties. Adults of both sexes are found in summer and autumn, and again in spring, but females have occurred even during the winter months.

Oxyptila praticola (C. L. Koch).
(Text-figs. 96, A ; 97, C)

Xysticus praticola, C. L. Koch, 1837 (2), I, p. 26.   *Thomisus incertus* J. Blackwall, 1861–4, p. 86.   *Oxyptila praticola* O. P.-Cambridge, 1879–81, p. 316 ; C. Chyzer and L. Kulczynski, 1891–7, I, p. 100 ; E. Simon, 1932, pp. 803, 811 ; A. Tullgren, 1944, p. 78.

DESCRIPTION. LENGTH : ♀ : 3–4 mm. ♂ : 2·5–3 mm. Both sexes are similar in colour, with ♂ sometimes slightly darker. CARAPACE : Sides dark brown or black, with reddish-brown central band and thoracic striæ. ABDOMEN : Greyish, heavily marked with black and brown spots and bars. LEGS : Brown, with femora, patellæ and tibiæ lined and annulated with dark brown. STERNUM : Has a distinct pattern, being yellow with a large brown spot or longitudinal line in the centre, and a large brown spot opposite the coxa of each of legs I-III, and one large brown spot at posterior end. EPIGYNE : Text-fig. 97, C. MALE PALP : Text-fig. 96, A ; external tibial apophysis has the end twisted into a tight spiral of one turn.

OCCURRENCE : This species is widespread, and is not rare in undergrowth, detritus, etc. ; it is commoner in the south than in the north. Adult in spring and summer.

Oxyptila trux (Blackwall).
(Text-figs. 96, B ; 97, D)

Thomisus trux J. Blackwall, 1846, p. 300, and 1861–4, p. 84.   *Oxyptila trux* O. P.-Cambridge, 1879–81, p. 320 ; C. Chyzer and L. Kulczynski, 1891–7, I, p. 99 ; E. Simon, 1932, pp. 804, 809 ; A. Tullgren, 1944, p. 74.

DESCRIPTION. LENGTH : ♀ : 4–5 mm. ♂ : 3–4 mm.

♀ : CARAPACE : Yellow-brown to brown, the central band (marked with some white at times) edged with two wide dark brown or black longitudinal lines ; clothed with a number of clavate hairs, particularly in area of central band, and some short hairs. ABDOMEN : Pale brownish with a variable number of broken transverse black or dark brown bars ; clothed with some clavate hairs, but not so many as

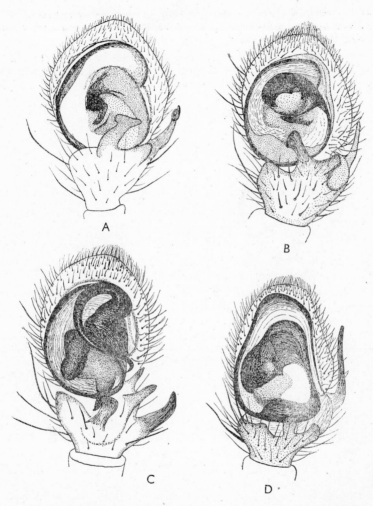

TEXT-FIG. 96.—Male palps (below) : A, *Oxyptila praticola;* B, *O. trux;* C, *O. atomaria;* D, *O. simplex.*

in some species. LEGS : Pale yellow to yellow-brown, usually unmarked. EPIGYNE : Text-fig. 97, D ; rather variable in appearance,
depending on the relative colouration of the parts.

♂ : CARAPACE : Dark brown to very dark brown on sides, marked
with paler areas near the edges ; central area yellow-brown suffused at
times anteriorly with dark brown ; hairs setaceous with hairs of clypeus
only slightly clavate. ABDOMEN : Pale brown to brown, variegated
with white and a rather variable number of black spots and bars.

LEGS : Femora I and II dark brown, or marked and spotted with brown ; remaining legs pale yellow to yellow-brown, occasionally with brown spots.   MALE PALP : Text-fig. 96, B.

OCCURRENCE : Perhaps the commonest species of the genus ; adults are to be found during most of the year.   Widespread throughout the country, in undergrowth, amongst grass, etc.

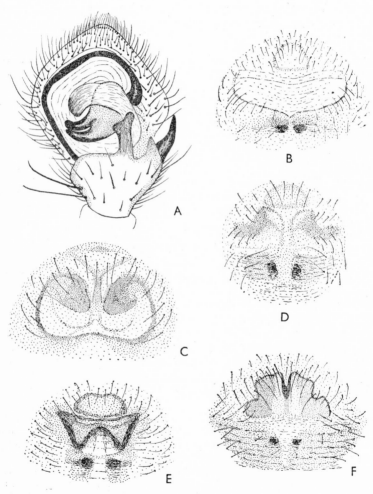

TEXT-FIG. 97.—Male palp (below) : A, *Oxyptila brevipes.*
Epigynes : B, *O. simplex;* C, *O. praticola;* D, *O. trux;* E, *O. brevipes;* F, *O. atomaria.*

Oxyptila simplex (O. P.-Cambridge).
(Text-figs. 96, D ; 97, B)

Thomisus simplex O. P.-Cambridge, 1862, p. 7951. *Oxyptila simplex* idem, 1879–81, p. 324 ; C. Chyzer and L. Kulczynski, 1891–7, I, p. 100 ; E. Simon, 1932, pp, 803, 809.

DESCRIPTION. LENGTH : ♀ : 4–5 mm. ♂ : 3–4 mm.

♀ : CARAPACE : Like *O. trux*, but slightly paler. ABDOMEN : Pale whitish-brown, with occasionally a very few black spots ; clothed with a number of short clavate hairs. LEGS : Uniform pale yellow to brown. EPIGYNE : Text-fig. 97, B.

♂ : CARAPACE : Sides brown to dark brown, variegated with lighter brown ; central band pale brown to brown, paler posteriorly ; clothed with few clavate hairs, like *O. trux*. ABDOMEN : Pale yellow-brown, white at the sides, marked with a few slightly darker spots and transverse bars. LEGS : Femora I and II yellow-brown to brown marked with a variable amount of dark brown to black ; remaining segments pale yellow to yellow-brown occasionally marked with a few brown spots. MALE PALP : Text-fig. 96, D, yellow-brown, with femur dark brown.

OCCURRENCE : In undergrowth, etc., mainly on sandhills apparently. Not common, and rarer in the north than in the south. Adult in spring and early summer.

Oxyptila atomaria (Panzer).
(Text-fig. 96, C ; 97, F)

Aranea atomaria G. W. F. Panzer, 1810, p. 19. *Thomisus pallidus* and *T. versutus* J. Blackwall, 1861–4, pp. 82–3. *Oxyptila atomaria* O. P.-Cambridge, 1879–81, p. 322 ; E. Simon, 1932, pp. 800, 809 ; A. Tullgren, 1944, p. 73 ; W. S. Bristowe, 1947, pl. 5.

DESCRIPTION. LENGTH : ♀ : 4–6 mm. ♂ : 3–4 mm.

♀ : CARAPACE : Sides light to dark brown with central band lighter, practically white at rear ; clothed with a number of very small clavate hairs. ABDOMEN : Brown to grey, with sometimes a few black spots ; clothed with a number of very small clavate hairs. LEGS : Almost uniform pale brown. EPIGYNE : Text-fig. 97, F.

♂ : CARAPACE : Dark reddish-brown at sides, with two wide black longitudinal lines bordering the central brown band ; no clavate hairs except for a few on clypeus. ABDOMEN : Like ♀ but slightly darker. LEGS : Yellow to yellow-brown, almost unmarked. MALE PALP : Text-fig. 96, C.

OCCURRENCE : Widespread and not uncommon in short grass, undergrowth, etc. Adult during spring and summer months.

Oxyptila brevipes (Hahn).
(Text-fig. 97, A, E)

Thomisus brevipes C. W. Hahn, 1831, p. 30. *Oxyptila flexa* O. P.-Cambridge, 1895, p. 117 ; W. S. Bristowe, 1939, p. 30. *O. brevipes* E. Simon, 1932, pp. 803, 811 ; A. Tullgren, 1944, p. 79.

DESCRIPTION. LENGTH : ♀ : 3 mm. ♂ : 2–2·5 mm.

♀ : CARAPACE : Dark brown, variegated with lighter brown ; central band brown anteriorly, white posteriorly, marked with brown dots carrying a few clavate hairs. ABDOMEN : Whitish, with a few broken transverse blackish bars, clothed with some very small clavate hairs. LEGS : Pale brown, prettily annulated and variegated (particularly on anterior legs) with very dark brown and white. EPIGYNE : Text-fig. 97, E ; has characteristic W-shaped marking.

♂ : CARAPACE : Sides very dark brown. ABDOMEN : Brown with numerous brown-black bars. LEGS : Pale brown, annulated and marked with dark brown, except for femora I which are very dark brown. MALE PALP : Text-fig. 97, A.

OCCURRENCE : Widespread but not common, throughout the more southern counties, usually in damp, marshy areas or near the sea. Adult in summer.

7. Genus **PHILODROMUS** C. A. Walckenaer 1825.

CHARACTERS OF GENUS. CARAPACE : Broader than long and relatively narrower in front than in genera *Xysticus* and *Oxyptila* (Text-fig. 89, A, B, C). EYES : Smaller and more uniform in size than in genera *Xysticus* and *Oxyptila*, in a smaller crescent-shaped group with the anterior row much the shortest ; posteriors slightly recurved, the medians further from each other than from the laterals (Text-fig. 89, C). ABDOMEN : Usually oval, not appreciably widened or truncated behind. LEGS : Relatively long, practically equal in length ; tibiæ with two or more pairs of spines ventrally ; tarsi, and sometimes metatarsi also, with scopulæ and claw tufts. EPIGYNES and PALPAL ORGANS : Show considerable specific variation.

These spiders, despite their relatively long legs, are still somewhat crab-like in general appearance. They can run very rapidly both forwards and sideways. Except for *P. fallax*, which occurs exclusively on sandhills and in other sandy places, all the species occur on low vegetation and are usually obtained by beating and sweeping.

The species can be split up for convenience into three groups, the members of which are best identified by reference to the descriptions and sex organs :

1. Tibia I armed ventrally with four to five pairs of spines .
    P. dispar
    —Tibia I armed ventrally with two to three pairs of spines . . . 2
2. Tibia I armed with three pairs of spines ventrally ; anterior median eyes equal to or smaller than the laterals . . .
    P. aureolus, P. emarginatus, P. rufus, P. margaritatus
    —Tibia I armed with two pairs of spines ventrally ; anterior median eyes greater than laterals . . . **P. fallax, P. histrio**

Philodromus dispar Walckenaer.
(Text-figs. 98, A ; 100, A)

Philodromus dispar C. A. Walckenaer, 1825, p. 89 ; J. Blackwall, 1861–4, p. 91 ; O. P.-Cambridge, 1879–81, p. 328 ; C. Chyzer and L. Kulczynski, 1891–7, I, p. 106 ; E. Simon, 1932, p. 843 ; A. Tullgren, 1944, p. 104.

DESCRIPTION. LENGTH : ♀: 4–5 mm. ♂: 4 mm.

♀: CARAPACE : Brown except for creamy wedge-shaped marking behind eyes ; sometimes marked with radiating cream striæ. ABDOMEN: Pale buff, sometimes with ill-defined brown folium, sometimes with some brown spots anteriorly and broken chevrons posteriorly. LEGS :

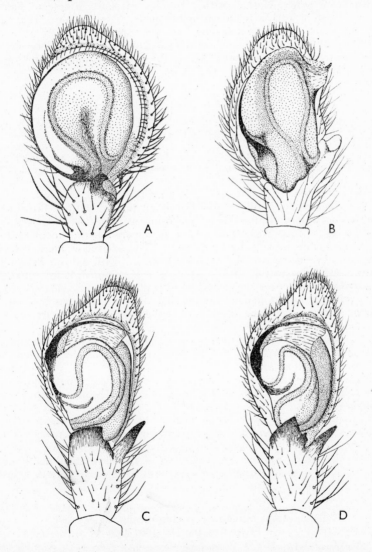

TEXT-FIG. 98.—Male palps (below) : A, *Philodromus dispar;* B, *P. emarginatus;* C, *P. anreolus;* D, *P. aureolus caespiticolis.*

Pale yellow-brown with a few brown spots ; tibiæ I armed ventrally with four to five pairs of spines. EPIGYNE : Text-fig. 100, A.

♂ : Often appears a shiny jet black in the field. CARAPACE : Dark brown with some darker radiating lines ; clothed with a number of short iridescent hairs. ABDOMEN : Has a deep blackish-brown folium with brown sides, clothed with a number of short, iridescent hairs. LEGS : Yellow with a few dark brown spots. MALE PALP : Text-fig. 98, A, yellow except for the dark brown tarsus.

OCCURRENCE : Common on low trees and bushes and in undergrowth, but less frequent in the north than in the south. Adult in spring and early summer.

Philodromus aureolus (Clerck).
(=P. aureolus (Olivier))
(Text-figs. 98, C ; 100, C)

Araneus aureolus C. Clerck, 1757, p. 133 ; A. G. Olivier, 1789, p. 225. *Philodromus aureolus* J. Blackwall, 1861-4, p. 99 ; O. P.-Cambridge, 1879-81, p. 329 ; C. Chyzer and L. Kulczynski, 1891-7, I, p. 108 ; E. Simon, 1932, p. 851 ; A. Tullgren, 1944, p. 115 ; B. J. Kaston, 1948, p. 436.

DESCRIPTION. LENGTH : ♀ : 5-6 mm. ♂ : 4 mm.

♀ : CARAPACE : Dull reddish-brown or brown, with a brownish-yellow or whitish central band enclosing at times a wedge-shaped marking ; clothed with some fine pale-coloured hairs ; ocular area devoid of spines. ABDOMEN : Dorsally brownish-yellow marked with a series of reddish-brown spots and chevrons ; with reddish brown or brown sides ; clothed with some fine pale-coloured hairs. LEGS : Brownish-yellow, practically unmarked ; tibiæ I armed ventrally with two pairs of rather pale-coloured spines and a small pair apically ; tarsal scopulæ well developed in ♀, much less so in ♂. EPIGYNE : Text-fig. 100, C.

♂ : Marked like ♀ but darker in colour, and has in nature a dull metallic hue reflected from the dense coating of iridescent hairs on the abdomen. MALE PALP : Text-fig. 98, C.

OCCURRENCE : By far the commonest of the genus. Found throughout the country in undergrowth, on bushes, etc. Adult in spring and summer.

A number of varieties of *P. aureolus* occur, in which the male palpal tibia and palpal organs, and the female epigyne, differ somewhat from the typical. The varieties are usually given sub-specific rank, and on the continent of Europe a whole series of intermediate forms seems to occur. In this country, the only well-established variety seems to be *P. aureolus cæspiticolis*.

Philodromus aureolus var. cæspiticolis Walckenaer.
(Text-figs. 98, D ; 100, E)

Philodromus cæspiticolis C. A. Walckenaer, 1825, p. 555 ; J. Blackwall, 1861-4, p. 95 ; O. P.-Cambridge, 1879-81, p. 331. *P. aureolus cæspiticolis* C. Chyzer and L. Kulczynski, 1891-7, I, p. 109.

Colour and size as *P. aureolus*. EPIGYNE : Text-fig. 100, E, differs considerably from that of *P. aureolus*. MALE PALP : Text-fig. 98, D, differs from *P. aureolus* in the ventral apophysis of the tibia, and in the disposition of the palpal organs (mainly in the convolution of the seminal duct), while the lateral tibial apophysis seems to be slightly narrower.

OCCURRENCE : In similar situations to *P. aureolus*, but rather less common.

Philodromus fallax Sundevall.
(Text-figs. 99, C ; 100, H)

Philodromus fallax J. C. Sundevall, 1833, p. 226 ; O. P.-Cambridge, 1879–81, p. 335 ; E. Simon, 1932, p. 847 ; A. Tullgren, 1944, p. 122 ; W. S. Bristowe, 1947, pl. 8.

DESCRIPTION. LENGTH : ♀ : 4·5–6 mm. ♂ : 4·5 mm. Both sexes are similar in colour, with the ♂ slightly darker. CARAPACE : Pale, sandy colour, mottled and marked with brown ; clothed with some short, pale hairs. EYES : Anterior medians distinctly greater than laterals. ABDOMEN : Sandy colour with a central longitudinal brown wedge-shaped marking followed by indistinct chevrons ; clothed thickly with short, light-coloured hairs. LEGS : Sandy, mottled and blotched with brown ; heavily clothed with fine hairs ; tarsal scopulæ very well developed, and well-defined scopulæ also present on metatarsi. EPIGYNE : Text-fig. 100, H, has a thick covering of light-coloured hairs. MALE PALP : Text-fig. 99, C, has a very narrow tarsus with inconspicuous palpal organs.

OCCURRENCE : This species cannot be mistaken for any other ; it is found only in sandy places, particularly on sand-dunes on the coast. In such localities it is widespread, but not always easy to discover because of its imitative colour. The ♂ is adult in April, and has vanished by early May ; the ♀ is mature in May and June.

Philodromus histrio (Latreille).
(Text-figs. 99, A ; 100, B)

Thomisus histrio P. A. Latreille, 1819, p. 36. *Philodromus elegans* J. Blackwall, 1861–4, p. 94 ; O. P.-Cambridge, 1879–81, p. 334. *P. histrio* C. Chyzer and L. Kulczynski, 1891–7, I, p. 107 ; E. Simon, 1932, p. 841 ; A. Tullgren, 1944, p. 113.

DESCRIPTION. LENGTH : ♀ : 6–7 mm. ♂ : ca. 6 mm. Both sexes are similar in colour, with the ♂ rather darker. CARAPACE : Sides dark red-brown with central yellow band, enclosing central reddish-brown marking, and ocular area suffused with red-brown ; head in ♀ with a number of long spines, directed forwards, but fewer in ♂. EYES : Anterior medians very slightly larger than laterals. ABDOMEN : Red-brown with anteriorly a red-brown rather diamond-shaped marking surrounded with yellow, followed by yellow chevrons and four rather prominent yellow spots towards the sides. LEGS : Red-brown annulated and marked with yellow ; tarsal scopulæ well developed, and scopulæ also present on metatarsi. STERNUM : Red-brown with central longitudinal yellow stripe, clothed thickly with hairs. Epigyne : Text-fig. 100, B. Male palp : Text-fig. 99, A, has only a minute lateral apophysis, and a rather narrow tarsus.

Occurrence : This species, which is large and prettily marked, is usually found on heather, and is widespread but rare. The ♂ is adult from end of March to end of April (depending on locality) and the ♀ is adult in April to June.

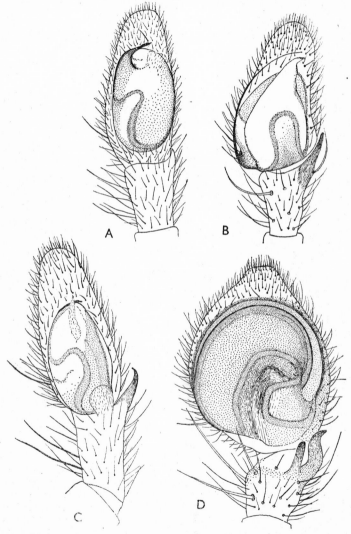

Text-fig. 99.—Male palps (below) : A, *Philodromus histrio;* B, *P. rufus;* C, *P. fallax;* D, *P. margaritatus.*

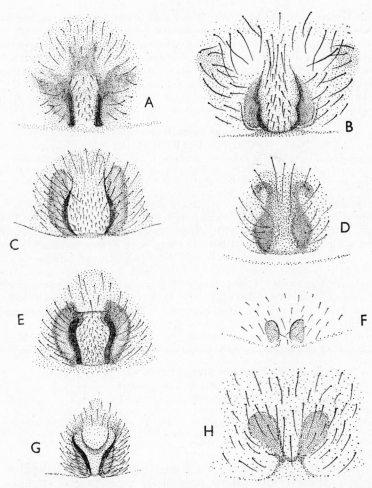

TEXT-FIG. 100.—Epigynes : A, *Philodromus dispar;* B, *P. histrio;* C, *P. aureolus;* D, *P. rufus;* E, *P. aureolus caespiticolis;* F, *P. margaritatus;* G, *P. emarginatus;* H, *P. fallax.*

Philodromus emarginatus (Schrank).
(Text-figs. 98, B ; 100, G)

Aranea emarginata F. von P. Schrank, 1803, p. 230.   *Philodromus lineatipes* O. P.-Cambridge, 1879–81, p. 538.   *P. emarginatus* idem, ibid. p. 333 ; C. Chyzer and L. Kulczynski, 1891–7, I, p. 107 ; E. Simon, 1932, p. 847 ; A. Tullgren, 1944, p. 110.

DESCRIPTION. LENGTH : ♀: 5–6 mm. ♂: 4–5 mm. The ♂ is slightly darker than the ♀. CARAPACE : Sides brown, marked with radiating cream lines ; central area cream to white marked anteriorly with brown lines and blotches ; head with a number of strong spines. ABDOMEN : Dull brown with some whitish spots and chevrons. LEGS : Brown to dark brown with faint white markings ; tarsal scopulæ well developed, and metatarsal scopulæ also present. EPIGYNE : Text-fig. 100, G. MALE PALP : Text-fig. 98, B, has large lateral apophysis, and tarsus is enlarged and rounded.

OCCURRENCE : On conifers ; frequent in a few localities, from Scotland to the south coast. Adult in May and June.

Philodromus rufus Walckenaer.
(Text-figs. 99, B ; 100, D)

Philodromus rufus C. A. Walckenaer, 1825, p. 91. P. clarkii J. Blackwall, 1861–4, p. 96 ; O. P.-Cambridge, 1879–81, p. 539. P. rufus C. Chyzer and L. Kulczynski, 1891–7, I, p. 107 ; E. Simon, 1932, p. 854 ; A. Tullgren, 1944, p. 117 ; B. J. Kaston, 1948, p. 434.

DESCRIPTION. LENGTH : ♀ : 3·5–4 mm. ♂ : 3 mm. CARAPACE : Pale brown at sides, and whitish fawn centrally. ABDOMEN : Pale buff, with only faint traces of pattern, more distinct in male ; armed with a number of spines. LEGS : Yellow, with numerous small brown or black spots ; armed ventrally with long pale spines ; tarsal scopulæ indistinct because of paleness of hairs, and no obvious metatarsal scopulæ. STERNUM : Pale yellow with some brown spots, particularly at edges. EPIGYNE : Text-fig. 100, D, has a number of pale hairs. MALE PALP : Text-fig. 99, B, is elongate. This species is in colour and size rather like a small, pale specimen of P. aureolus.

OCCURRENCE : Rare ; on bushes and low herbage in wooded areas in a few of the more southern counties. Adult in May and June.

Philodromus margaritatus (Clerck).
(=P. levipes (Linnaeus))
(Text-figs. 99, D ; 100, F)

Araneus margaritatus C. Clerck, 1757, p. 130. A. levipes Linnaeus, 1758, p. 624. Philodromus pallidus J. Blackwall, 1861–4, p. 93. P. margaritatus O. P.-Cambridge, 1879–81, p. 326 ; C. Chyzer and L. Kulczynski, 1891–7, I, p. 106 ; E. Simon, 1932, p. 846. P. levipes W. S. Bristowe, 1939, p. 32, and 1947, pls. 6, 7 ; A. Tullgren, 1944, p. 108.

DESCRIPTION. LENGTH : ♀ : 5–6 mm. ♂ : 4–5 mm. CARAPACE : Whitish, mottled with brown particularly on sides and on head ; clothed with light hairs, but no spines on head. EYES : Anterior medians distinctly smaller than laterals. ABDOMEN : Greenish-white with two prominent darker spots about half-way to spinners, followed by series of broken dark-coloured chevrons (pattern more distinct in ♂ than ♀) ; clothed with light-coloured hairs except for the two dark spots which have brown hairs. LEGS : Pale yellow with some dark brown annulations and spots ; armed with numerous long, very pale spines and hairs ; tarsal scopulæ distinct though formed of rather pale-coloured hairs (scopulæ less developed in ♂). STERNUM : Pale whitish-yellow, with numerous whitish hairs. EPIGYNE : Text-fig. 100, F, clothed with many short hairs. MALE PALP : Text-fig. 99, D. The whole spider has a flattened form.

OCCURRENCE : Very rare. On the trunks of trees. A variety in which the carapace and abdomen were mainly a clear, chalky white in colour, with darker markings, occurred on the lichen-covered trunks of apple trees in O. Pickard-Cambridge's garden at Bloxworth. Recorded only in a few southern counties and in Scotland. Adult in May-June.

8. Genus **THANATUS** C. L. Koch 1837 (2).

CHARACTERS OF GENUS. This genus differs from *Philodromus* in the relative position of the eyes, and in the relative lengths of the legs. CARAPACE : Scarcely longer than wide. EYES : Anterior row closer together, and posterior row more strongly recurved, than in *Philodromus;* posterior eyes equidistant (Text-fig. 89, D) ; anterior medians appreciably smaller than laterals. ABDOMEN : Oval, not appreciably enlarged or truncated behind. LEGS : Relatively shorter and stouter than in *Philodromus*, with legs IV rather longer than the remainder ; tibiæ armed ventrally with three pairs of spines ; tarsi and metatarsi armed with scopulæ. The two species are rare.

Thanatus striatus C. L. Koch.
(Text-fig. 101, A)

Thanatus striatus C. L. Koch, 1845, p. 92 ; E. Simon, 1932, p. 858 ; A. Tullgren, 1944, p. 119 ; B. J. Kaston, 1948, p. 438. *T. hirsutus* O. P.-Cambridge, 1879–81, p. 337.

DESCRIPTION. LENGTH : ♀ : 4–5 mm. An adult ♂ could not be found amongst the collections in this country. CARAPACE : Yellow-brown with two lateral bands of dark brown and a median brown stripe behind the posterior eyes ; spotted with brown ; clothed with long coarse black hairs. ABDOMEN : Yellowish or reddish-yellow with a sharply defined pattern composed of a central dark brown lanceolate marking ending in a point about half-way to the spinners, with, on either side, some dark brown irregular longitudinal stripes ; sides dark brown ; clothed with coarse black hairs. LEGS : Yellow-brown to brown, mottled with darker brown, and armed with large numbers of black hairs. STERNUM : Yellow-brown, heavily spotted with dark brown. EPIGYNE : Text-fig. 101, A. The depth of colour varies somewhat, but the abdominal pattern is always clear.

OCCURRENCE : Amongst grass and undergrowth in woods, on sand-hills, in fens, in a number of northern as well as southern counties. Uncommon except in a few localities. Adult in May and June, though recognisable immature specimens can be found throughout the summer.

Thanatus formicinus (Clerck).
(=*T. formicinus* (Olivier))
(Text-fig. 101, B, D)

Araneus formicinus C. Clerck, 1757, p. 134 ; A. G. Olivier, 1789, p. 226. *Thanatus formicinus* O. P.-Cambridge, 1895, p. 118 ; C. Chyzer and L. Kulczynski, 1891–7, 1, p. 114 ; E. Simon, 1932, p. 861 ; A. Tullgren, 1944, p. 121 ; B. J. Kaston, 1948, p. 438.

DESCRIPTION. LENGTH : ♀ : up to 8–9 mm. ♂ : 5–7 mm. Both sexes are similar in colour, with ♂ slightly darker. CARAPACE :

Margins dark reddish-brown, with central marking paler ; clothed fairly thickly with white silky hairs, particularly in centre, and some coarse dark hairs. ABDOMEN : Yellow-brown to brown with a very distinct dark brown lanceolate marking ending in a point half-way to the spinners, followed by two longitudinal dark lines and dark spots ; clothed with coarse hairs and numerous short silky whitish hairs. LEGS : Brown, streaked with slightly darker brown and clothed with numerous dark hairs and short, prone, white hairs. STERNUM : Yellow-brown, with some coarse black hairs and a number of prone white hairs. EPIGYNE : Text-fig. 101, B, is covered thickly with silky white hairs. MALE PALP : Text-fig. 101, D.

OCCURRENCE : This species has been captured in two localities only in this country, viz., on Beaulieu Heath (Hampshire) and in Ashdown Forest (near Forest Row, Sussex). Adult probably in spring.

9. Genus **TIBELLUS** E. Simon 1875.

CHARACTERS OF GENUS. CARAPACE : Appreciably longer than wide. EYES : The change in position of the eyes has gone further than in the genus *Thanatus*, and the eyes of the anterior row, with the posterior median pair, form a small compact hexagonal group from which the posterior laterals are conspicuously removed (Text-fig. 89, E). ABDOMEN : Long and cylindrical or cigar-shaped (Text-fig. 101, C). LEGS : Relatively long, bearing scopulæ on both tarsi and metatarsi.

This genus contains two closely similar species, formerly confused with one another. They are very active spiders, found on coarse grasses, rushes, etc. When disturbed, they run with great rapidity up the stems of grasses ; when at rest they extend their four anterior legs forwards and the four posterior legs backwards along a stem, in this way becoming very inconspicuous. The two species can be separated with certainty only by their genitalia.

Tibellus maritimus (Menge).
(Text-figs. 101, C ; 102, B, D)

Thanatus maritimus A. Menge, 1866–79, p. 398 (♂ only). *T. oblongus* idem, ibid, p. 396 (♀ only). *Tibellus oblongus* C. Chyzer and L. Kulczynski, 1891–7, I, p. 115 ; E. Simon, 1932, p. 864 ; W. S. Bristowe, 1939, p. 33. *T. maritimus* A. R. Jackson, 1911, p. 387 ; O. P.-Cambridge, 1911, p. 46 ; A. Tullgren, 1944, p. 124 ; B. J. Kaston, 1948, p. 441.

DESCRIPTION. LENGTH : ♀: up to 10 mm. ♂: 8 mm. This species is of a sandy or straw colour (♀) or often greyish (♂), with a darker cental band on the abdomen. It has usually (but not invariably) a number of fairly large brown spots on the dorsal surface of the abdomen on either side of the central marking, and on the margins of the carapace and on the legs. EPIGYNE : Text-fig. 102, D. MALE PALP : Text-fig. 102, B ; the palpal organs viewed from below and to the inside have the base of the embolus broad and screw-like, with the tip pointed.

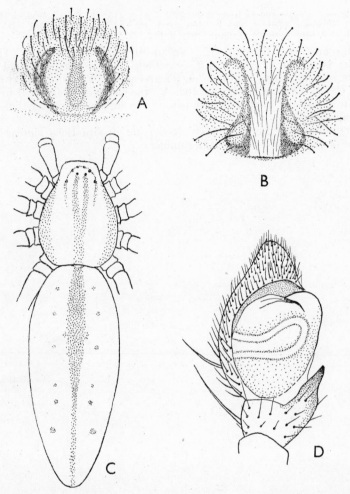

Text-fig. 101.—Epigynes : A, *Thanatus striatus* ; B, *T. formicinus* ; C, dorsal side of body of *Tibellus maritimus* ; D, *T. formicinus*, male palp (below).

Occurrence : On coarse grasses, rushes, etc., in damp places, on sandhills and rough ground, etc. This species, though widespread, appears to be less common than the next ; adult in summer.

Tibellus oblongus (Walckenaer).
(Text-fig. 102, A, C)

Aranea oblonga C. A. Walckenaer, 1802, p. 228.   *Philodromus oblonga* J. Blackwall, 1861–4, p. 100.   *Thanatus oblongus* A. Menge, 1866–79, p. 396 (♂ only).   *T. maritimus* idem, ibid, p. 398 (♀ only).   *T. parallelus* C. L. Koch 1837, (2), I, p. 28.   *Tibellus parallelus* C. Chyzer and L. Kulczynski, 1891–7, I, p. 115 ; E. Simon, 1932, p. 864 ; W. S. Bristowe, 1939, p. 33. *T. oblongus* A. R. Jackson, 1911, p. 387 ; O. P.-Cambridge, 1911, p. 46 ; A. Tullgren, 1944, p. 124 ; B. J. Kaston, 1948. p, 440.

DESCRIPTION. LENGTH : ♀ : up to 10 mm. ♂ : 8 mm. This spider is similar in colour to *T. maritimus*, but is usually devoid of spots, except for two faint ones on the abdomen. EPIGYNE : Text-fig. 102, C. MALE PALP : Text-fig. 102, A ; the palpal organs viewed from below and to the inside have the base of the embolus narrower than in *T. maritimus*.

OCCURRENCE : Very common ; occurring in situations similar to those of *T. maritimus*. Adult in summer.

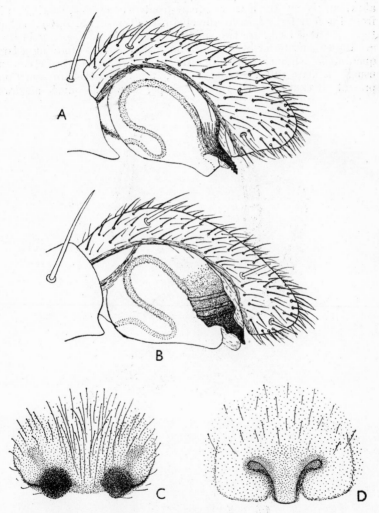

TEXT-FIG. 102.—Male palps (from inside and above): A, *Tibellus oblongus;* B, *T. maritimus.*
Epigynes: C, *T. oblongus;* D, *T. maritimus.*

14. Family SALTICIDÆ.

CHARACTERS OF FAMILY. This family comprises those spiders commonly known as "jumping spiders." They are characterised above all else by the massive square-fronted CARAPACE, bearing on its front the four large forward-directed eyes (Text-fig. 9, B, C) ; behind these, set well back, are two small eyes, and behind these again there are the two posterior eyes of medium size, the whole forming a large quadrangle. LEGS : Normally rather short, with two tarsal claws and usually a claw tuft (Text-fig. 6, C) ; tarsal scopulæ are sometimes present. STERNUM : Of variable shape, sometimes much narrowed

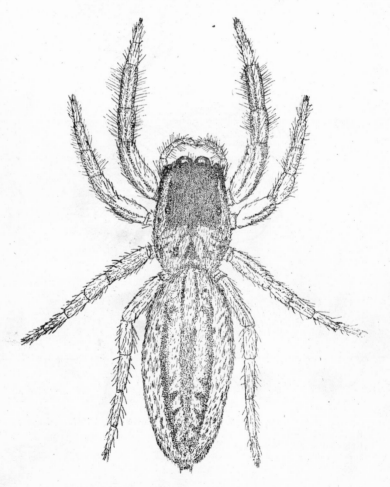

TEXT-FIG. 103.—*Marpissa pomatia* ♀ (SALTICIDÆ).

in front. CHELICERÆ : Armed on inner margin with 0, 1 or several teeth ; in some species the cheliceræ are much enlarged and projecting in the male. The MALE PALP usually has a tibial apophysis and some-times a femoral apophysis.

The spiders of this family are clothed to a greater or less degree with iridescent squamose hairs and pubescence of various colours. Several species are considered to be ant-mimics. They are diurnal in habit, and are frequently encountered in grass and undergrowth, etc., in hot sunshine. They spin no snare, but usually leap upon their prey. The males indulge in courtship displays with the females.

The 32 British spiders of this family are included in 17 genera, which can be separated according to the following key :

KEY TO GENERA.

1. Ocular trapezium slightly longer than broad : pedicel visible from above : ant-like spider. . . . (14) **Synageles**
——Ocular trapezium very slightly broader than long ; pedicel visible from above ; sternum about three times as long as broad with coxæ II well separated from coxæ III (Text-fig. 117, D) ; ant-like spider (Text-fig. 116) . . . . . . (15) **Myrmarachne**
——Ocular trapezium appreciably broader than long ; pedicel not visible from above, not particularly ant-like . . . 2

2. Tibiæ and metatarsi I without stout spines ventrally, but with long, fine hairs only ; " zebra spiders " with typical black and white colouration . . . (1) **Salticus**
——Tibiæ and metatarsi I with pairs of strong spines ventrally 3

3. Tarsi I and II armed ventrally with dense scopulæ to at least half their length 4
——Tarsi I and II not armed with scopulæ, or only at the tip 5

4. Legs IV shorter than legs III. . . . . (13) **Phlegra**
——Legs IV longer than legs III. . . . . (12) **Ælurillus**

5. Ocular trapezium appreciably broader behind than in front 6
——Ocular trapezium not broader behind than in front . . 8

6. No spines on legs III and IV . . . . . (6) **Ballus**
——Legs III and IV with at least a few stout spines . . . 7

7. Posterior eyes set practically half-way along carapace ; ocular trapezium nearly as long as broad, and ca. 1·3 times as wide behind as in front ; legs III and IV with few spines ; abdominal pattern obscure . . (4) **Bianor**
——Posterior eyes set back from front about one-third of length of carapace ; ocular trapezium appreciably broader than long, and ca. 1·1–1·15 times as wide behind as in front ; legs III and IV with several stout spines ; clear and distinctive abdominal pattern . . . (17) **Pellenes**

8. Sternum narrowed in front, with coxæ I close together (*i.e.*, not much more than their own diameter apart) (Text-fig. 107, C) 9
——Sternum not greatly narrowed in front 10

9. Patella I practically as long as tibia I . . (3) **Marpissa**
——Patella I considerably shorter than tibia I . (5) **Hyctia**

10. Metatarsi IV with spines reduced practically to stout hairs : tibiæ IV with no spines . . . . (7) **Neon**
——Metatarsi IV with normal spines (these are fine and thin in *Heliophanus*) 11

11. Patella + tibia of leg III practically equal in length to patella + tibia of leg IV 12
——Patella + tibia of leg III appreciably shorter than patella + tibia of leg IV 13

12. Posterior eyes equal in diameter to anterior laterals ; inner cheliceral margin with bifid tooth . . (16) **Hasarius**
——Posterior eyes rather less in diameter than anterior laterals ; inner cheliceral margin with simple tooth (11) **Evarcha**

13. Tibiæ IV more than twice or nearly twice as long as tibiæ III ; outer edge of cheliceræ with a group of two to four teeth on a small protuberance 14
——Tibiæ IV about 1·5 times as long as tibiæ III ; outer edge of cheliceræ with one large and one small tooth, not on a protuberance 15

14. Tibiæ IV about 2·5–3 times as long as tibiæ III ; carapace very squat . . . . (10) **Attulus**
——Tibiæ IV about twice as long as tibiæ III ; carapace less squat . . . . (9) **Sitticus**

15. Spines on metatarsi many and large and stout ; tarsi I–III with a long trichobothrium, tarsi IV with two long trichobothria . . . . (8) **Euophrys**
——Spines on metatarsi few and small and fine ; tarsi I–IV with two long trichobothria . . . . . (2) **Heliophanus**

1. Genus **SALTICUS** P. A. Latreille 1804 (1).

CHARACTERS OF GENUS. This genus includes the familiar black and white " zebra spider " of sunny walls, etc. EYES : The ocular trapezium is about one-third broader than long. STERNUM : Narrowed in front. CHELICERÆ : With one large tooth on inner margin, and two smaller ones on outer margin ; cheliceræ of ♂ greatly elongated and projecting (Text-fig. 104, D). LEGS : Tibiæ and metatarsi I armed ventrally with hairs only, and no paired spines. The three species are readily separated by the genitalia, and usually by their patterns.

Salticus scenicus (Clerck).

(=*S. scenicus* (Linnaeus))

(Text-figs. 104, A, D ; 105, A, B)

Araneus scenicus C. Clerck, 1757, p. 117. *Aranea scenica* Linnaeus, 1758, p. 623.
Salticus scenicus J. Blackwall, 1861–4, p. 47 (ad partem) ; F. Dahl, 1926, p. 25 ;
E. Simon, 1937, pp. 1202, 1204 ; A. Tullgren, 1944, p. 19 ; W. S. Bristowe, 1947,
pl. 16 ; B. J. Kaston, 1948, p. 453. *Epiblemum scenicum* O. P.-Cambridge, 1879–81,
p. 392 ; C. Chyzer and L. Kulczynski, 1891–7, I, p. 11.

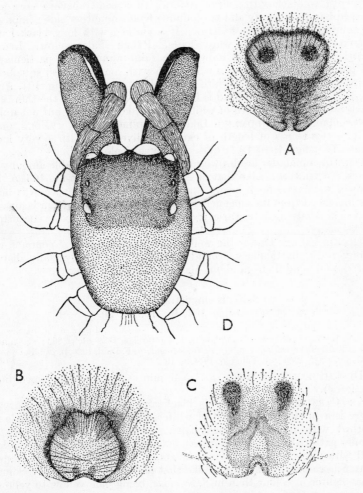

TEXT-FIG. 104.—Epigynes : A, *Salticus scenicus;* B, *S. cingulatus;* C, *S. zebraneus.*
D, male cheliceræ of *S. scenicus.*

DESCRIPTION. LENGTH : ♀ : 5–7 mm. ♂ : 5–6 mm. (including chelicerae).

♀ : CARAPACE : Very dark brown to black, somewhat darker on the head than on thorax ; clothed rather thickly with iridescent squamose hairs ; there is a patch of white hairs behind the anterior eyes, and two small triangular patches of white hairs just behind and inside of the posterior eyes ; the carapace is thickly covered with black hairs, and the lower margin has a thick fringe of white hairs. ABDOMEN : Brownish to black with a clear pattern ; there is a transverse crescent-shaped band anteriorly and two oblique bands on either side composed of shining white squamose hairs ; it is clothed with long black hairs interspersed with some white hairs. PALP : Pale yellow. LEGS : Mottled brown to yellow-brown with faint annulations particularly on posterior legs. STERNUM : Blackish with many whitish squamose hairs, and also some long white hairs. EPIGYNE : Text-fig. 104, A.

♂ : CARAPACE : The head is black, somewhat rugose; the thorax is dark brown ; the pattern of white hairs is like that of ♀ but not quite so pronounced. ABDOMEN : Like ♀. CHELICERÆ : Very long, one-half to two-thirds of length of carapace, divergent, with a very long fang (Text-fig. 104, D) ; dark brown in colour. LEGS : Legs I black, the remainder are brown mottled with a considerable amount of black. STERNUM : Like that of ♀. MALE PALP : Text-fig. 105, A, B, brown, with tarsi dark brown and white at tips ; the species is best distinguished from its congeners by the palpal tibia seen from below.

A completely melanic variety, with no white markings, has occurred occasionally.

OCCURRENCE : This is the well-known " zebra spider," common on sunny walls, particularly around buildings. It is universally distri-buted, and is adult from about May to August.

Salticus cingulatus (Panzer).
(Text-figs. 104, B ; 105, C, D)

Aranea cingulata Panzer, 1797, p. 22. *Salticus scenicus* (ad partem), J. Blackwall, 1861–4, p. 47. *Epiblemum cingulatum* O. P.-Cambridge, 1879–81, p. 393 ; C. Chyzer and L. Kulczynski, 1891–7, I, p. 11. *Salticus cingulatus* F. Dahl, 1926, p. 24 ; E. Simon, 1937, pp. 1202, 1206 ; A. Tullgren, 1944, p. 19.

DESCRIPTION. LENGTH : ♀ : 5–6 mm. ♂ : 5–6 mm (including chelicerae).

♀ : CARAPACE : The head is black and the thorax dark brown ; there is a broad central band of white squamose hairs ; the whole is clothed with numerous black hairs. ABDOMEN : Greyish, with a similar pattern to that of *S. scenicus*, but with the oblique bands broader and with a few chevrons giving the spider a more striped appearance than *S. scenicus*. STERNUM : Like that of *S. scenicus*. LEGS : Some-what lighter in colour than in *S. scenicus*, being pale yellow to yellow-brown with a few blackish patches or annulations. PALP : Pale yellow. EPIGYNE : Text-fig. 104, B, has an aperture of characteristic shape.

♂ : CARAPACE : Resembles that of ♀ but has fewer white squamose hairs. ABDOMEN : Pattern is rather less pronounced than in ♀. CHELICERÆ : Very long and divergent, almost as long as carapace. LEGS : Yellow-brown suffused with brown, except legs I which are brown, suffused with dark brown. MALE PALP : Text-fig. 105, C, D, brown with some squamose hairs, and whitish at the tip ; the species is best distinguished from its congeners by the palpal tibia seen from below.

OCCURRENCE : Normally found on tree trunks or palings, in woods, etc., away from habitations. Widespread ; adult in summer.

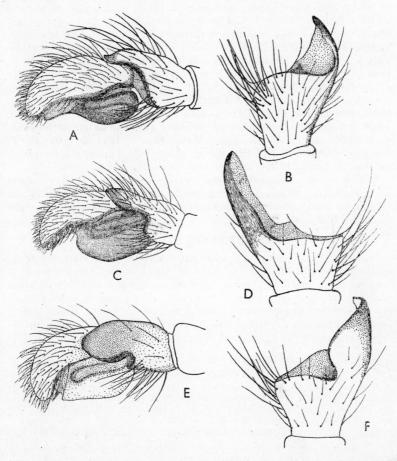

TEXT-FIG. 105.—Male palps : A, *Salticus scenicus* (side) ; B, do. tibia (below) ; C, *S. cingulatus* (side) ; D, do. tibia (right palp below) ; E, *S. zebraneus* (side) ; F, do. tibia (below).

Salticus zebraneus (C. L. Koch).
(Text-figs. 104, C ; 105, E, F)

Calliethera zebranea et *varia* C. L. Koch, 1837, p. 31. *Epiblemum zebraneum* C. Chyzer and L. Kulczynski, 1891–7, I, p. 11. *Epiblemum affinitatum* O. P.-Cambridge, 1879–81, p. 394 ; A. R. Jackson, 1908, p. 17. *Salticus zebraneus* E. Simon, 1937, pp. 1202, 1207. *S. olearii* F. Dahl, 1926, p. 24 ; A. Tullgren, 1944, p. 20.

DESCRIPTION. LENGTH : ♀ : 3·5–4 mm. ♂ : ca. 3 mm (including cheliceræ).

♀ : CARAPACE : Dark brown with the head black ; clothed fairly thickly with whitish squamose hairs which reflect a metallic sheen ; the lower margin of the carapace and the clypeus have a thick fringe of white squamose hairs. ABDOMEN : Black with some patches of white squamose hairs, but without a markedly striped appearance. STERNUM : Yellowish, suffused with black and clothed with few hairs. LEGS : Yellow suffused and annulated vaguely with blackish (particularly on femora). PALP : Pale yellow. EPIGYNE : Text-fig. 104, C, is very different from those of *S. scenicus* and *S. cingulatus*.

♂ : CARAPACE : Resembles that of ♀ but has fewer squamose hairs. ABDOMEN : Like that of ♀. CHELICERÆ : Fairly long and divergent, but somewhat less long relatively than in *S. scenicus* and *S. cingulatus*. LEGS : Yellow to yellow-brown suffused and annulated with black, particularly the posterior legs. MALE PALP : Text-fig. 105, E, F, blackish with patella and tibia rather paler ; tibial apophysis seen from outside, and from below, is large and wide.

OCCURRENCE : This species appears to be very rare. It has occurred on Bloxworth Heath (Dorset), near Lyndhurst (Hampshire), in Richmond Park (Surrey), near Plaistowe (Sussex) and in the Channel Islands. It is adult May-June.

2. Genus HELIOPHANUS C. L. Koch 1833 (3).

CHARACTERS OF GENUS. Spiders with relatively long, narrow bodies, black or greenish-black in colour with the legs and palps yellow or brown. They are found on low vegetation. EYES : Ocular trapezium nearly twice as broad as long. CLYPEUS : Very narrow, a fraction of the diameter of the anterior central eyes. MALE PALP : Has a strong femoral apophysis (Text-fig. 106, A, B, D). The three species can be separated readily by their genitalia.

Heliophanus cupreus (Walckenaer).
(Text-fig. 106, A, E, G)

Aranea cuprea C. A. Walckenaer, 1802, p. 245. *Salticus cupreus* (ad partem) J. Blackwall, 1861–4, p. 31. *Heliophanus cupreus* O. P.-Cambridge, 1879–81, p. 395 ; C. Chyzer and L. Kulczynski, 1891–7, I, p. 8 ; F. Dahl, 1926, p. 42 ; E. Simon, 1937, pp. 1159, 1169 ; A. Tullgren, 1944, p. 52.

DESCRIPTION. LENGTH : ♀ : 5–6 mm. ♂ : about 4 mm.

♀ : CARAPACE : Rugose ; head black with metallic sheen, and thorax very dark brown shading to black at rear ; clothed with some black hairs and some white squamose hairs. ABDOMEN : Black with a line (sometimes very narrow) of white hairs across the anterior end and sides ; two flecks of white hairs towards the rear are sometimes only poorly developed ; it is clothed with shining squamose hairs. STERNUM : Black and shiny with some white hairs. LEGS : Femora yellowish with black longitudinal striæ and black spots ; sometimes almost completely black ; the remaining segments are yellow-brown suffused with some blackish streaks. PALP : Yellow to yellow-brown, but sometimes suffused and marked with much black. EPIGYNE : Text-fig. 106, G ; reddish processes of variable shape often project from the aperture, obscuring its appearance.

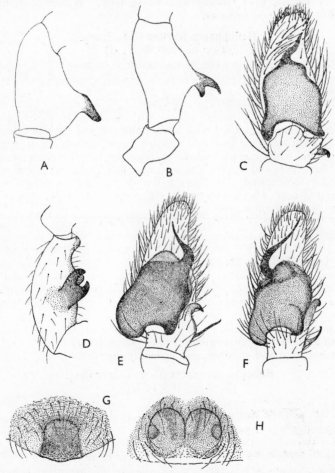

TEXT-FIG. 106.—Male palps : A, *Heliophanus cupreus:* femur (side) ; F, do. (below) ; B, *H. flavipes:* femur (side) ; F, do. (below) ; C, *H. expers* (below) ; D, do. : femur (side).
Epigynes : G, *H. cupreus;* H, *H. flavipes.*

♂ : CARAPACE : Completely black, rugose, and shining with a metallic sheen ; clothed with black hairs and with some white squamose hairs at the edges. ABDOMEN : Black, clothed with iridescent squamose hairs. LEGS : Femora are black, suffused with a little yellow ; the remaining segments are yellow-brown suffused with variable amounts of black. MALE PALP : Text-fig. 106, A, E ; dark-brown to black ; femoral apophysis is not bifid at the end, cf. *H. flavipes* and *H. expers* ; the stylus of the palpal organs is on the outer side.

OCCURRENCE : A common species in the undergrowth, low vegetation, etc., of woods, open spaces and waste land. Widely distributed. Adult in spring and summer.

Heliophanus flavipes C. L. Koch.
(Text-fig. 106, B, F, H)

Heliophanus flavipes C. L. Koch, 1848, p. 64 ; O. P.-Cambridge, 1879–81, p. 398 ; E. Simon, 1937, pp. 1163, 1169. *H. ritteri*, F. Dahl, 1926, p. 43 ; A. Tullgren, 1944, p. 54.

DESCRIPTION. LENGTH : ♀ : 5–6 mm. ♂ : 3·5 mm.

♀ : CARAPACE : Slightly rugose with a metallic sheen, almost completely black ; clothed with black hairs and some white squamose hairs. ABDOMEN : A uniform greyish-black except for a vaguely defined thin white line around the anterior and anterior sides ; clothed with black hairs and some white squamose hairs. LEGS : Clear yellow to yellow-brown with sometimes a few dark markings on coxæ and femora. PALP : Clear pale yellow. EPIGYNE : Text-fig. 106, H, has a more or less circular opening.

♂ : CARAPACE : The head is black and the rest very dark brown ; it is rugose with a metallic sheen, and has a few whitish hairs on the sides. ABDOMEN : Uniform greyish-black with some shining squamose hairs particularly at anterior end. LEGS : Yellow-brown to brown, suffused in parts (particularly on femora) with black streaks and markings. MALE PALP : Text-fig. 106, B, F ; brown with femur and tarsus suffused with black, but rather lighter in colour than in *H. cupreus;* the femoral apophysis is bifid ; the stylus of the palpal organs is on the inner side.

OCCURRENCE : Found commonly in the same situations as *H. cupreus*. Adult in spring and summer, and generally distributed.

Heliophanus expers (O. P.-Cambridge).
(Text-fig. 106, C, D)

Salticus expers O. P.-Cambridge, 1871, p. 401. *Heliophanus expers* idem, 1879–81, p. 396. ? *H. viriatus* E. Simon, 1868, p. 686 ; 1937, pp. 1166, 1167.

DESCRIPTION. LENGTH : ♂ : 4 mm. The ♀ is not known.

♂ : CARAPACE : Dark, rich black, with the head shining black with a metallic sheen ; it is rugose and has some white hairs at the edges and sides. ABDOMEN : Black with a line of shining white squamose hairs around the anterior and sides, and with two longitudinal rows of white squamose hairs. LEGS : Dark brown suffused with considerable black, particularly on femora. MALE PALP : Text-fig. 106, C, D, dark brown suffused with some black ; the femoral apophysis is bifid at the tip, transverse to the segment, and there is a second small apophysis ; the palpal organs have the stylus more or less central, and there is only one small tibial apophysis instead of two as in the other species.

OCCURRENCE : This is an exceedingly rare species, the only specimen known having been taken at Bloxworth (Dorset) in 1870.

3. Genus **MARPISSA** C. L. Koch 1846 (1).

CHARACTERS OF GENUS. The two members of this genus are fairly large, of rather flattened form, and handsomely marked (Text-fig. 103). CARAPACE : Rather oval. EYES : The ocular trapezium is about 1·5 times broader than long, parallel-sided. CHELICERÆ : With one tooth on inner margin and two on outer margin. STERNUM : Greatly narrowed in front (Text-fig. 107, C). The two species can be distinguished by their genitalia, patterns and habitats.

Marpissa muscosa (Clerck).
(= *M. rumpfi* (Scopoli))
(Text-fig. 107, B, D)

Araneus muscosus C. Clerck, 1757, p. 116. *A. rumpfi* J. A. Scopoli, 1763, p. 401. *Salticus tardigradus* J. Blackwall, 1861–4, p. 63. *Marpessa muscosa* O. P.-Cambridge, 1879–81, p. 554. *Marptusa muscosa* C. Chyzer and L. Kulczynski, 1891–7, I, p. 15. *Marpissa muscosa* E. Simon, 1937, p. 1207. *M. rumpfi* F. Dahl, 1926, p. 40 ; A. Tullgren, 1944, p. 45.

DESCRIPTION. LENGTH : ♀ : 8 mm. ♂ : 8 mm.

♀ : CARAPACE : The head is mainly black, particularly round the eyes, and rugose ; the thorax is a deep reddish-brown, and the whole is clothed fairly thickly with white and black hairs. ABDOMEN : Blackish with a central pattern composed of angular whitish chevrons ; anteriorly it is spotted with white and reddish-brown. STERNUM : Yellowish to brown and mottled with black ; clothed with numerous fine white hairs. LEGS : Legs I are stout and massive, dark reddish brown or brown with tarsi paler ; the remainder are brown to yellow-brown, with legs III and IV sometimes faintly annulated with black. EPIGYNE : Text-fig. 107, D, thickly covered with white hairs.

♂ : CARAPACE : The head is shiny black and rugose, and clothed with some white hairs ; behind the head, on either side, are two roughly circular orange-brown areas ; the remainder is black, clothed with black and white hairs. ABDOMEN : Has a pretty pattern composed of light and dark markings. STERNUM : Dark-brown clothed with numerous white hairs. LEGS : The femora are dark brown to black ; the remaining parts are yellow-brown to brown, suffused with longitudinal black bars and spots, and annulated with black in places. MALE PALP : Text-fig. 107, B, dark brown ; the tarsus is large and rounded, and the palpal organs are relatively complex.

OCCURRENCE : This species has a flattened form and lives beneath the loose bark on trees, posts, etc. (*e.g.*, hop poles in Kent) in the southern counties, It is a striking and handsome species, particularly the ♂. It is uncommon, and is adult in April.

P

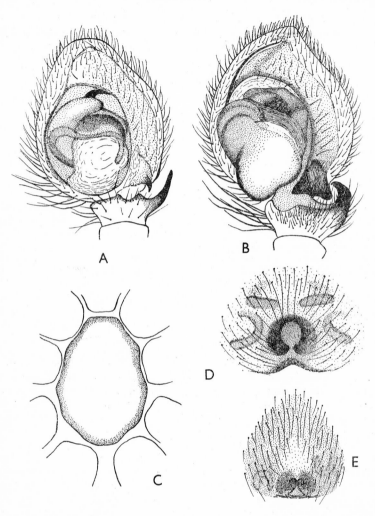

Text-fig. 107.—Male palps (below): A, *Marpissa pomatia;* B, *M. muscosa.* Epigynes: D, *M. muscosa;* E, *M. pomatia.* C, Sternum: *Marpissa.*

Marpissa pomatia (Walckenaer).
(Text-figs. 103 ; 107, A, E)

Aranea pomatia C. A. Walckenaer, 1802, p. 244. *Salticus blackwalli* et ♀ *promptus* J. Blackwall, 1861–4, pp. 59, 62. *Marpessa pomatia* O. P.-Cambridge, 1879–81, p. 555. *Marptusa pomatia* C. Chyzer and L. Kulczynski, 1891–7, I, p. 16. *Marpissa pomatia* E. Simon, 1937, p. 1208.

DESCRIPTION. LENGTH : ♀: 8–10 mm. ♂ : 6–7 mm.

♀ : CARAPACE : The head is deep black with a metallic lustre, and is clothed with a number of long, black hairs and numerous short white ones ; the thorax is orange-brown with the fovea black, from which radiate a number of broken black lines, and is also clothed with black and white hairs. ABDOMEN : Yellow-brown thickly spotted with black, with a central yellow-brown dentated band, narrowed in front and with an irregular black margin ; there is, however, some variation in the abdominal pattern. STERNUM : Pale yellow-brown thickly margined with black. LEGS : Yellow-brown, not annulated, but with tibiæ and metatarsi of legs I (in particular) spotted and marked with black. EPIGYNE : Text-fig. 107, E : somewhat variable in appearance, and clothed with long, white hairs.

♂ : CARAPACE : Similar to that of ♀ but with thorax more heavily marked with black. ABDOMEN : A uniform blackish colour. EYES : Anteriors fringed with longish white hairs. STERNUM : Like that of ♀. LEGS : Yellow-brown, heavily marked and streaked with black ; tibiæ I and metatarsi I in particular are heavily blackened, and femora I are darkened and have a metallic sheen. MALE PALP : Text-fig. 107, A, yellow-brown spotted with black ; the tarsus is large and rounded.

OCCURRENCE : This handsome spider has occurred in two or three localities only (Dorset, Cambridgeshire and Lancashire) ; it is common in Wicken Fen (Cambridgeshire), where it is found in the heads of *Phragmites*, but also amongst low vegetation. It is adult in May and June.

4. Genus **BIANOR** G. and E. Peckham 1885.

CHARACTERS OF GENUS. There is a single British species. CARAPACE : Only slightly longer than broad. EYES : Ocular trapezium is about one-third wider behind than in front. CHELICERÆ : One tooth on inner margin and two on outer margin.

Bianor ænescens (Simon).
(Text-fig. 108, F, G, H, I)

Attus œnescens E. Simon, 1868, p. 628. *Oedipus œnescens* C. Chyzer and L. Kulczynski, 1891–7, I, p. 46. *Bianor œnescens* A. R. Jackson, 1908, p. 13 ; E. Simon, 1937, p. 1219. *B. aurocinctus* F. Dahl, 1926, p. 34 ; A. Tullgren, 1944, p. 33.

DESCRIPTION. LENGTH : ♀: 4 mm. ♂ : 3·5 mm. The spider has a dull metallic appearance in nature.

♀ : CARAPACE : The head is dark brownish-black with a metallic lustre ; the thorax is brown ; the whole is clothed fairly thickly with whitish and black hairs. ABDOMEN : Almost uniform grey with no pattern, and is thickly covered with squamose hairs. STERNUM : Brown with a slight metallic lustre. LEGS : Femora and tibiæ of legs I are massive and swollen, as in the ♂ but rather less so, and brown in colour ; metatarsi and tarsi I are yellow ; the remaining legs are yellow with the femora suffused with black. EPIGYNE : Text-fig. 108, I.

♂ : CARAPACE : Shiny black shading to dark brown posteriorly ; at times it is entirely dark brown except around the eyes where it is black ; it is clothed with metallic shining squamose hairs, and is very rugose or even pitted. ABDOMEN : Black with a few paler spots and chevrons towards the rear ; it is clothed with squamose and normal hairs. LEGS : Femora I are dark blackish-brown, with the patellæ, tibiæ and metatarsi a rich brown and the tarsi blackish-brown ; femora and tibiæ I are massive and swollen, and tibiæ and patellæ I in particular are armed thickly beneath with thick black coarse plumose hairs (Text-fig. 108, F) ; the remaining legs are yellow-brown. MALE PALP : Text-fig. 108, G, H, dark brown.

OCCURRENCE : This very squat, dark-coloured species has occurred in a few localities only, viz., in Isle of Wight, Surrey, Gloucestershire, and Lancashire. It is found amongst heather or short grass, etc., and is adult in spring, summer and autumn.

5. Genus **HYCTIA** E. Simon 1876.

CHARACTERS OF GENUS. The single British species is long and narrow, with legs I massive. STERNUM : Greatly narrowed in front.

Hyctia nivoyi (Lucas).
(Text-fig. 108, A, B)

Salticus nivoyi H. Lucas, 1846, p. 183. *Hyctia nivoyi* O. P.-Cambridge, 1879–81, p. 560 ; C. Chyzer and L. Kulczynski, 1891–7, I, p. 15 ; E. Simon, 1937, p. 1212.

DESCRIPTION. LENGTH : ♀ : 4–6 mm. ♂ : 4–5 mm.

♀ : CARAPACE : Orange-brown, with darker brown sides and fovea ; the area around the eyes is suffused with black ; the head in particular is very rugose and clothed with short, white hairs and a few black ones ; the carapace is nearly twice as long as broad. ABDOMEN : Yellow to yellow-brown with three longitudinal rows of dark spots or a central black line and a row of black blotches on either side ; the sides are black ; it is about three times as long as broad, and clothed with very fine hairs. STERNUM : About twice as long as its widest part, much narrowed anteriorly with coxæ I nearly touching. LEGS : Femora I are very swollen, and tibiæ I are also somewhat swollen, the whole leg being very massive, a dark reddish-brown in colour ; the remaining legs are normal, yellow to yellow-brown with a few dark spots. EPIGYNE : Text-fig. 108, B, is rather indefinite and variable in appearance.

♂ : CARAPACE : Similar in colour to the ♀, but a darker reddish-brown with the eyes surrounded with black and the sides practically black ; there are tufts of white hairs behind the anterior eyes ; it is very rugose, and nearly twice as long as broad. ABDOMEN : Long and narrow ; yellow to brownish with a central black line, with the sides black and some black chevrons posteriorly ; it is clothed with white and black hairs. STERNUM : Long, as in ♀ ; yellow reticulated with black, or all black. LEGS : The first pair are very massive, as in ♀ ;

they are dark brown with a metallic sheen except for the tarsi and the apices of the metatarsi which are yellow ; the remaining legs are yellow to yellow-brown, suffused and annulated with black. MALE PALP : Text-fig. 108, A, dark brown to blackish with the tarsus practically black.

This is a thin, narrow-bodied spider, and its massive front legs make it readily identifiable. It is almost unable to leap, but when disturbed runs rapidly backwards with its anterior legs extended in front of the head, somewhat resembling a large chelifer.

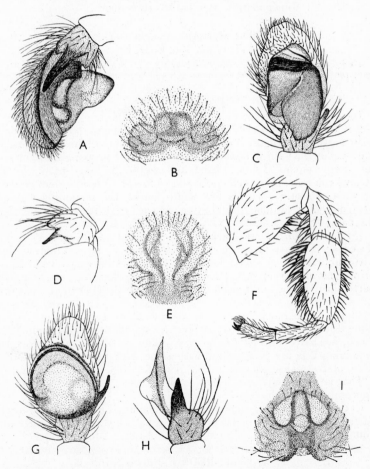

TEXT-FIG. 108.—Male palps : A, *Hyctia nivoyi* (side) ; C, *Ballus depressus* (below) ; D, do. tibia (side) ; G, *Bianor œnescens* (below) ; H , do. (side). Epigynes : B, *Hyctia nivoyi* ; E, *Ballus depressus* ; I, *Bianor œnescens*. F, *Bianor œnescens*. Leg I of male.

OCCURRENCE : A rare species, occurring in marshy areas and on sand-hills. Rather southern in distribution, no records existing further north than Yorkshire.

6. Genus **BALLUS** C. L. Koch 1850.

CHARACTERS OF GENUS. There is a single British species, which has a somewhat flattened form. CARAPACE : Rather flat, with highest point just behind the eyes. EYES : Ocular trapezium about twice as broad as long, and about 1·25 times as broad behind as in front. CHELICERÆ : Inner margin with two to three teeth.

Ballus depressus (Walckenaer).
(Text-fig. 108, C, D, E)

Aranea depressa C. A. Walckenaer, 1802, p. 242 (♀). *Salticus obscurus* (♂) J. Black-wall, 1861–4, p. 53. *Ballus depressus* O. P.-Cambridge, 1879–81, p. 399 ; C. Chyzer and L. Kulczynski, 1891–7, I, p. 47 ; F. Dahl, 1926, p. 34 ; E. Simon, 1937, p. 1149 ; A. Tullgren, 1944, p. 32.

DESCRIPTION. LENGTH : ♀ : 5 mm.   ♂ : 4 mm.
♀ : CARAPACE : Dark blackish-brown becoming rather less dark posteriorly, very rugose ; clothed with some white hairs. ABDOMEN : Pale yellowish with a broad red-brown central marking and sides of the same colour. LEGS : Tarsi and metatarsi I are pale whitish-yellow, the remaining segments being suffused with considerable dark brown and clothed with a few white hairs ; the remaining legs are whitish-yellow, annulated and streaked with dark brown, particularly the basal segments. EPIGYNE : Text-fig. 108, E.
♂ : CARAPACE : Dark blackish-brown, shading to deep black round the eyes ; it is extremely rugose and has a metallic sheen, and is clothed with only a few very short, fine hairs. ABDOMEN : Very dark reddish-brown, becoming somewhat less dark posteriorly ; it is rather rugose particularly at the anterior end, and there is little trace of any pattern. LEGS : Femora I (seen from the side) are very wide and swollen, dark brown to black in colour ; patellæ I are rather paler brown ; tibiæ I are blackish-brown to black, very swollen with a metallic sheen, in sharp contrast to the pale yellow metatarsi and tarsi ; the remaining legs are pale yellow with some dark brown spots, annula-tions and streaks. MALE PALP : Text-fig. 108, C, D, dark brown.
This is a squat, short-legged spider ; the ♂ is very different in appearance from the ♀.
OCCURRENCE : Fairly common in wooded areas in the more southern parts of the country, being obtained usually by beating bushes and young trees (particularly young oaks). Adult in May to July.

7. Genus **NEON** E. Simon 1876.

CHARACTERS OF GENUS. CARAPACE : The head is distinctly longer than the thorax. EYES : The ocular trapezium is about 1·25 times as broad as long. CLYPEUS : Narrow, only about one-quarter of diameter of anterior median eyes. LEGS : Short, with only a few weak spines on posterior legs. The two British species are small, and can be separated with certainty only by their genitalia, although *N. valentulus* is normally darker-coloured than *N. reticulatus*.

Neon reticulatus (Blackwall).
(Text-fig. 109, C, F)

Salticus reticulatus J. Blackwall, 1853, p. 14 ; 1861–4, p. 60. *Neon reticulatus* O. P.-Cambridge, 1879–81, p. 404 ; C. Chyzer and L. Kulczynski, 1891–7, I, p. 45 ; W. Falconer, 1912, p. 323 ; F. Dahl, 1926, p. 38 ; E. Simon, 1937, p. 1184 ; A. Tullgren, 1944, p. 40.

DESCRIPTION. LENGTH : ♀ : 2–3 mm. ♂ : 2–2·5 mm.

♀ : CARAPACE : Yellow-brown becoming slightly darker posteriorly ; the eyes are surrounded thickly with black ; it has few hairs. ABDOMEN : Pale whitish-yellow reticulated with black, and with a number of black chevrons becoming more distinct posteriorly. LEGS : Pale yellow-brown, the anteriors being annulated and suffused with black. EPIGYNE : Text-fig. 109, C, is closely similar to that of *N. valentulus*, but the relative proportions of the parts are different.

♂ : This is much darker than the ♀, with a metallic sheen when freshly caught. CARAPACE : Like that of ♀, but pale yellow with the black margins around the eyes more pronounced, and with the ocular area, sides and radiating striæ suffused with black. ABDOMEN : Resembles that of ♀, but the reticulated appearance is more pronounced, with more black margins. STERNUM : Yellow, edged with black. LEGS : Femora I and patellæ I are yellow, suffused with much black ; tibiæ I are black with a metallic sheen ; metatarsi I are blackish, while tarsi I are white ; the remaining legs are pale yellow, reticulated and faintly annulated with black. MALE PALP : Text-fig. 109, F, brown, suffused and reticulated with some black ; the palpal organs are closely similar to those of the next species, and the differences are best seen from the inner side.

OCCURRENCE : This little spider is common in the detritus of woods, in the north as well as the south of the country. It appears to be adult at most seasons.

Neon valentulus Falconer.
(Text-fig. 109, D, G)

Neon valentulus W. Falconer, 1912, p. 321 ; A. Tullgren, 1944, p. 41.

DESCRIPTION. LENGTH : ♀ : 2–2·5 mm. ♂ : 2–2·5 mm.

♀ : This resembles *N. reticulatus* in appearance, but is darker. It differs from that species in having LEGS I black except for the tarsi which are very pale yellow, suffused with some black at the bases, and the coxæ which are also pale yellow ; also in having the remaining legs heavily annulated in black. PALP : Suffused with much black. EPIGYNE : Text-fig. 109, D.

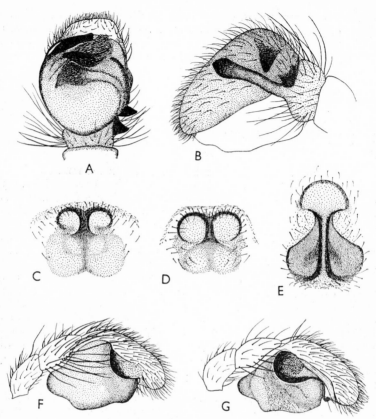

TEXT-FIG. 109.—Male palps : A, *Pellenes tripunctatus* (below) ; B, do. (side) ;
F, *Neon reticulatus* (inside) ; G, *Neon valentulus* (inside).
Epigynes : C, *Neon reticulatus;* D, *N. valentulus;* E, *Pellenes tripunctatus.*

♂ : This is very like *N. reticulatus,* but is darker, differing in the
following points : LEGS : I are almost wholly sooty black with only
the tips of the tarsi white ; the remaining legs are heavily suffused
with black, the tips of tarsi II being white. STERNUM : Heavily
reticulated with black. MALE PALP : Text-fig. 109, G, sooty black.

OCCURRENCE : This species has occurred only in Wicken and
Chippenham Fens (Cambridgeshire), where it is not uncommon at
times amongst detritus, grass, etc. It is adult in May and June.

8. Genus **EUOPHRYS** C. L. Koch 1834.

CHARACTERS OF GENUS. Small spiders, often of speckled appearance.
CARAPACE : Thorax longer than head. EYES : Ocular trapezium
twice as broad as long, and parallel-sided. CHELICERÆ : With one

tooth on inner margin and two smaller ones on outer margin. LEGS :
With strong spines ventrally ; tarsi I–III have one long trichobothrium dorsally, while tarsi IV have two. The species can be
separated readily by their colour and genitalia.

Euophrys frontalis (Walckenaer).
(Text-figs. 110, A, D ; 111, B)

Aranea frontalis C. A. Walckenaer, 1802, p. 246. *Salticus frontalis* J. Blackwall,
1861–4, p. 52. *Euophrys frontalis* O. P.-Cambridge, 1879–81, p. 403 ; C. Chyzer and
L. Kulczynski, 1891–7, I, p. 43 ; E. Simon, 1937, pp. 1172, 1176. *E. maculata* F. Dahl,
1926, p. 35 ; A. Tullgren, 1944, p. 35.

DESCRIPTION. LENGTH : ♀ : 3–5 mm. ♂ : 2–3 mm.

♀ : CARAPACE : Yellow-brown, with the head suffused with black
and with a metallic lustre, and the whole clothed with numerous
fine hairs. EYES : Anteriors are fringed with white hairs. ABDOMEN :
Pale whitish-yellow with longitudinal rows of black blotches. STERNUM :
Pale whitish-yellow, clothed with numerous hairs. LEGS and PALP :
Yellow-brown, not annulated. EPIGYNE : Text-fig. 111, B.

♂ : CARAPACE : Dark yellow-brown, with the head deep black
with a metallic lustre ; the whole is clothed with black and white
hairs. EYES : Anteriors fringed with vivid orange hairs. ABDOMEN :
Yellow-brown with a central row of black chevrons and irregular black
bands on either side. LEGS : Tarsi I contrast sharply with the rest
of legs I, being white and clothed with white hairs ; metatarsi I are
deep black, tibiæ are olive-black, the remainder shading off gradually
to coxæ I which are olive-green ; the dark-coloured segments, particularly the femora, have a deep bluish-green metallic sheen by
reflected light ; the remaining legs are yellow-brown except for
metatarsi II and tibiæ II which are darker and have a metallic sheen.
MALE PALP : Text-figs. 110, A, D ; the femur is dark brown to black,
the remaining segments being yellow-brown ; the patella and tibia
are thickly clothed with long, stout, white hairs on the inside and
above ; the tibia has a long, thin, light-coloured apophysis on the
outer side.

OCCURRENCE : Common, of widespread occurrence in grass, low
undergrowth, etc. Adult during spring and early summer.

Euophrys molesta O. P.-Cambridge.
(Text-fig. 111, D)

Euophrys molesta O. P.-Cambridge, 1912, p. 93. *? E. herbigrada*, E. Simon, 1937, pp.
1175, 1177, 1252.

DESCRIPTION. LENGTH : ♀ : 3–3·5 mm. ♂ : 2·5 mm. This
species closely resembles *E. frontalis*.

♀ : CARAPACE : The head is shiny black, sharply defined, and
indented at the fovea, with a metallic hue ; the thorax is a rich brown
or dark brown ; the whole is clothed with long white hairs and some
black ones. CLYPEUS : Has numerous white hairs. EYES : Anteriors

are fringed with white hairs. ABDOMEN : Whitish-yellow with a mottled pattern of black, much more sharply defined than in *E. frontalis;* it is clothed with long black hairs. STERNUM : Pale yellow with a blackish margin. LEGS : Yellow-brown with no (or only very indistinct) annulations. PALP : Pale yellow. EPIGYNE : Text-fig. 111, D, very similar to *E. frontalis*, but is distinguishable in the examples seen. This sex can be distinguished from *E. frontalis*, which it resembles closely, by the more pronounced abdominal pattern, the black head with the indentation (notch) at the fovea, and (less readily) by the epigyne.

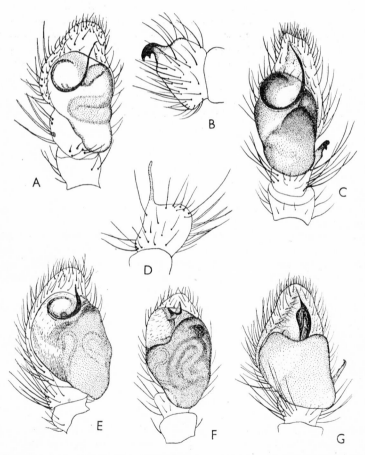

TEXT-FIG. 110.—Male palps : A, *Euophrys frontalis* (below) ; D, do. tibia (above and to outside) ; B, *E. lanigera*, tibia (side) ; C, do. (below) ; E, *E. petrensis* (below) ; F, *E. æquipes* (below) ; G, *E. erratica* (below).

♂ : CARAPACE : The head is a deep shining black, with an indentation at the fovea as in the ♀ ; the remainder is very dark brown, shading to black at the rear and sides ; the whole is clothed with a few black hairs. EYES : The anteriors are not fringed noticeably with hairs. ABDOMEN : Black, with two longitudinal rows of white spots or bars. STERNUM : Black with many whitish hairs. LEGS : Legs I are dark brown except for the tarsi which are yellow-brown ; femora I and tibiæ I are thickly clothed beneath with squamose hairs ; the remaining legs are also dark except for the tarsi which are yellow-brown. MALE PALP : Pale yellow with the femur and coxa suffused with blackish ; there is no thick cluster of white hairs on the tibia as in *E. frontalis;* there is no tibial apophysis ; the palpal organs appear to be practically identical with those of *E. frontalis.* This sex differs from *E. frontalis* in the abdominal pattern, the pronounced indentation in the black pattern of the head, in the absence of orange hairs round the anterior eyes, and in the absence of long white hairs and the tibial apophysis on the palps.

OCCURRENCE : It is of very local occurrence, having been taken only at Whitsand Bay (Cornwall) and Mewstone and Plymouth (Devon). Adult in summer.

Euophrys petrensis C. L. Koch.
(Text-figs. 110, E ; 111, C)

Euophrys petrensis C. L. Koch, 1837, p. 34 ; O. P.-Cambridge, 1879–81, p. 406 ; F. Dahl, 1926, p. 37 ; E. Simon, 1937, p. 1181 ; A. Tullgren, 1944, p. 36.

DESCRIPTION. LENGTH : ♀ : 3 mm. ♂ : 3 mm.

♀ : CARAPACE : The head is black, with a metallic lustre, and the thorax is very dark brown. ABDOMEN : Greyish-black, with a few small whitish spots. STERNUM : Yellow-brown, mottled with black, and with numerous hairs. LEGS : Femora I are black with a metallic lustre, and the remaining femora are suffused with a good deal of black ; the remaining segments are yellowish-brown annulated with black. PALP : Clear pale yellow. EPIGYNE : Text-fig. 111, C.

♂ ; CARAPACE : Yellow-brown spotted with dark brown, with the head deep black. EYES : Anteriors fringed with orange hairs. ABDOMEN : Black, clothed with whitish hairs. LEGS : Legs I and II are dark brown to black, except for the tarsi and metatarsi which may be lighter ; the remaining legs have the femora black, the other segments being yellow annulated clearly with black. MALE PALP : Text-fig. 110, E; dark brown to black with the tarsus sometimes lighter; the tibia is furnished with many long glistening white hairs ; there is a tibial apophysis.

OCCURRENCE : Uncommon, except in certain localities in the south, *e.g.*, Beaulieu Heath (Hampshire), where it occurs on heather and other low vegetation. It has occurred on mountains in Cumberland at 2,500 ft. Adult April to June, the male vanishing usually by about mid-May.

Euophrys erratica (Walckenaer).
(Text-figs. 110, G ; 111, F)

Attus erratica C. A. Walckenaer, 1825, p. 46. *Salticus distinctus* J. Blackwall, 1861–4, p. 54. *Pseudeuophrys callida* F. Dahl, 1926, p. 38 ; A. Tullgren, 1944, p. 39. *Euophrys erratica* O. P.-Cambridge, 1879–81, p. 558 ; C. Chyzer and L. Kulczynski, 1891–7, I, p. 40 ; E. Simon, 1937, p. 1180.

DESCRIPTION. LENGTH : ♀ : 3–4 mm. ♂ : 3–4 mm.

♀ : CARAPACE : The head is black with a metallic hue, the black area being widely indented at the rear, rather as in *E. molesta;* the thorax is a rich brown ; the whole is clothed with long whitish hairs, there being a clump of white hairs in the fovea. EYES : Anteriors

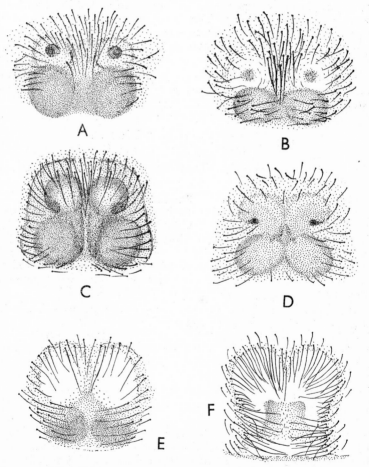

TEXT-FIG. 111.—Epigynes : A, *Euophrys æquipes;* B, *E. frontalis;* C, *E. petrensis;* D, *E. molesta;* E, *E. lanigera;* F, *E. erratica.*

are circled with whitish hairs. ABDOMEN : Blackish with a white bar across the anterior end, and followed by longitudinal rows of white spots and white chevrons. STERNUM : Yellow-brown, clothed with hairs. LEGS : Yellow to yellow-brown, the anteriors being very lightly annulated with darker brown, and the posteriors more strongly annulated with black. PALP : Pale whitish-yellow. EPIGYNE : Text-fig. 111, F, rather indistinct.

♂ : This is practically identical in colour with the ♀ ; the abdominal pattern is slightly more pronounced and the legs are less distinctly annulated. MALE PALP : Text-fig. 110, G, whitish-yellow with the tarsus brown.

OCCURRENCE : Found on walls, etc., and appears to be more common in northern England. Adult in May and June.

Euophrys æquipes (O. P.-Cambridge).
(Text-figs. 110, F ; 111, A)

Salticus æquipes O. P.-Cambridge, 1871, p. 399. *Euophrys æquipes* idem, 1879–81, p. 404 ; C. Chyzer and L. Kulczynski, 1891–7, p. 43 ; F. Dahl, 1926, p. 37 ; E. Simon, 1937, p. 1180 ; A. Tullgren, 1944, p. 37.

DESCRIPTION. LENGTH : ♀ : 2–3 mm. ♂ : 2 mm.

♀ : CARAPACE : The head is black with a metallic sheen and the thorax is yellow-brown ; the whole is clothed with black and white hairs. ABDOMEN : Blackish, with brownish spots and bars, and clothed with whitish hairs. STERNUM : Blackish with a small yellowish area in the centre. LEGS : Pale yellow, annulated sharply with black. PALP : Yellow. EPIGYNE : Text-fig. 111, A.

♂ : The general colour is very similar to the ♀. EYES : Anteriors are fringed with white hairs. ABDOMEN : Dull black. LEGS : Annulated as in the ♀, but femora I are darker with a slight metallic sheen. MALE PALP : Text-fig. 110. F, yellow, with no tibial apophysis.

OCCURRENCE : Uncommon, occurring only in the southern counties, on hot, sunny banks, and sandy places. It is rather small, yet leaps considerable distances. Adult during the summer months.

Euophrys lanigera (Simon).
(Text-figs. 110, B, C ; 111, E)

Attus laniger E. Simon, 1871, p. 171. *Euophrys lanigera*, idem, 1937, p. 1178 ; W. S. Bristowe, 1930, p. 352.

DESCRIPTION. LENGTH : ♀ : 4·5 mm. ♂ : 3·5–4 mm.

♀ : CARAPACE : The head is black, clothed with numerous white hairs ; the thorax is dark brownish-black with some white hairs, and a central row of white hairs. EYES : Anteriors fringed with white and a few orange hairs. ABDOMEN : Blackish-brown, with some paler chevrons anteriorly, followed by two light-coloured spots and more chevrons posteriorly ; it is clothed with black and whitish hairs, and there is a clump of white hairs at the front. STERNUM : Dark brown, with numerous hairs. LEGS : Brown to yellow-brown, heavily marked and streaked with dark brown or black ; femora I are almost completely dark brown. PALP : Pale yellow. EPIGYNE : Text-fig. 111, E.

♂ : CARAPACE : The head is black or practically black, with a metallic lustre, clothed with numerous white hairs ; the thorax is dark brown to black with a narrow yellowish central band clothed thickly with white hairs. EYES : Anteriors are fringed with a few whitish-orange hairs. ABDOMEN : Brown, with a pattern composed of two whitish parallel longitudinal bands opening out posteriorly, followed by whitish chevrons ; it is clothed with white and black hairs, and there is a clump of white hairs anteriorly. STERNUM : Dark brown with a metallic lustre, and with numerous hairs. LEGS : Legs I are dark brown to black with a metallic lustre, with the exception of the tarsi which are yellow-brown ; legs II–IV have the femora black or dark brown, with the remaining segments yellow-brown annulated and streaked considerably with dark brown. MALE PALP : Text-fig. 110, B, C, pale yellow with the tarsus suffused with some brown.

OCCURRENCE : Found only in or near habitations in a few localities in the southern part of the country, e.g. Devonshire, Hampshire, London ; usually on the inside walls of houses (though it also occurs outside). Adults seem to occur at most seasons.

9. Genus **SITTICUS** E. Simon 1901.

CHARACTERS OF GENUS. Dull-coloured spiders with numerous dark hairs, though often with a pretty abdominal pattern. CARAPACE : More elevated than in *Euophrys*. EYES : Ocular trapezium about twice as broad as long. CHELICERÆ : Outer margin with two to six teeth on a common tubercle ; inner margin without teeth. LEGS : IV much longer than III, with tibia IV nearly twice tibia III. One or both claws on tarsus IV with numerous minute teeth (cf. *Attulus*). The species can be separated by their genitalia (at times with difficulty), size and pattern.

Sitticus pubescens (Fabricius).
(Text-figs. 112, A ; 113, A)

Aranea pubescens J. C. Fabricius, 1775, p. 438. *Salticus sparsus* J. Blackwall, 1861–4, p. 49. *Attus pubescens* O. P.-Cambridge, 1879–81, p. 408 ; C. Chyzer and L. Kulczynski, 1891–7, I, p. 21. *Sitticus pubescens* E. Simon, 1937, p. 1186 ; B. J. Kaston, 1948, p. 460. *S. truncorum* F. Dahl, 1926, p. 30 ; A. Tullgren, 1944, p. 25.

DESCRIPTION. LENGTH : ♀ : 4–5 mm. ♂ : 4 mm.

♀ : CARAPACE : The head is black and the remainder dark brown suffused with black ; it is thickly clothed with coarse black hairs interspersed with some white ones. ABDOMEN : Blackish, thickly clothed with coarse black hairs interspersed with a few white ones ; there is an ill-defined pattern (sometimes more pronounced) of white spots and bars, due partly to white hairs. STERNUM : Yellowish, mottled with black, and clothed at the edges with long white hairs. LEGS : Brown, suffused and annulated with black. PALP : Brown to dark brown, suffused with some black. EPIGYNE : Text-fig. 113, A.

♂ : CARAPACE : Dark blackish-brown to black, with a metallic sheen in the ocular area ; it is clothed mainly with white hairs, but there are also a few coarse black ones. ABDOMEN : Like that of ♀. LEGS : Dark brown, the posterior ones suffused and annulated with black ; they are clothed with white hairs and a few black ones. MALE PALP : Text-fig. 112, A, dark brown, with the tarsus black ; clothed with some white hairs ; the tibia has a large black apophysis.

OCCURRENCE : On the interior walls, windows, etc., of buildings, and occasionally outside. Generally distributed and adult at all seasons.

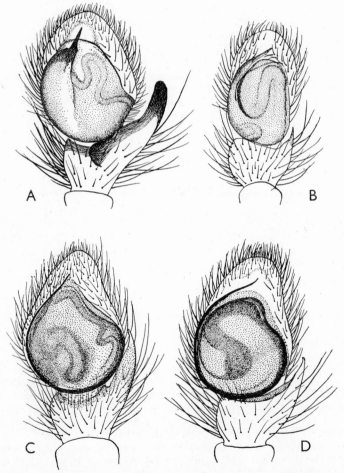

TEXT-FIG. 112.—Male palps (below) : A, *Sitticus pubescens;* B, *Attulus saltator;* C, *Sitticus rupicola;* D, *S. floricola.*

Sitticus caricis (Westring).
(Text-fig. 113, B)

Attus caricis N. Westring, 1861, p. 576 ; O. P.-Cambridge, 1879–81, p. 563 ; C. Chyzer and L. Kulczynski, 1891–7, I, p. 23.　*Dendryphantes hastatus* O. P.-Cambridge, 1885 (1), p. 11, and subsequently.　*Sitticus caricis* F. Dahl, 1926, p. 29 ; E. Simon, 1937, pp. 1190, 1193 ; A. Tullgren, 1944, p. 26.

DESCRIPTION.　LENGTH :　♀ : 3–3·5 mm.　♂ : 3 mm.

♀ : CARAPACE : Dark brown, shading to black on the head, which has a somewhat metallic tinge ; it is clothed with numerous black and white hairs.　EYES : Anteriors fringed with orange and black hairs. ABDOMEN : Dark-brownish, clothed with numerous black and brown hairs ; there is a very ill-defined pattern of paler chevrons posteriorly. STERNUM : Brown, with a few white hairs at the edges.　LEGS : Yellow-brown, with annulations absent or very ill-defined.　PALP : Yellow.　EPIGYNE : Text-fig. 113, B.

♂ : This is coloured like the ♀, but with the head a darker black and with fewer hairs.　PALP : Brown to dark brown ; the palpal organs seem to be practically identical in appearance with those of *S. rupicola*, but the present species is readily distinguished from the latter by its size and general appearance.

OCCURRENCE : Amongst grass, etc., in swamps, but uncommon. Adult in spring and autumn ; found only in the southern part of the country.

Sitticus floricola (C. L. Koch).
(Text-figs. 112, D ; 113, C)

Euophrys floricola C. L. Koch, 1837, p. 34.　*Sitticus floricola* E. Simon, 1937, pp. 1191, 1194.　*S. littoralis* F. Dahl, 1926, p. 33 ; A. Tullgren, 1944, p. 30.　*Attus floricola* C. Chyzer and L. Kulczynski, 1891–7, I, p. 22.

DESCRIPTION.　LENGTH :　♀ : 4·5–5 mm.　♂ : 4 mm.

♀ : CARAPACE : The head is black and the thorax dark brown ; it is clothed with black hairs and some white ones ; there is a small patch of white hairs in the fovea, a row of white hairs behind the anterior eyes, and the clypeus is clothed thickly with long white hairs.　EYES : Anteriors surrounded with white and a few orange hairs.　ABDOMEN : Blackish-brown with two very distinct white patches composed of white hairs about midway, and two pairs of smaller white patches in front of, and behind, respectively, these larger patches ; it is clothed with white hairs anteriorly and black hairs elsewhere.　STERNUM : Blackish, fringed with white hairs.　LEGS : Orange-brown, annulated with dark brown, and clothed with black and a few white hairs.　PALP : Yellow to yellow-brown, clothed fairly thickly with long white hairs. EPIGYNE :　Text-fig. 113, C, obscured by long white hairs.

♂ : CARAPACE : Rich reddish-brown, with the head darker with a slight metallic tinge, and black around the eyes ; it is clothed with some black hairs, and has a row of white hairs behind the anterior eyes and on the clypeus ; there are conspicuous patches of white hairs

between the posterior eyes, in the fovea, and at the sides. EYES :
Anteriors fringed with white and some orange hairs. ABDOMEN :
Like that of ♀. STERNUM : Rich brownish, with a margin of white
hairs. LEGS : Orange-brown suffused with brown on the femora.
MALE PALP : Text-fig. 112, D, orange-brown, thickly clothed with
white hairs above and on the inside of the tibia and patella ; the palpal
organs appear to be distinguishable from those of *S. rupicola* by the
arrangement of the convoluted seminal duct.

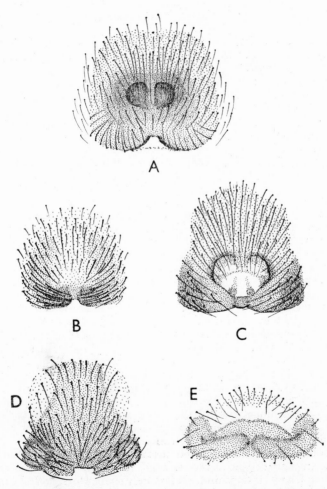

A

B

C

D   E

TEXT-FIG. 113.—Epigynes : A, *Sitticus pubescens;* B, *S. caricis;* C, *S. floricola;*
    D, *S. rupicola;* E, *Attulus saltator.*

R

OCCURRENCE : Hitherto found in one locality only, viz., in a swamp in Delamere Forest (Cheshire), where it is quite common. It is found adult in May-June, usually spun up in the white heads of the cotton-grass which grows at the edges of a swampy pond.

Sitticus rupicola (C. L. Koch).
(Text-figs. 112, C ; 113, D)

Euophrys rupicola C. L. Koch, 1837, p. 34. *Attus floricola* O. P.-Cambridge, 1879-81, p. 564. *A. mancus* idem, 1896, p. 62. *Sitticus rupicola* F. Dahl, 1926, p. 31 ; E. Simon, 1937, pp. 1192, 1194 ; A. Tullgren, 1944, p. 28. *Attus rupicola* C. Chyzer and L. Kulczynski, 1891-7, I, p. 23. (The identity of the spider we describe under this name is not absolutely certain, but we believe it to be referable to this species.)

DESCRIPTION. LENGTH : ♀: 7 mm. ♂: 4–5 mm. This species closely resembles *S. floricola* in general appearance and pattern, but is darker in colour.

♀: CARAPACE : The head is black with a metallic sheen, and the thorax is dark brown to black ; it is clothed with black hairs and some white ones ; there are bands of white hairs behind the anterior eyes and on the clypeus, but these are not so thick as in *S. floricola;* there is a patch of white hairs in the fovea. EYES : Anteriors fringed with white hairs and a few orange ones. ABDOMEN : Blackish, with a pretty pattern of whitish-grey (clothed with white hairs) similar to that of *S. floricola,* but with in addition a central row of chevrons and a broad band (not always very pronounced) around the front and sides. STERNUM : Dark brown, fringed with long white hairs. LEGS : Brown, annulated and suffused vaguely with black, clothed with black and some white hairs. PALP : Brown, suffused with some dark brown, clothed with long white hairs, but not quite so thickly as in *S. floricola.* EPIGYNE : Text-fig. 113, D, clothed with long whitish hairs.

♂: CARAPACE : Dark brown, with eyes surrounded thickly with black and with metallic sheen on head ; it is clothed with numerous black hairs, and has a row of white hairs behind the anterior eyes, and numerous white hairs at the sides ; there are two small areas of white hairs in central fovea. EYES : Anteriors are fringed with white and a few orange hairs. ABDOMEN : Black, with six clear white spots, composed of white hairs, disposed as in *S. floricola;* there are also some faintly-defined chevrons, and a narrow band of white hairs across the front. STERNUM : Dark brown, clothed with white hairs. LEGS : Dark brown, suffused with blackish, particularly on the femora. MALE PALP : Text-fig. 112, C, brown, with clumps of white hairs on the upper sides of the femur and patella, but fewer on the inner side than in *S. floricola;* the palpal organs seem to be indistinguishable from those of *S. caricis.*

OCCURRENCE : Has occurred in two localities only on the south coast, amongst shingle at the sea edge, viz., at Shoreham (Sussex) and Hayling Island (Hampshire). It is closely similar to *S. floricola*, but can be distinguished by its different habitat, by slight differences in the sexual organs and by its colour and pattern.

10. Genus **ATTULUS** E. Simon 1889.

CHARACTERS OF GENUS. The single British species differs from *Sitticus* as shown in the generic key. LEGS : Claws on tarsi IV with 3 or 4 stout teeth (cf. *Sitticus*).

Attulus saltator (Simon).
(Text-figs. 112, B ; 113, E)

Salticus floricola J. Blackwall, 1861–4, p. 55. *Attus saltator* E. Simon, 1868, p. 611 ;
O. P.-Cambridge, 1879–81, p. 410 ; C. Chyzer and L. Kulczynski, 1891–7, I, p. 26.
Attulus saltator E. Simon, 1937, p. 1199. *Sitticulus saltator* F. Dahl, 1926, p. 29 ;
A. Tullgren, 1944, p. 22.

DESCRIPTION. LENGTH : ♀ : 3·5–4 mm. ♂ : 3 mm.

♀ : CARAPACE : Brown to dark brown, shading practically to black anteriorly ; it is thickly clothed with long black hairs and some white ones, and there are some squamose hairs on the head. EYES : Anteriors are fringed with white hairs. ABDOMEN : Brown with an ill-defined pattern of whitish hairs ; thickly clothed with long black and white hairs. STERNUM : Yellow-brown, wide in front. LEGS : Yellow-brown with faint brown annulations, particularly on the posterior legs ; armed with very stout spines. PALP : Pale yellow. EPIGYNE : Text-fig. 113, E.

♂ : CARAPACE : Like that of the ♀ but with fewer hairs. EYES : Anteriors more thickly fringed with hairs than the ♀. ABDOMEN : Like that of ♀ but with more white hairs. LEGS : As ♀. PALP : Text-fig. 112, B, pale whitish-yellow, clothed thickly with white hairs.

OCCURRENCE : Found exclusively on sandhills and in sandy areas, where its colour harmonises with its surroundings. It leaps considerable distances. It has been taken mainly in the southern half of England (but also as far north as Lancashire), and does not appear to be very common. Adult in May–June.

11. Genus **EVARCHA** E. Simon 1902.

CHARACTERS OF GENUS. The two members of this genus are handsome spiders of moderate size. They have powerful legs subequal in length. EYES : The ocular trapezium is not quite twice as broad as long. CLYPEUS : About one-half the width of the diameter of the anterior central eyes. CHELICERÆ : Inner margin with a simple tooth (cf. *Hasarius*).

Evarcha falcata (Clerck).
(= *E. blancardi* (Scopoli))
(Text-fig. 114, A, C, E)

Araneus falcatus and *flammatus* C. Clerck, 1757, pp. 124–5. *A. blancardi* J. A. Scopoli,
1763, p. 402. *Salticus coronatus* J. Blackwall, 1861–4, p. 50. *Hasarius falcatus*
O. P.-Cambridge, 1879–81, p. 412. *Ergane falcata* C. Chyzer and L. Kulczynski,
1891–7, I, p. 37. *Evarcha blancardi* F. Dahl, 1926, p. 50 ; A. Tullgren, 1944, p. 61.
E. flammata E. Simon, 1937, pp. 1240–1.

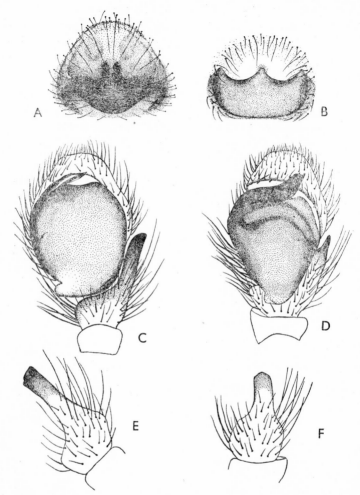

TEXT-FIG. 114.—*Epigynes:* A, *Evarcha falcata;* B, *E. arcuata.*
Male palps : C, *Evarcha falcata* (below) ; E, do., tibia (side and above) ;
D, *E. arcuata* (below) ; F, do., tibia (side and above).

DESCRIPTION. LENGTH : ♀ : **7 mm.** ♂ : **5 mm.**
♀ : CARAPACE : The head is black and furnished with shining metallic squamose hairs ; the thorax is dark brown to brown, becoming black posteriorly, and clothed with some white and black hairs. EYES : Anteriors are fringed with some yellowish or whitish hairs. ABDOMEN : Greyish with some vague lighter spots and chevrons ; clothed with some prone whitish hairs and some long black hairs. STERNUM :

Yellow-brown to dark brown, clothed with fine hairs. LEGS : Yellow to dark brown with no appreciable annulations ; legs I rather darker in colour than the remainder. EPIGYNE : Text-fig. 114, A.

♂ : CARAPACE : The head is a brilliant black with a metallic sheen, thickly clothed with prone shining hairs ; the thorax is dark brown becoming black posteriorly and is clothed with stout black hairs ; there are some white hairs, particularly at the sides. EYES : Anteriors fringed with whitish to yellow hairs. ABDOMEN : Encircled with shining white hairs, inside which on either side are two longitudinal black bands reaching almost to the spinners and clothed with black hairs ; centrally there is a grey band with some reddish-brown spots and chevrons, and clothed with greyish hairs. STERNUM : Brown with some white hairs. LEGS : Legs I have the femora massive, dark brown to black in colour and clothed with a few white hairs ; the remaining segments of legs I are dark brown except for the tarsi which are yellow ; the femora of the remaining legs are very dark, with the remaining segments yellow to brown. MALE PALP : Text-fig. 114, C, E, brown, clothed with white hairs.

OCCURRENCE : Fairly common in wooded areas, where it can be obtained by sweeping and beating the low vegetation, and is often to be seen leaping from plant to plant. Widespread ; adult in May to July.

Evarcha arcuata (Clerck).
(= E. marcgravii (Scopoli))
(Text-fig. 114, B, D, F)

Araneus arcuatus C. Clerck, 1757, p. 125. *A. marcgravii* J. A. Scopoli, 1763, p. 401. *Hasarius arcuatus* O. P.-Cambridge, 1879–81, p. 565. *Ergane arcuata* C. Chyzer and L. Kulczynski. 1891–7, I, p. 37. *Evarcha arcuata* E. Simon, 1937, pp. 1238, 1241. *E. marcgravii* F. Dahl, 1926, p. 51 ; A. Tullgren, 1944, p. 62.

DESCRIPTION. LENGTH : ♀ : 7 mm. ♂ : 5–6 mm.

♀ : CARAPACE : The head is shiny black, clothed with some shining hairs ; the thorax is brown to dark brown, clothed with coarse black hairs and prone pale coloured squamose hairs. ABDOMEN : Yellowish-grey with an ill-defined blackish pattern (clearer than in *E. falcata*) of chevrons and spots ; it is clothed with black hairs and prone whitish hairs. STERNUM : Yellow with a blackish centre. LEGS : Yellow-brown with no annulations. EPIGYNE : Text-fig. 114, B.

♂ : CARAPACE : The head is black with a metallic lustre ; the thorax is dark brown shading to black posteriorly and at the sides ; the whole is clothed with hairs as in ♀. EYES : Anteriors fringed with whitish hairs. ABDOMEN : Almost unicolorous, a blackish-grey, with some shining hairs and some coarse black ones. STERNUM : Dark brown clothed with white hairs. LEGS : Femora I are enlarged and dark blackish-brown in colour ; tibiæ I are somewhat thickened and almost black, while metatarsi and tarsi I are yellow suffused with brown ; the remaining legs have the femora dark brown and the other segments brown to yellow-brown suffused with darker brown but not annulated.

MALE PALP : Text-fig. 114, D, F, dark brown suffused with black
the tibia is furnished with some white hairs.

OCCURRENCE : Found in the more southern counties only (commonly
in some localities) on heather and low vegetation. Adult in summer.

12. Genus ÆLURILLUS E. Simon 1884.

CHARACTERS OF GENUS. The single British species is handsomely
marked. CARAPACE : High and broad, with head appreciably shorter
than thorax. CLYPEUS : Almost as wide as the diameter of the anterior
central eyes. EYES : Ocular trapezium about 1·5 times as broad as
long, parallel-sided. LEGS : Tarsi with scopulæ ; legs IV longer than
legs III.

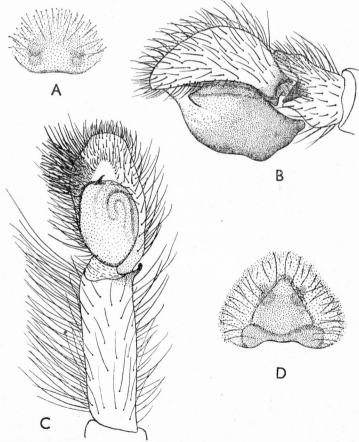

TEXT-FIG. 115.—Epigynes : A, *Hasarius adansoni;* D, *Aelurillus v-insignitus.*
Male palps : B, *Aelurillus v-insignitus* (side) ; C, *Hasarius adansoni* (below).

Ælurillus v-insignitus (Clerck).
(=Æ. insignitus (Olivier))
(Text-fig. 115, B, D)

Araneus littera v-insignitus C. Clerck, 1757, p. 121. *A. insignita* A. G. Olivier, 1789, p. 220. *Ælurops v-insignitus* O. P.-Cambridge, 1879–81, p. 416. *Ælurillus littera-v-notatus* Dahl, 1926, p. 48. *Æ. insignitus* A. Tullgren, 1944, p. 58. *Æ. v-insignitus* C. Chyzer and L. Kulczynski, 1891–7, I, p. 29 ; E. Simon, 1937, p. 1227.

DESCRIPTION. LENGTH : ♀ : 6–7 mm. ♂ : 4–5 mm.

♀ : CARAPACE : Black, heavily clothed with coarse black hairs and white squamose hairs. EYES : Anteriors fringed with white, black and orange hairs. ABDOMEN : Black, heavily clothed with coarse black hairs, and shining white hairs which form an ill-defined pattern of spots and chevrons ; the abdomen is only slightly longer than the carapace, giving the spider a squat appearance. STERNUM : Blackish, fringed with numerous white hairs, and narrowed in front. LEGS : Yellow-brown with blackish annulations and spots, heavily clothed with coarse black hairs and some white ones ; tarsi I have scopulæ extending to more than one-half of their length. PALP : Yellow-brown. EPIGYNE : Text-fig. 115, D.

♂ : CARAPACE : The head is black, with the remainder very dark brown, the whole having a metallic sheen ; it is clothed with coarse black hairs and some white hairs ; there is a white inverted V in the head area. EYES : Anteriors fringed with white and black hairs. ABDOMEN : Blackish, clothed with black hairs, with a well-defined central band of shining white hairs. STERNUM : Like that of ♀. LEGS : Like those of ♀ but somewhat darker. MALE PALP : Text-fig. 115, B, brown, thickly clothed on upper side with pale yellow or whitish hairs.

OCCURRENCE : Uncommon, occurring only in the southern counties, amongst low undergrowth on heaths. Adult in spring and summer.

13. Genus PHLEGRA E. Simon 1876.

CHARACTERS OF GENUS. The single British species has a clear and definite pattern in ♀. CLYPEUS : Almost as wide as the diameter of the anterior median eyes. EYES : Ocular trapezium nearly twice as broad as long. CHELICERÆ : Have two dissimilar teeth on outer margin and a relatively long tooth on inner margin. LEGS : Tarsi with scopulæ ; legs III longer than legs IV.

Phlegra fasciata (Hahn).
(Text-fig. 117, A, B)

Attus fasciatus C. W. Hahn, 1826, p. 182. *Phlegra fasciata* O. P.-Cambridge, 1879–81, p. 414 ; C. Chyzer and L. Kulczynski, 1891–7, I, p. 33 ; F. Dahl, 1926, p. 27 ; E. Simon, 1937, pp. 1222, 1224 ; A. Tullgren, 1944, p. 21 ; B. J. Kaston, 1948, p. 460.

DESCRIPTION. LENGTH : ♀ : 6–7 mm. ♂ : 5–6 mm.

♀ : CARAPACE : The head is dark brownish-black ; the remainder is reddish-brown, with two paler stripes furnished with white hairs running backwards from the posterior eyes ; the whole is clothed with black hairs, and some white squamose hairs on the head ; the clypeus is clothed with long white hairs. ABDOMEN : Whitish with two broad brown longitudinal stripes running the whole length, becoming narrower behind ; it is clothed thickly with white hairs and some brown hairs. STERNUM: Yellow-brown clothed with white and brown hairs. LEGS : Stout, orange-brown to yellow-brown, legs I and II being furnished with well-defined scopulæ extending to one-half or more of the length of the tarsi. PALP : Orange-brown. EPIGYNE : Text-fig. 117, B.

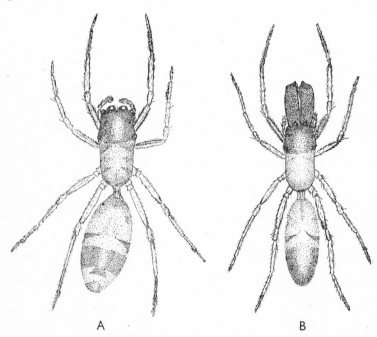

A   B

TEXT-FIG. 116.—*Myrmarachne formicaria:* A, ♀; B, ♂.

♂ : CARAPACE : The head is blackish, the remainder being reddish-brown ; there is but little trace of the paler stripes behind the posterior eyes ; the whole is clothed with prone white hairs and some long black hairs. ABDOMEN : Blackish-brown, somewhat reticulated ; it is clothed with shining prone hairs and some long black hairs. STERNUM : Like that of ♀. LEGS : Dark brown, clothed with long black hairs and some shining prone ones. MALE PALP : Text-fig. 117, A, brown with the end of the tarsus pale yellow to white and clothed thickly with short white hairs.

OCCURRENCE : This is a rare spider, which has occurred sparingly on a few sandhills along the south coast. Adult in May to July.

14. Genus **SYNAGELES** E. Simon 1876.

CHARACTERS OF GENUS : The only species is ant-like, with a long narrow body. EYES : The ocular trapezium is very slightly longer than broad. STERNUM : About twice as long as broad. CHELICERÆ : With one tooth on inner margin. PEDICEL : Visible from above.

Synageles venator (Lucas).
(Text-fig. 118, D, E, F)

Salticus venator H. Lucas, 1836, p. 1.   *Synageles venator* C. Chyzer and L. Kulczynski, 1891–7, I, p. 6 ;   F. Dahl, 1926, p. 39 ;   E. Simon, 1937, p. 1155 ;   A. Tullgren, 1944, p. 43.

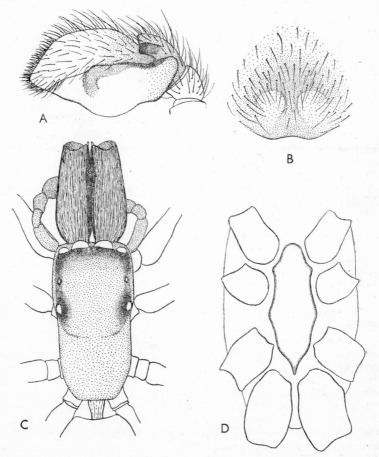

TEXT-FIG. 117.—A, *Phlegra fasciata:* male palp (side). B, do.: epigyne. C, *Myrmarachne formicaria:* male carapace and cheliceræ (above). D, do.: sternum.

DESCRIPTION. LENGTH : ♀: 3·5–4 mm. ♂: 3 mm.

♀: CARAPACE : At least twice as long as wide ; brown suffused heavily with black anteriorly, around the eyes and on the sides ; rather rugose, particularly on the head ; clothed fairly thinly with white and black hairs. EYES : The ocular trapezium is very slightly longer than broad. PEDICEL : Clearly visible from above. ABDOMEN : Rather wider behind than in front, greyish-brown with two broad curved white lines across it, roughly half-way to the spinners. STERNUM : About twice as long as broad, blackish-brown with few hairs. LEGS : Brown, often with longitudinal dark brown or black lines ; there are no spines on posterior tibiæ and metatarsi. PALP : Pale yellow. EPIGYNE : Text-fig. 118, D.

♂ : This sex is very similar in colour to the ♀. LEGS I are rather more massive. MALE PALP : Text-fig. 118, E, F, brown.

OCCURRENCE : This is a very rare spider, which has been taken only on a few sandhills around the coasts, and in a fen (Huntingdonshire). Adult in spring to summer. It is very ant-like in appearance.

15. Genus **MYRMARACHNE** W. S. MacLeay 1839.

CHARACTERS OF GENUS. The only species is ant-like, with a long narrow body (Text-fig. 116). EYES : Ocular trapezium nearly as long as broad. STERNUM : About three times as long as broad (Text-fig. 117, D). CHELICERÆ : With several teeth on inner margin ; chelicaræ strongly developed in ♂ (Text-fig. 117, C). PEDICEL : Visible from above.

Myrmarachne formicaria (Degeer).
(Text-figs. 116, A, B ; 117, C, D ; 118, A, B, C)

Aranea formicaria Degeer, 1778, p. 293. *Salticus formicarius* J. Blackwall, 1861–4, p. 64 ; O. P.-Cambridge, 1879–81, p. 568 ; C. Chyzer and L. Kulczynski, 1891–7, I, p. 4. *Myrmarachne formicarius* E. Simon, 1937, p. 1150. *M. joblotii* F. Dahl, 1926, p. 23 ; A. Tullgren, 1944, p. 17.

DESCRIPTION. LENGTH : ♀: 5–6 mm. ♂: 5–6·5 mm. (including chelicaræ).

♀: CARAPACE : The head is dark blackish-brown, particularly at the edges, and is very rugose with a metallic sheen ; the head is elevated sharply from the thoracic area, which is reddish-orange and much less rugose ; the carapace is more than twice as long as broad, and is clothed with some long hairs. EYES : The ocular trapezium is slightly broader than long. PEDICEL : Clearly visible from above. ABDOMEN : Pale whitish-yellow anteriorly, followed by a black chevron, and then blackish at the rear (Text-fig. 116, A). STERNUM : Yellow, about three times as long as broad, with coxæ II and III well separated (Text-fig. 117, D). LEGS : Pale yellow to yellow-brown but with metatarsi I jet black, tibiæ I suffused with black apically, femora I blackish above, and tibiæ IV and metatarsi IV suffused with brownish.

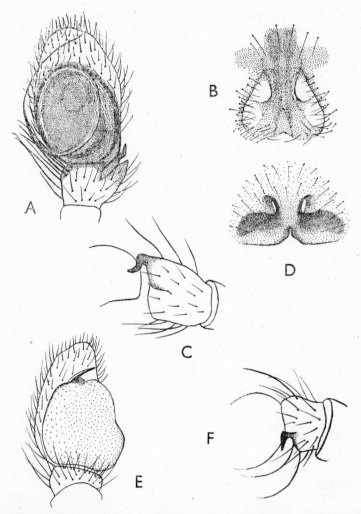

TEXT-FIG. 118.—Male palps: A, *Myrmarachne formicaria* (below); C, do., tibia (side); E, *Synageles venator* (below); F, do., tibia (side).
Epigynes: B, *Myrmarachne formicaria;* D, *Synageles venator.*

PALPS: The femora are orange-brown, the remainder being black; they are broadened at the end with swollen tarsi and tibiæ. EPIGYNE: Text-fig. 118, B.

♂: The general colour resembles that of ♀ (Text-fig. 116, B). CHELICERÆ: Strongly projecting in front, almost as long as the carapace (Text-fig. 117, C), a shining blackish-brown in colour, and rugose ; the fang is also almost as long as the carapace, and lies parallel to the long axis of the body. MALE PALP : Text-fig. 118, A, C.

OCCURRENCE : Rare, though not infrequent in a few localities on the south coast ; *e.g.* a number of specimens have been taken in recent years in Parkhurst Forest and near Shanklin (Isle of Wight). It is a long slender spider with a superficial resemblance to the ant *Formica rufa* Linn. It does not jump, but runs about in grass, etc., sometimes in company with ants. It is adult in May-July, and is recognisable at once in the field.

16. Genus **HASARIUS** E. Simon 1871.

CHARACTERS OF GENUS. Closely similar to *Evarcha*, from which it differs mainly in the relative size of the posterior eyes and in having a bifid tooth on inner cheliceral margin. The sex organs are quite distinct in type from those of *Evarcha*.

Hasarius adansoni (Audouin).
(Text-fig. 115, A, C)

Attus adansoni V. Audouin, 1826. *Hasarius adansoni* O. P.-Cambridge, 1879–81, p. 566 ; E. Simon, 1937, p. 1243 ; W. S. Bristowe, 1947, pl. 15 ; B. J. Kaston, 1948, p. 493.

DESCRIPTION. LENGTH : ♀ : 8 mm. ♂ : 6–7 mm.

♀ : CARAPACE : The head is dark reddish-brown becoming black centrally and at the sides ; the thorax is orange-brown shading off to dark brown behind ; the whole is clothed with white hairs, particularly at the sides. ABDOMEN : Greyish, slightly mottled, clothed with short white and brownish hairs. LEGS : Brown to dark brown with stout spines and fine whitish hairs. STERNUM : Yellow, clothed with short hairs. EPIGYNE : Text-fig. 115, A, very small.

♂ : CARAPACE : Very similar to that of ♀, but rather more vivid colouration, with a metallic sheen in the black areas. ABDOMEN : Blackish with a wide transverse crescentic band of white hairs across the front, and two small areas of white hairs towards the rear. STERNUM : Like that of ♀. LEGS : Darkish-brown, the femora being suffused and streaked with olive-green. MALE PALP : Text-fig. 115, C, yellow-brown with the tarsus rather darker ; long with the tibia longer than the tarsus, which is small and narrow ; the patella and tibia are thickly clothed with long, fine white hairs. This handsome species has a squat appearance, with the carapace almost as long as the abdomen.

OCCURRENCE : Not a true British species, but established in some hot-houses throughout the country.

17. Genus **PELLENES** E. Simon 1876.

CHARACTERS OF GENUS. The single species has a clear and well-defined pattern. EYES : Posterior row is wider than the anterior row.

Pellenes tripunctatus (Walckenaer).
(Text-fig. 109, A, B, E)

Aranea tripunctata C. A. Walckenaer, 1802, p. 247. *Pellenes tripunctatus* O. P.-Cambridge, 1889, p. 122 ; C. Chyzer and L. Kulczynski, 1891—7, I, p. 36 ; F. Dahl, 1926, p. 49 ; E. Simon, 1937, p. 1230 ; A. Tullgren, 1944, p. 59.

DESCRIPTION. LENGTH : ♀ : 6 mm. ♂ : 4–5 mm. The two sexes are similar in colour with the ♂ rather darker. CARAPACE : A deep rich blackish-brown, clothed (particularly on head) with prone yellowish-white hairs, and some black hairs. EYES : Anteriors fringed with orange hairs. ABDOMEN : Brown, mottled with black, darker anteriorly ; there is a central longitudinal band of glistening white hairs followed by three white spots, the first spreading transversely out into an arc ; it is clothed with numerous long black hairs. LEGS : Legs I are very dark reddish-brown with the femora enlarged ; the remainder are dark brown ; they are clothed with numerous very long fine hairs. EPIGYNE : Text-fig. 109, E. MALE PALP : Text-fig. 109, A, B, very dark brown, with numerous white glistening hairs on the upper side ; there are two black pointed apophyses on the tarsus.

OCCURRENCE : This species has been found but once, at Folkestone (Kent) in 1888, when both sexes were taken. It has never been re-discovered and may have been the result of a chance importation of a cocoon.

15. Family OXYOPIDÆ.

CHARACTERS OF FAMILY. General appearance as in Text-fig. 119. Integument has scale-like, as well as normal, hairs. EYES : Text-fig. 11, A, B ; all dark. ABDOMEN : Tapering behind ; spinners terminal. CHELICERÆ : With few teeth or none. LEGS : With long erect spines (Text-fig. 119). Trochanters with a shallow notch. Tarsi with no scopulæ. Tarsal claws three ; the paired claws pectinate, with many teeth (10–20 in *Oxyopes*, cf. LYCOSIDÆ), median claw with two to three teeth. The spiders of this family spin no snare or regular retreat.

Genus **OXYOPES** P. A. Latreille 1804.

CHARACTERS OF GENUS. EYES : Text-fig. 11, A, B. CHELICERÆ : Inner margin with one tooth, outer with one to two.

Oxyopes heterophthalmus Latreille.
(Text-figs. 11, A, B ; 119 ; 120)

Oxyopes heterophthalmus P. A. Latreille, 1804 (2), p. 280. *Sphasus lineatus* J. Black-wall, 1861–4, p. 43. *Oxyopes lineatus* O. P.-Cambridge, 1879–81, p. 552. *O. heterophthalmus* C. Chyzer and L. Kulczynski, 1891–7, I, p. 48 ; A. R. Jackson, 1910, p. 20 ; O. P.-Cambridge, 1910, p. 63 ; E. Simon, 1937, p. 1144.

DESCRIPTION. LENGTH : ♀ : 5–6 mm. ♂ : 5·5–6·5 mm. CARA-PACE and ABDOMEN : Appearance as in Text-fig. 119. Colouration dark brown and cream. EYES : Text-fig. 11, A, B. STERNUM : Deep brown, with a longitudinal lighter yellow stripe. CHELICERÆ : Some-what conical and tapering, each with a brown central streak and a similar darkening at apical ends on outside. LEGS : With numerous long spines, which are striking (Text-fig. 119). Yellow, with brown streaks and other markings. EPIGYNE : Text-fig. 120, A. MALE PALP : Text-fig. 120, B.

OCCURRENCE : Near Lyndhurst and Brockenhurst (New Forest). These spiders spin no snare, but run on the ground and jump from branch to branch of heather and other vegetation.

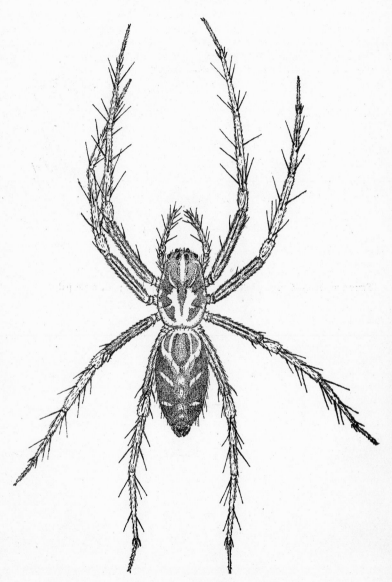

TEXT-FIG. 119.—*Oxyopes heterophthalmus* ♀ (OXYOPIDÆ).

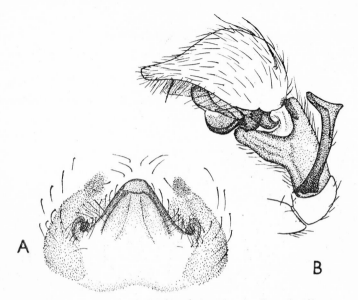

TEXT-FIG. 120.—*Oxyopes heterophthalmus:* A, epigyne ; B, male palp.

16. Family LYCOSIDÆ.

CHARACTERS OF FAMILY. CARAPACE: The outline never very different from that shown in Text-figs. 121 ; 122, D, E ; together with the abdomen, covered thickly with fine hairs, whose colour makes up or reinforces the visible pattern. EYES: All dark ; in three rows :

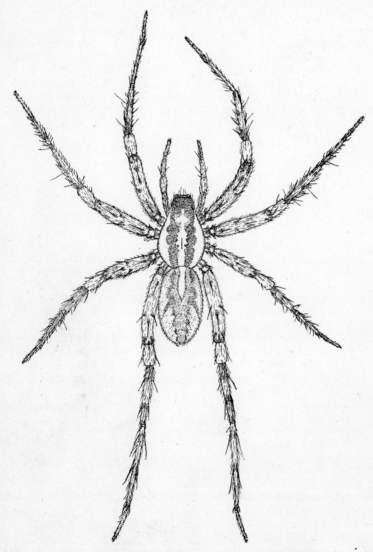

TEXT-FIG. 121.—*Lycosa tarsalis* var. *herbigrada* (LYCOSIDÆ).

S

first row contains four small eyes, second row two very much larger eyes, third row with two large eyes with a slightly backward glance. (The second and third rows can be looked upon as being one very strongly recurved row ; consequently for purposes of description we shall refer to the eyes in the second row as " posterior median " and those in the third row as " posterior lateral," in conformity with descriptions for most other families.) Trapezium, formed by the four large eyes, a little narrower in front than behind (Text-fig. 10, A, B) (cf. PISAURIDÆ). ABDOMEN : Colouration and pattern various but ground plan of design and outline shown in Text-fig. 121. CHELICERÆ : Robust, with teeth (two or three in the inner row). LEGS : Order of length, IV, I, II, III. Armed with spines. Apical ventral margin of each trochanter notched (Text-fig. 10, E. cf. AGELENIDÆ). Three tarsal claws, the paired claws with few teeth (cf. PISAURIDÆ). MALE PALP : With no tibial apophysis (cf. PISAURIDÆ).

KEY TO THE GENERA.

Note.—This is a homogeneous family and its subdivision into genera is almost impossible by the strict use of a dichotomous key which makes use of characters other than the sexual organs. Nevertheless it is felt that a key, albeit imperfect, will probably provide the most useful guide in the first place, if the obvious exceptions to its workings have been noted. Subsequent reference to the form of the sexual organs will always allow of a species being placed at least in the correct genus.

1. Anterior row of eyes *strongly* procurved (as seen from in front). Patella of palps white in both sexes (a character visible in the field). Posterior spinners the longest, the basal segment wider apically than at the base (Text-fig. 122, A) . . . . . . (7) **Aulonia**.
——Anterior row of eyes not *strongly* procurved. Palpal patella not white. Posterior spinners not noticeably the longest, nor wider apically than at the base 2
2. Head noticeably elevated with almost vertical sides (Text-fig. 122, B). Clypeus wide, at least twice diameter of lateral, and usually twice diameter of anterior median eye. Metatarsus IV longer than (or at least as long as) patella and tibia together (except in *L. rubrofasciata*) . (1) **Lycosa**.
——Head not noticeably elevated, with sloping sides. Clypeus narrow, equal to about diameter of an anterior median (1·5 diameters in *Xerolycosa*), and less than twice diameter of an anterior lateral eye (1·5–2 diameters in *Xerolycosa*). Metatarsus IV shorter than (or not longer than) patella and tibia together 3
3. Median light band of carapace well defined and clear of markings, but for the fovea. Cheliceræ with two teeth in the inner row 4
——Median light band of carapace with darker markings, or absent. Cheliceræ with three teeth in the inner row (except some species of *Trochosa*, q.v.) 5

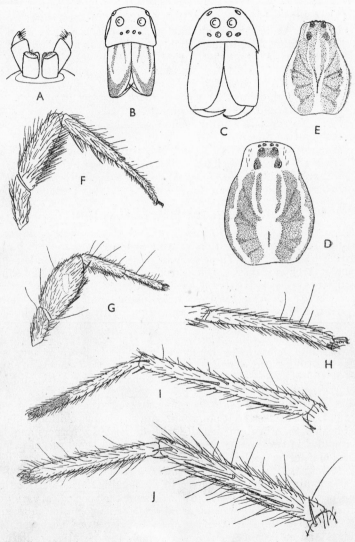

Text-fig. 122.—A, *Aulonia albimana*, spinners. B, head and chelicerae of *Lycosa*. C, do., *Trochosa*. D, carapace of *Trochosa*. E, do., *Pirata*. F, leg I of *Tarentula barbipes* ♂. G, do., *T. cuneata*. H, tarsus of *Xerolycosa*. I, metatarsus and tarsus of *Lycosa agrestis* ♂. J, do., *L. purbeckensis* ♂.

4. Tarsi I with trichobothria disposed as in Text-fig. 122,
F, G . . . . (3) **Tarentula**.
——Tarsi I with trichobothria as in Text-fig. 122, H (2) **Xerolycosa**.
5. Carapace, though possibly having light areas, yet with
no definite longitudinal light band. Ground colour
black (with sometimes light markings) or blackish
brown . . . . (5) **Arctosa**.
——Carapace with or without a median band, but with a more
or less well-defined V-shaped mark just in front of
the fovea and pointing backwards (Text-fig. 122, E).
♀ : No *apical* ventral spine on tibia I. General
colouration brown . . . . . . (6) **Pirata**.
——Carapace with a median light band, with markings other
than a V, usually two longitudinal bars in the anterior half
(Text-fig. 122, D). ♀ : Apical ventral spines present on
tibia I. General colouration brown . . (4) **Trochosa**.

1. Genus **LYCOSA** P. A. Latreille 1804.

CHARACTERS OF GENUS : CARAPACE : notably narrowed in front
(Text-fig. 121), normally with a central and two lateral light bands
on darker background. (These vary in shape, the lateral bands being
frequently broken ; they are of considerable value in distinguishing
the different species.) HEAD : noticeably elevated, with almost vertical
sides. CLYPEUS : Wide, at least twice diameter of anterior lateral
eye. EYES : Text-fig. 122, B. ABDOMEN : Pattern varies, but of
the type shown in Text-fig. 121. LEGS : Slender, attenuated apically :
IVth pair, notably the longest, give a characteristic appearance
when running. Metatarsus IV longer than (or at least as long as)
patella and tibia together (except in *L. rubrofasciata*). Their markings
various (and constituting another useful character for distinguishing
species).

The species of the genus are conveniently grouped as follows :

Group I. EPIGYNE : With a prominent conspicuous chitinous plate,
wider behind than in front, usually with its posterior corners angular
(but rounded in two cases). MALE PALP : Central apophysis of palpal
organs blunt, never aculeate : *Lycosa arenicola, L. agricola, L. agrestis,
L. purbeckensis, L. monticola, L. tarsalis.*

It is not always an easy matter to distinguish the species of this
Group, of which some members may be no more than ecological varieties
of others. Their sexual organs are all similar and sometimes difficult
to distinguish and reliance must often be placed on variations in
markings and other minor characters, which, though usually, are not
always constant.

Group II. EPIGYNE : Various, but with the chitinous tongue much
smaller relatively to the epigynal area. MALE PALP : Median apophysis
slender and pointed (except in *L. proxima* and *L. hortensis*) : *Lycosa
pullata, L. prativaga, L. amentata, L. nigriceps, L. lugubris, L. hortensis,
L. proxima.*

This group is less homogeneous and the species identifiable without great difficulty by the sexual organs, as well as by other characters.

Group III. Epigynes and Male palp : Text-fig. 131, A, D, E. Two rather large and quite distinct species, resembling one another closely : *Lycosa trailli, L. paludicola.*

Group IV. Epigyne and Male palp : Text-fig. 131, B, C, F. Metatarsus IV shorter than patella and tibia together. Head less elevated than in other species, and its sides more sloping : *Lycosa rubrofasciata.*

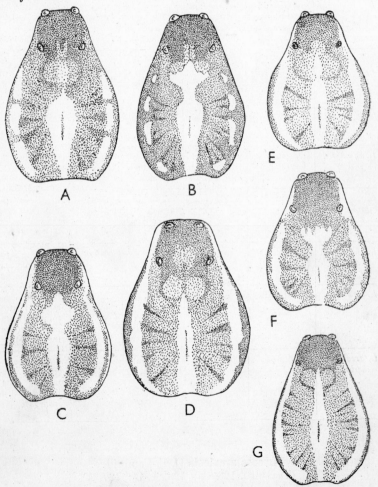

Text-fig. 123.—Carapace (above) ♀: A, *Lycosa arenicola;* B, *L. agricola;* C, *L. agrestis;* D, *L. purbeckensis;* E, *L. tarsalis;* F, *L. tarsalis* var. *herbigrada;* G, *L. monticola.*

Group I.

The following table will be found useful in separating the species of this Group, although it should always be borne in mind that variation is likely to occur, either naturally or owing to the action of spirit on specimens of different ages.

Species	♀ ♂		♀	♂	♂
	Anterior end of light median carapace band	Lateral light carapace bands	Legs	Darkening of tarsi I	Palpal organs (Text-fig. 124)
L. arenicola	Pointed or blunt.	Broken	Annulations obscure, if any.	Nearly to base.	Apophysis (a) slender and tapering (seen ventrally).
L. agricola	Dilated	Broken	Clearly annulated.	Nearly to base.	Apophysis (a) long but not attenuated.
L. agrestis	Dilated (sometimes pointed, v.p.256.)	Continuous or broken (v.p. 256).	Annulations more or less distinct.	On apical $\frac{1}{3}-\frac{1}{2}$.	Apophysis (a) blunt.
L. purbeckensis	Pointed	Continuous	Annulations absent or very obscure.	None	Apophysis (a) blunt.
L. monticola	Pointed	Continuous	Partly annulated.	None	Apophysis (a) somewhat attenuated.
L. tarsalis	Pointed	Continuous	Partly annulated.	None	Marginal sclerite (b) prominent and jagged (seen from side).
L. tarsalis var. herbigrada	Dilated	Continuous	Partly annulated.	None	Marginal sclerite (b) prominent and jagged (seen from side).

Lycosa arenicola O. P.-Cambridge.
(Text-figs. 123, A ; 125, A, B ; 127, A)

Lycosa arenicola O. P.-Cambridge, 1875, p. 253; 1879–81, p. 373; F. P. Smith, 1907 (1), p. 14; F. Dahl, 1908, p. 261, and 1927, p. 51; A. Holm, 1947, p. 31. *Pardosa arenicola* E. Simon, 1937, pp. 1056, 1074.

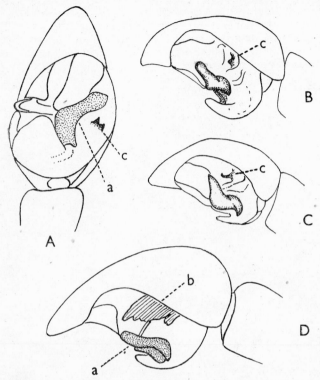

TEXT-FIG. 124.—Male palps : A, *Lycosa agrestis* and *purbeckensis* (below) ; B,
do. (below and to left side) ; C, *L. monticola* (do.) ; D, *L. tarsalis* (side).

DESCRIPTION. LENGTH : ♀ : 6-8 mm. ♂ : 5·5-6·5 mm. CARA-
PACE : Text-fig. 123, A. Dark brown, almost black. The lighter
median stripe varies somewhat and is often not well defined. (In some
specimens it is almost continuous to just behind the posterior median
eyes, but does not form here a regular dilation. In long-preserved
specimens this region may become much lighter than the surrounding
field, suggesting a dilation such as occurs in *L. agricola*, but the markings
as a whole are never so distinct as in that species.) Lateral bands often
very indistinct, broken up by bars very variable in width. CLYPEUS :
Yellow with a darker mark below the anterior eyes ; sides of head
mottled. ABDOMEN : Dark brown ; pattern very obscure ; a lighter
median stripe is flanked and followed by five to six lighter blotches,
diminishing in size and separated by narrow transverse bars of the field
colour (rather more distinct in the male). Abdominal markings as a
whole similar in the male, but usually darker. STERNUM : Dark brown
to black, with sometimes, in females, a lighter median stripe on the

anterior half. CHELICERÆ: Yellow; apices darkened as in *L. monticola;* there are three longitudinal, black, tapering streaks, the central, and sometimes the outer, ones reaching the apex. LEGS: ♀: Femora with long streaks dorsally, or obscurely annulated; sometimes uniformly dark. Tibiæ and metatarsi with apical, and usually basal, ends darkened obscurely. (Sometimes these marks amount to

TEXT-FIG. 125.—Male palps: A, *Lycosa arenicola* (side); B, do. (below); C, *L. agricola* (side); D, do. (below).

annulations, sometimes the whole segment is uniformly dark brown.) ♂ : Legs rather lighter, femoral markings less distinct. Tarsi I deep brown, almost to the base. EPIGYNE : Text-fig. 127, A. Somewhat variable and very like that of *L. agricola*. MALE PALP : Text-fig. 125, A, B. Viewed ventrally the long tapering apophysis is characteristic. The spider appears almost black as it runs about. It can be distinguished from *L. agricola* by the median carapace band ; the outlines of the bands are much less clearly defined than in that species.

OCCURRENCE : A rare species of southern counties. Found also in Eire (Co. Galway). It occurs amongst shingle on the coasts, but has also been taken inland. Males adult May and June ; females may be found throughout the spring and summer.

Lycosa agricola Thorell.
(Text-figs. 123, B ; 125, C, D ; 127, B)

Lycosa agricola T. Thorell, 1856, p. 61. *L. fluviatilis* J. Blackwall, 1861–4, p. 31. *L. agricola* O. P.-Cambridge, 1879–81, p. 598 ; C. Chyzer and L. Kulczynski, 1891–7, I, p. 55 ; F. P. Smith, 1907 (1), p. 15 ; A. Holm, 1947, p. 30. *L. fluviatilis* F. Dahl, 1908, p. 259, and 1927, p. 52. *Pardosa agricola* E. Simon, 1937, pp. 1057, 1070.

DESCRIPTION. LENGTH : ♀ : 5·5–7·5 mm. ♂ : 4·5–5·5 mm. CARAPACE : Markings (Text-fig. 123, B) disposed much as in *L. arenicola*, but very clear-cut. Median band dilated anteriorly (though not always in males) ; lateral bands divided by wide, dark bars and sometimes almost obliterated in males ; clypeus usually of a lighter yellow. ABDOMEN : Pattern of the usual *Lycosa* type. Lighter patches following the anterior median stripe usually lighter than in *L. arenicola* and much more distinct, especially in males. STERNUM : Dark ; a mark as in *L. arenicola* sometimes present. CHELICERÆ : Yellow. The streaks usually clear and continuous in the male, broken or quite absent in the female. LEGS : ♀ : Very clearly annulated ; annulations on femora clear but somewhat irregular and broken. ♂ : Obscurely annulated. Tarsi I deep brown, nearly to the base (cf. *L. agrestis*). EPIGYNE : Text-fig. 127, B. MALE PALP : Text-fig. 125, C, D. Viewed ventrally the median apophysis is long but not slender nor tapering as in *L. arenicola*. The sexual organs of both sexes resemble those of *L. arenicola* fairly closely, and reliance must be placed to some extent on the clear carapace markings, with the dilated median band in the female.

OCCURRENCE : A northern species. It seems to prefer the sandy banks of rivers and lakes. Locally abundant. Adult in spring or early summer.

Lycosa agrestis Westring.
(Text-figs. 122, I ; 123, C ; 124, A, B ; 126, A, B ; 127, C)

Lycosa agrestis N. Westring, 1861, p. 480 ; C. Chyzer and L. Kulczynski, 1891–7, I, p. 56. *L. decipiens* O. P.-Cambridge, 1903, p. 161. *L. agrestis* F. P. Smith, 1907 (1), p. 16 ; F. Dahl, 1908, p. 262, and 1927, p. 49 ; A. Holm, 1947, p. 29. *Pardosa agrestis* E. Simon, 1937, pp. 1056, 1071.

DESCRIPTION.   LENGTH :   ♀ : 6–6·5 mm.   ♂ : about 4·5 mm.   CARA-
PACE :   ♀ : Brown, with whitish hairs on fore part and head. Markings
very variable ; lateral light bands, if not broken, continued round head.
The following varieties have been recognised, according to carapace
pattern :

LIGHT CARAPACE BANDS

	MEDIAN	LATERAL
L. agrestis Westring. .	Dilated in front	Continuous (about equal in width to median).
var. *pseudoagricola* Dahl . †	Dilated in front	Broken (as in Text-fig 123, B)
var. *pseudomonticola* Sim.. ‡	Pointed in front	Continuous

† F. Dahl, 1908, p. 221.
‡ E. Simon, 1937, p. 1071. (See also R. de Lessert, 1910, p. 509. Fig. 222.)

(Between the lateral bands and margin there is sometimes a darker
stripe, but it may be faint or represented only by dots.)   ♂ : Similar,
but darker, sometimes almost black ; lateral bands may be reduced or
scarcely visible.   ABDOMEN : Dark brown, with normal *Lycosa* pattern
(as in *L. monticola*) but usually very obscure. STERNUM : ♀ : Variable ;
light to dark brown, usually with lighter region in anterior half.
♂ : Dark, nearly uniform. CHELICERÆ : Light yellow, sometimes
darkened apically. LEGS : ♀ : Light, often greenish, yellow. Femora
with dorsal black marks, sometimes extending to ventral sides and even
forming irregular annulations ; other segments (except tarsi) more or
less clearly annulated.   ♂ : Femora similar, other segments clear yellow,
except for dark apical one-third to one-half of tarsi I (sometimes,
however, not distinct). EPIGYNE : Text-fig. 127, C. This is variable,
but the tongue is almost always broader at the posterior margin than
in *L. monticola*, and differs from those of the other species except *L.
purbeckensis*, whose epigyne seems not distinguishable from this.
MALE PALP : Indistinguishable with certainty from that of *L.
purbeckensis* (Text-fig. 126, A) although the tooth (*c*) (Text-fig. 124,
A, B) is generally more pointed and the median apophysis usually has
a rather more jagged outline.

As indicated above, the species varies greatly in the carapace pattern.
The form *pseudoagricola* (as in Text-fig. 123, B) is that most usually met
with in this country and this is readily identifiable.   (The pattern is
much less clear cut than in *L. agricola*, which, moreover, has a different
epigyne). The normal form (Text-fig. 123, C) is also distinct, but if the
median band is pointed in front (*pseudomonticola*) the spider becomes
nearly identical with *L. purbeckensis*, which may be but another variety
of it, although *L. agrestis* is usually smaller, with the leg markings clearer.
If the epigynal tongue happens to be very narrow, there might be difficulty in separating the species from *L. monticola*, but all specimens
examined hitherto are clear enough.   In the male the numerous long

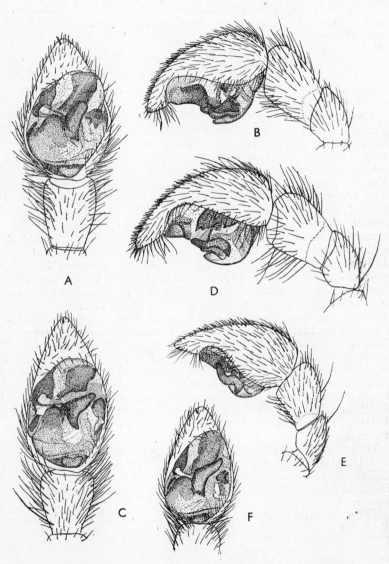

TEXT-FIG. 126.—Male palps : A, *Lycosa agrestis* and *purbeckensis* (below) ; B, do. (side) ; C, *L. tarsalis* (below) ; D, do. (side) ; E, *L. monticola* (side) ; F, do. (below).

hairs on metatarsi and tarsi I in *L. purbeckensis* (Text-fig. 122, I, J) serve as a distinguishing character.

OCCURRENCE : A southern species. Very rare. Open heaths, grassland, chalk pits.

Lycosa purbeckensis (F. O. P.-Cambridge.)
(Text-figs. 122, J ; 123, D ; 124, A, B ; 126, A, B ; 127, D)

Pardosa purbeckensis F. O. P.-Cambridge, 1895, p. 32 ; *Lycosa purbeckensis* F. P. Smith, 1907 (1), p. 18.

DESCRIPTION. LENGTH : ♀ : 7–9 mm. ♂ : 6–7 mm. CARAPACE : Text-fig. 123, D. Lateral stripes continue round the head ; clypeus with a darker region in the middle. ABDOMEN : Dark brown, pattern very obscure, as in *L. arenicola* and *L. agrestis*, with two converging rows of small white spots, visible in living specimens. CHELICERÆ : Variable ; yellow-brown, sometimes with the usual streaks and darkening towards the apices. LEGS : ♀ : Femora with dark longitudinal blotches on upper sides only ; tibiæ dark brown (usually almost uniform) (cf. *L. agrestis*) ; metatarsi with dark marks almost amounting to annulations, especially on III and IV. ♂ : With dark blotches only on dorsal and basal parts of femora. Metatarsi and tarsi I with many long hairs (Text-fig. 122, J) (cf. *L. agrestis* and *L. monticola*). In some localities this spider is almost black when alive, but the colouration varies and tends to fade in long-preserved specimens. EPIGYNE : Text-fig. 127, D. MALE PALP : Text-fig. 126, A, B. Viewed ventrally the median apophysis (*a*) is blunt-ended, and the little tooth (*c*) (Text-fig. 124, A, B) is distinct from that of *L. monticola* (Text-fig. 124, C). (NOTE. These teeth (*c*) are best looked at as indicated in Text-fig. 124, B, C. They can be almost invisible if the palp is viewed ventrally or in some dark, fresh specimens.) The spider resembles *L. agrestis* closely and may be only a variety of it. A small form, found in the north, has been named *L. purbeckensis* var. *minor* F. O. P.-Cambridge, but as it appears to be identical with the larger form in all but size, it is doubtful whether it should be regarded as a separate variety.

OCCURRENCE : Widely distributed, but almost always on mud flats and the shores, especially, of estuaries ; but it has been found on a cliff top and may be able to survive inland. Very local but abundant in some places. Males adult in early May, females throughout the summer.

Note.—E. Simon (1937, pp. 1065, 1072, 1129) considers that *L. purbeckensis* F. O. P.-Camb. (together with *L. mixta* Kulczynski) probably amounts to no more than a variety of *L. tarsalis* Thorell and that it could be assigned with reason to either *L. tarsalis* Thor. or to *L. monticola* (Clerck). Confusion might well have arisen if the females only were considered, since the epigynes do vary considerably. The male palp of this species, however, as will be seen, lacks the large jagged marginal sclerite of *L. tarsalis* and differs in the parts (*a*) and (*c*) from *L. monticola*, and it seems to be quite distinct from either of them. It bears on the other hand a very close resemblance to the palp of *L. agrestis* Westr. and only breeding experiments could decide whether or not *L. purbeckensis* were a variety of that species. The females are sometimes practically indistinguishable.

Lycosa monticola (Clerck).
(=L. monticola Sundevall)
(Text-figs. 123, G ; 124, C ; 126, E, F ; 127, E)

Araneus monticola C. Clerck, 1757, p. 92. *Lycosa monticola* C. J. Sundevall, 1833 p. 175. *L. exigua* J. Blackwall, 1836, p. 490, and 1861–4, p. 29 (in part). *L. monticola* O. P.-Cambridge, 1879–81, p. 388 ; C. Chyzer and L. Kulczynski, 1891–7, I, p. 56 ; F. P. Smith, 1907 (1), p. 17 ; F. Dahl, 1908, p. 256, and 1927, p. 48 ; A. Holm, 1947, p. 29. *Pardosa monticola* E. Simon, 1937, pp. 1068, 1074.

DESCRIPTION. LENGTH : ♀ : 4·5–6 mm. ♂ : 4·5–5·5 mm. There is considerable variation in the depth of ground colour of living specimens from black to a light chocolate brown. CARAPACE : Text-fig. 123, G. ♀ : Chocolate brown with darker radiating striæ. The light yellow-brown median and lateral bands very well defined and clear ; the median starts as a point between posterior lateral eyes and is also pointed behind. Lateral bands unbroken and usually continued round clypeus (though with occasionally a darker break at each side of the head). Sometimes a second narrow light band can be made out just within the margin. ♂ : Similar, but in general darker ; median light band often extends, as white hairs, to front of head. All bands usually a little narrower than in ♀. ABDOMEN : Pattern typical of genus, not especially well defined, though very pretty in some specimens. Brown median stripe in fore part edged with black and followed by a series of transverse bars (sometimes ill defined) joined, at their ends, with black curved bars diminishing in size towards the spinners and which are often continuous. STERNUM : ♀ : Dark brown. ♂ : Black, often with an ill-defined lighter region in the middle, and occasionally at the sides. CHELICERÆ : Yellow. ♀ : A dark loop in apical region runs parallel with inner margin, leaving a light yellow region between them. ♂ : Similar but whole segment rather more attenuated. LEGS : ♀ : Rather light yellow-brown with black streaks and blotches on femora, sometimes extending to their under sides. Tibiæ and metatarsi annulated more or less distinctly (especially on III and IV). ♂ : Only femora marked above with dark streaks and blotches, often ill defined ; remaining segments light. EPIGYNE : Text-fig. 127, E. MALE PALP : Text-fig. 126, E, F. The little tooth (c) (Text-fig. 124, C) is distinct from that of *L. purbeckensis*.

OCCURRENCE : Widespread and rather common, locally abundant in open heaths and meadows throughout the country. Males adult in May, females throughout the spring and summer.

Lycosa tarsalis Thorell.
(Text-figs. 123, E ; 124, D ; 126, C, D ; 127, F)

Lycosa tarsalis T. Thorell, 1856, p. 53. *L. exigua* J. Blackwall, 1836, p. 490, and 1861–4 p. 29. (ad partem), *L. palustris* O. P.-Cambridge, 1879–81, p. 287 ; C. Chyzer and L. Kulczynski, 1891–7, I, p. 56 ; F. P. Smith, 1907 (1), p. 20 ; A. Holm, 1947, p. 28. *L. tarsalis* F. Dahl, 1908, p. 265, and 1927, p. 47. *Pardosa tarsalis* E. Simon, 1937, pp. 1064, 1072.

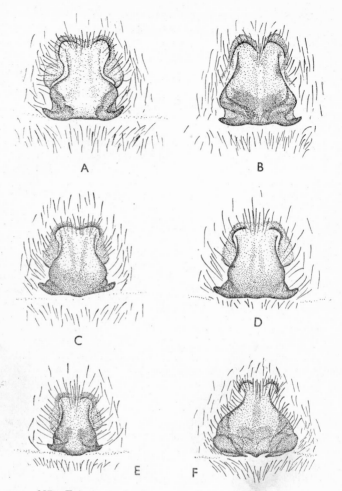

TEXT-FIG. 127.—Epigynes: A, *Lycosa arenicola*; B, *L. agricola*; C, *L. agrestis*; D, *L. purbeckensis*; E, *L. monticola*; F, *L. tarsalis*.

DESCRIPTION. LENGTH : ♀: 4·5–6 mm. ♂: 4·5–5·5 mm. CARAPACE (Text-fig. 123, E) and ABDOMEN : Very like that of *L. monticola*. STERNUM : ♀: Dark brown, usually with a central lighter region, reaching sometimes to anterior margin, and more or less distinct lateral bands. ♂: Darker, almost black. CHELICERÆ : Like *L. monticola*, but lighter ; the dark loop often indistinct. LEGS : Very like *L. monticola*. EPIGYNE : Text-fig. 127, F. The rounded posterior edges are characteristic, but considerable variation is possible. MALE PALP : Text-figs. 126, C, D ; 124, D. The process (*b*) is more developed than in the other species and is jagged at the apical end ; it is very clear viewed from the outside but not striking when viewed ventrally.

The general appearance of this spider is very like that of *L. monticola* and not unlike that of *L. purbeckensis* (especially after preservation).

OCCURRENCE : Widespread, locally abundant, especially in open heathy country. With it often occurs a variety *herbigrada* (see below) and *L. monticola*. Males adult in May, females throughout the spring and summer.

<h2 style="text-align:center">Lycosa tarsalis var. herbigrada Blackwall.</h2>

(Text-figs. 121 ; 123, F)

Lycosa herbigrada J. Blackwall, 1857, p. 285, and 1861–4, p. 22 ; O. P.-Cambridge, 1879–81, p. 384 ; F. P. Smith, 1907 (1), p. 19. *Pardosa herbigrada* G. H. Carpenter, 1898, p. 20 ; E. Simon, 1937, pp. 1064, 1071. *Lycosa palustris* A. Holm, 1947, p. 28.

DESCRIPTION. CARAPACE : Covered with a greyish pubescence. Light bands disposed as in Text-fig. 123, F, the median being dilated in front. ABDOMEN : Text-fig. 121. Sides of posterior region lightish grey, covered with almost white hairs and giving the spider a very characteristic appearance as it runs. The pair of black streaks running outwards and backwards across the sides over this region are very typical. STERNUM : ♀ : Very variable, but usually yellow-brown with some darker patches. ♂ : From uniform black to nearly colour of ♀. CHELICERÆ : Like *L. tarsalis*, but loops darker in males, approaching those of *L. monticola*. LEGS : Like *L. tarsalis*. EPIGYNE and MALE PALP : Indistinguishable from *L. tarsalis*.

This description applies to the extreme and very distinct variety, which was for long considered a separate species. It usually occurs on heaths, especially on the dark soil amongst heather. In some localities it is accompanied by *L. tarsalis* and collections have been made containing specimens with intermediate carapace patterns in both sexes, but these have always been found to have the typical abdominal pattern of var. *herbigrada*. The white hairs, which give this variety its distinct appearance in the field, are, in some localities, replaced by a rather browner pubescence. It has been found that *L. tarsalis* will mate with var. *herbigrada* and that fertile eggs are produced.

OCCURRENCE : Widely distributed and abundant locally. On open heaths, usually on bare, dark soil amongst heather. Adult in May.

<h2 style="text-align:center">Group II</h2>

<h3 style="text-align:center">Lycosa pullata (Clerck).</h3>

(Text-fig. 128, C, D, E)

Araneus pullatus C. Clerck, 1757, p. 104. *Lycosa obscura* J. Blackwall, 1841, p. 611, and 1861–4, p. 28. *L. pullata* O. P.-Cambridge, 1879–81, p. 357 ; C. Chyzer and L. Kulczynski, 1891–7, I, p. 57 ; F. P. Smith, 1907 (1), p. 21 ; F. Dahl, 1908, p. 235, and 1927, p. 44 ; A. Holm, 1947, p. 32. *Pardosa pullata* E. Simon, 1937, pp. 1065, 1081. (F. P. Smith (*loc. sit.*) wrongly gave the name *L. pullata* Olivier, and was followed by W. S. Bristowe, 1939–41, p. 40. A. G. Olivier's name (1789, p. 217) was *Aranea erratica*.)

DESCRIPTION. LENGTH : ♀ : 4–6 mm. ♂ : 4–4·5 mm. CARAPACE : Dark brown ; yellow-brown bands not well defined, the median often dilated in front, lateral bands continuous, or broken by faint, narrow transverse bars. (Males from Co. Galway, Eire, have been taken in which the median and lateral bands are covered with white hairs, giving the appearance of *L. monticola*.) Head black. ABDOMEN : Dark reddish-brown with black markings. Pattern normal for the genus, usually better defined in males. STERNUM : Brown, often with an obscure yellowish median wedge, starting from anterior border, which is narrower and better defined in males. LEGS : Variable in depth of colour, usually reddish-brown. Annulations, if any, very obscure (cf. *L. prativaga*). EPIGYNE : Text-fig. 128, E. The form of the anterior edge is very characteristic and distinct from that of *L. prativaga*. The median septum is usually narrower than in that species, although specimens are occasionally met with in which it is nearly if not quite as broad. (This character, by itself, is not therefore of use in separating these species.) MALE PALP : Text-fig. 128, C, D. The median apophysis appears not nearly to reach the edge of the alveolus when seen from outside (cf. *L. prativaga*).

OCCURRENCE : Almost ubiquitous, and usually abundant. Probably the commonest species of the genus. Adult in April and early May ; adult females continue throughout the summer and autumn.

Lycosa prativaga L. Koch.
(Text-fig. 128, A, B, F)

Lycosa prativaga L. Koch, 1870, p. 43. *L. prativaga* and *L. riparia* O. P.-Cambridge, 1879–81, pp. 380, 381. *L. prativaga* C. Chyzer and L. Kulczynski, 1891–7, I, p. 57 ; F. P. Smith, 1907 (1), p. 22. *L. riparia* F. Dahl, 1908, p. 412, and 1927, p. 45. *Pardosa prativaga* E. Simon, 1937, pp. 1061, 1080. *Lycosa prativaga* A. Holm, 1947, p. 32.

DESCRIPTION. LENGTH : ♀ : 4·5–6 mm. ♂ : 4–5 mm. This species resembles *L. pullata* fairly closely and differs from it in the following respects : CARAPACE : Lateral bands often broken into isolated patches, their edges irregular. ABDOMEN : Dark brown with black markings ; in preserved specimens the pattern is not clear (but better defined in males). In the living spiders, on the other hand, a black and white pattern (due to hair colour) is distinct and often very beautiful. LEGS : Clearly annulated in both sexes (cf. *L. pullata*). EPIGYNE : Text-fig. 128, F. This is smaller than in *L. pullata* and lacks the inflexion of the anterior margin ; the median septum is almost always broader. MALE PALP : Text-fig. 128, A, B. The tibia has some scattered white hairs at the base. The alveolus, seen ventrally (Text-fig. 128, B) is not so broad as in *L. pullata*, and the proportions of the sexual organs are different. Viewed from outside (Text-fig. 128, A) the median apophysis appears nearly to reach the edge of the alveolus. The hairs on the tarsus are usually thicker and stouter.

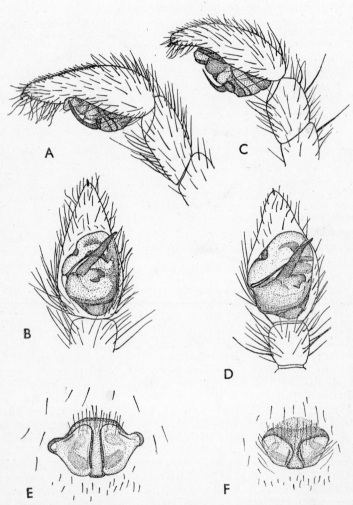

TEXT-FIG. 128.—Male palps: A, *Lycosa prativaga* (side); B, do. (below); C, *L. pullata* (side); D, do. (below).
Epigynes: E, *L. pullata;* F, *L. prativaga.*

OCCURRENCE : Widespread, often abundant locally.   Not so common as *L. pullata*, although the two species are often found together.   Fields, heaths, waste ground, marshes.   Males adult in April and early May ; females throughout spring and summer.

Note on *L. pullata* and *L. prativaga.*—Although the sexual organs of these two species appear distinct and easily recognisable, the males of one species have been seen to copulate with females of the other repeatedly in captivity and fertile eggs have occasionally been produced.   It is quite possible that they may interbreed in nature, which would account for the fact that specimens are sometimes met with, which have the sexual organs of one species with the colouration nearly that of the other, or intermediate between the two.   The decision as to whether the species are truly distinct or are but variations one of another must await the result of further investigation.

Lycosa amentata (Clerck).
(=*L. saccata* (Linnaeus))
(Text-fig. 129, A, B, G)

Araneus amentatus C. Clerck, 1757, p. 96.   *Aranea saccata* Linnaeus, 1758, p. 623 (in part), J. Blackwall, 1861–4, p. 26.   *L. amentata* O. P.-Cambridge, 1879–81, p. 370 ; C. Chyzer and L. Kulczynski, 1891–7, p. 58.   *L. saccata* F. P. Smith, 1907 (1), p. 23 ; F. Dahl, 1908, pp. 227, and 1927, p. 41 ;   A. Holm, 1947, p. 34.   *Pardosa amentata* E. Simon, 1937, pp. 1066, 1082.

DESCRIPTION.   LENGTH :   ♀ : 5·5–8 mm.   ♂ : 6–6·5 mm.   CARAPACE : Ground colour dark brown.   Median lighter band yellow-brown, of the same general form as in *L. agrestis* (Text-fig. 123, C) (the light hairs reach front of head in living female).   ABDOMEN : Greyish-olive in life, becoming deep red-brown in spirit.   Lighter stripe on anterior half edged more or less definitely with a number of black dots. Following this is a tapering brown area flanked by four to five pairs of crescent-shaped black marks of diminishing size, which are especially visible in the living spider.   The sides densely mottled with black. STERNUM : Dark brown, a pale band sometimes reaching from anterior border to about the middle.   CHELICERÆ :   ♀ :   Yellow-brown, variously marked with darker brown stripes and blotches, apices light. ♂ : Darker but similarly marked.   LEGS : ♀ : Annulated, except tarsi. ♂ : Femora annulated, tibiæ obscurely, with only very faint marks on metatarsi.   EPIGYNE : Text-fig. 129, G.   MALE PALP : Text-fig. 129, A, B.   The palps are used in courtship and have the tibiæ and tarsi clothed with dense black hairs.

OCCURRENCE : In almost all situations exposed to sunshine, provided that they are not too dry.   One of the commonest and most abundant spiders.   Males adult in April and early May ; females adult throughout spring and summer.

Lycosa nigriceps Thorell.
(Text-fig. 129, C, D, H)

Lycosa nigriceps T. Thorell, 1856, p. 55 (♂ not ♀) ; p. 56 ♀ ;   O. P.-Cambridge, 1879–81, p. 382 ;   F. P. Smith, 1907 (1), p. 24 ;   F. Dahl, 1908, p. 247, and 1927, p. 46 ;   A. Holm, 1947, p. 31.   *Pardosa nigriceps* E. Simon, 1932, pp. 1062, 1076.

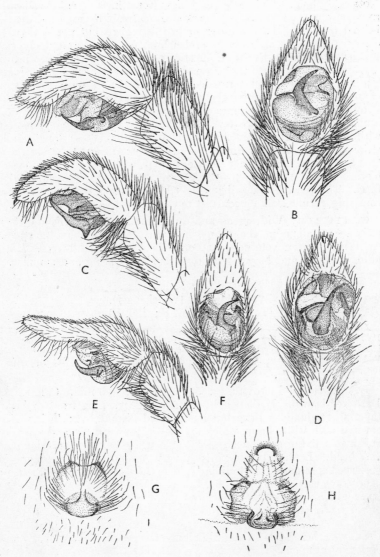

TEXT-FIG. 129.—Male palps: A, *Lycosa amentata* (side); B, do: (below); C, *L. nigriceps* (side); D, do. (below); E, *L. lugubris* (side); F, do (below). Epigynes: E, *L. amentata;* H, *L. nigriceps.*

DESCRIPTION. LENGTH : ♀: 5–6·5 mm. ♂: 4–5 mm. CARAPACE : Noticeably long. Lighter bands yellow (sometimes greenish-yellow in living specimens), less clearly marked in males. Median band dilated behind the eyes (and often darker in this region) but not noticeably constricted. Lateral bands unbroken and continued round clypeus. ♂ has white hairs on the head. ABDOMEN : Markings chocolate-brown on a yellow-brown field ; pattern similar to L. amentata but not very clearly defined. On posterior half lighter regions alternate with ill-defined darker bars forming chevrons. ♂ generally darker. STERNUM : Brown (♂ darker), sometimes with a median yellowish stripe, widest at mid-point, which may extend whole length. Remaining region often with irregular brown blotches. CHELICERÆ : Yellow ; longitudinal stripes brown (absent or broken in ♀). LEGS : Yellow-brown with no true annulations, but upper sides of femora with three to four darker blotches. EPIGYNE : Text-fig. 129, H. MALE PALP : Text-fig. 129, C, D. The dense black hairs on the tibiæ and tarsi, which are used in courtship, form a striking contrast to the yellow legs and white head.

OCCURRENCE : Widespread and rather common. Heaths and open places. It, alone in the genus, has partly arboreal habits and is frequently beaten from gorse and other bushes and small trees. Males adult in April and May ; females throughout spring and summer.

Lycosa lugubris (Walckenaer).
(Text-figs. 129, E, F ; 130, E)

Aranea lugubris C. A. Walckenaer, 1802, p. 239. *Lycosa lugubris* J. Blackwall, 1861–4, p. 27 ; O. P.-Cambridge, 1879–81, p. 374 ; C. Chyzer and L. Kulczynski, 1891–7, I, p. 58 ; F. P. Smith, 1907 (1), p. 25 ; A. Holm, 1947, p. 33. *Lycosa chelata* F. Dahl, 1908, p. 244, and 1927, p. 43. *Pardosa lugubris* E. Simon, 1937, pp. 1065, 1085.

DESCRIPTION. LENGTH : ♀: 5–6 mm. ♂: 4–5 mm. CARAPACE : Dark red-brown. Median light band broad, reaching front of head, tapering gradually a little but not pointed behind. ♂: This region covered with white hairs, which extend to front of head and are very striking in living specimens. ♀: Some white hairs on anterior part and head. Lateral bands narrow, very obscure or even absent in preserved specimens, but in living spiders there are two parallel narrow bands each side consisting of light hairs, the outer one continuous, the inner broken. ABDOMEN : Pattern typical of genus, sometimes visible in old specimens, but generally very obscure. Rather like that of L. amentata in living spiders. STERNUM : Reddish-brown to black. ♂: Usually darker. CHELICERÆ : Colour of carapace, with streaks and darkening at apex usually visible. ♂: Darker. LEGS : ♀: Annulated, usually including metatarsi. ♂: Femora dark brown or black (except at apex), the rest light yellow or brown, the contrast being rather striking. EPIGYNE : Text-fig. 130, E. This requires careful comparison with L. proxima and L. hortensis. MALE PALP : Text-fig. 129, E, F.

OCCURRENCE : Widespread and locally very abundant. It never seems to occur very far from woods. Males adult in April and early May ; females throughout spring and summer.

Lycosa hortensis Thorell.
(Text-fig. 130, A, B, F)

Lycosa hortensis ♀ + *annulata* T. Thorell, 1872, III, p. 299. *L. annulata* O. P.-Cambridge, 1879-81, p. 372 ; C. Chyzer and L. Kulczynski, 1891-7, I, p. 57 ; F. P. Smith, 1907 (1), p. 26. *L. hortensis* F. Dahl, 1908, p. 248 ; 1927, p. 31. *Pardosa hortensis* E. Simon, 1937, pp. 1064, 1085.

DESCRIPTION. LENGTH : ♀ : 4·5–5·5 mm. ♂ : 3·5–4·5 mm. CARAPACE : Chocolate brown, cephalic area dark. Median band of general form of that of *L. agrestis* (Text-fig. 123, C.) the anterior dilation being a little darker than the rest. Lateral bands broken and edges dentate. Clypeus yellow (♂ brown). ABDOMEN : Pattern typical of genus, indistinct and yellowish on a light to chocolate brown ground. Following the anterior median stripe are five pairs of lighter marks set at an angle with a black dot in each. STERNUM : Dark brown ; no clear markings, a little lighter towards the middle. CHELICERÆ : Yellow-brown with normal markings (Text-fig. 122,B.). LEGS : Annulated clearly on femora and tibiæ, less clearly on metatarsi (not at all on tarsi) ; not quite so distinct in males. EPIGYNE : Text-fig. 130, F. This needs to be compared carefully with those of *L. lugubris* and *L. proxima*. MALE PALP : Text-fig. 130, A, B. The femur and patella are yellow, contrasting sharply with the dark brown tibia and tarsus. There are some white hairs (not easy to see) on the ventral side of the tibia. The palp has to be distinguished from that of *L. proxima*, in which, however, the tibia is differently shaped as seen from the side, and the colour contrast mentioned above does not occur in that species.

OCCURRENCE : Widespread, though most records refer to the southern counties. Rather local, but then sometimes abundant. Clearings in woods, waste ground, chalk pits and the sea shore. Adult about the second half of April. The male often has a very short season, females continue into the summer. (The female bears a superficial resemblance to *L. amentata* but can usually be distinguished in the field by its clearer carapace markings and darker cephalic region.)

Lycosa proxima C. L. Koch.
(Text-fig. 130, C, D, G)

Lycosa (Pardosa) proxima C. L. Koch, 1848 (1), XV, p. 53. *Lycosa proxima* O. P.-Cambridge, 1878. p. 125 and 1879-81 p. 378 ; C. Chyzer and L. Kulczynski, 1891-7, I p. 57 ; F. P. Smith, 1907 (1), p. 26. *L. proxima* sub-sp. *tenuipes* F. Dahl, 1908, p. 251, and 1927, p. 33. *Pardosa proxima* E. Simon, 1937, pp. 1068, 1085.

DESCRIPTION. LENGTH : ♀ : 5·5–6·5 mm. ♂ : 4·5–5 mm. CARAPACE : Very dark brown ; the bands rather bright yellow, the median tapered before and behind and thickest about the mid point. Lateral bands usually, but not always, broken into three parts. ABDOMEN :

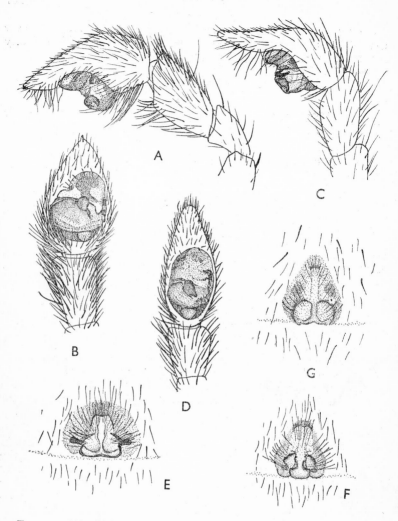

TEXT-FIG. 130.—Male palps: A, *Lycosa hortensis* (side); B, do. (below);
C, *L. proxima* (side); D, do. (below).
Epigynes: E, *L. lugubris*; F, *L. hortensis*; G, *L. proxima*.

Brown to black; pattern often obscure or quite invisible, especially
in males. STERNUM: Dark brown with a narrow light central band in
fore half, sometimes absent in males. CHELICERÆ: Yellow, darkened
at apices and much darker in males. LEGS: ♀: Annulated to tibiae
and sometimes to metatarsi (annulations rather irregular). ♂: Only
femora annulated as a rule. EPIGYNE: Text-fig. 130, G. This
requires careful comparison with that of *L. lugubris* and *L. hortensis*.

MALE PALP : Text-fig. 130, C, D. This is not unlike that of *L.
hortensis* (q.v.) the only other species to have so short a median
apophysis in the sexual organs.

OCCURRENCE : A southern species. Local. Waste places, marshy
ground. Males adult April and May ; females continue into the
summer.

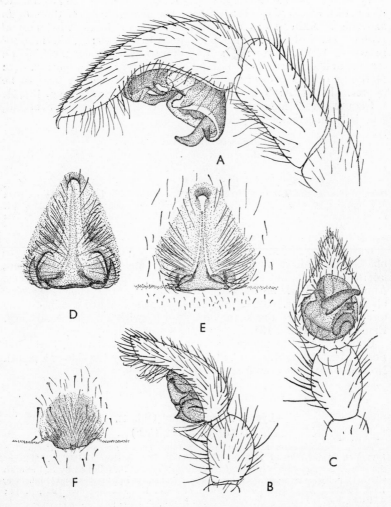

TEXT-FIG. 131.—Male palps : A, *Lycosa trailli* (side) ; B, *L. rubrofasciata* (side) ;
C, do. (below).
    Epigynes : D, *L. trailli;* E, *L. paludicola;* F, *L. rubrofasciata.*

Group III
Lycosa traillii O. P.-Cambridge.
(Text-fig. 131, A, D)

Lycosa traillii O. P.-Cambridge,1873 (2), p. 524, and 1879–81, p. 545 ; F. P. Smith, 1907 (1), p. 27.

DESCRIPTION. LENGTH : ♀ : 7–8 mm. ♂ : 6·5–7 mm. CARAPACE : Very dark, the bands very obscure and sometimes impossible to distinguish at all (they seem to have the general form of those of *L. amentata*). ABDOMEN : Very dark brown or black with normal pattern very obscure. STERNUM and CHELICERÆ : Uniform dark brown or black. LEGS : ♀ : Dark brown with black mottling on femora and obscure, ill-defined annulations on other segments. ♂ : Markings even less clear ; all segments, except femora, tend to be lighter. EPIGYNE : Text-fig. 131, D. MALE PALP : Text-fig. 131, A.

OCCURRENCE : Mountains in the north of England and in Scotland, especially on screes. Very local.

Lycosa paludicola (Clerck).
(= *L. paludicola* Walckenaer)
(Text-fig. 131, E)

Araneus paludicola C. Clerck, 1757, p. 94. *Lycosa paludicola* C. A. Walckenaer, 1825, p. 16. *L. fumigata* C. L. Koch, 1834 (3), p. 123–4, and 1848 (1), XIV, p. 100 ; F. P. Smith, 1907 (1), p. 27. *L. paludicola* T. Thorell, 1856, p. 59, and 1872, p. 304. C. Chyzer and L. Kulczynski, 1891–7, I, p. 59 ; O. P.-Cambridge, 1902 (1), p. 29 ; F. Dahl, 1908, p. 223, and 1927, p. 40 ; A. Holm, 1947, p. 35. *Pardosa paludicola* E. Simon, 1937, pp. 1066, 1086.

DESCRIPTION. LENGTH : ♀ : 9 mm. CARAPACE : Deep brown to black, with light brown bands. Median band dilated behind head, lateral dentate, but not broken, and continued round clypeus. ABDOMEN : Dark brown with grey mottlings, the whole appearing black at first sight. STERNUM : A broad, pale band discernible in the fore half. LEGS : Black to dark brown, with no clear markings. EPIGYNE : Text-fig. 131, E.

OCCURRENCE : In an open grassy area, cleared of trees, Parkhurst Forest, Isle of Wight, and at Plaistowe, Sussex (by the side of a pond). No males have yet been found in Britain.

Group IV
Lycosa rubrofasciata (Ohlert).
(Text-fig. 131, B, C, F)

Trochosa rubrofasciata E. Ohlert, 1865, p. 10. *Lycosa farrenii* O. P.-Cambridge 1871, p. 395, and 1879–81, p. 546. (O. P.-Cambridge's statement (1903, p. 160) that the species is synonymous with *L. ferruginea* L. Koch, 1870, followed by F. P. Smith (1907 (1), p. 28), is incorrect, as pointed out by Smith, 1907 (2), p. 188, and Cambridge, 1908, p. 182.) *Hygrolycosa rubrofasciata* F. Dahl, 1908, p. 366, and 1927, p. 14 ; A. Holm, 1947, p. 11. *Lycosa rubrofasciata* E. Simon, 1937, p. 1108.

DESCRIPTION. LENGTH : ♀ : 5·5–6 mm. ♂ : about 5·5 m. CARAPACE : Chocolate brown in darker parts. Median light band yellow-brown, extending whole length from just behind posterior median eyes. This is parallel-sided and flanked by stripes of the chocolate ground colour, also parallel-sided and equal in width to the median band. Outside these are wide, light lateral bands, broken by longitudinal rows of irregular dark spots. ABDOMEN : Red-brown. Median stripe lighter and reaching at least to the mid point, flanked by two pairs of light spots and dark divergent marks, directed obliquely backwards. It is followed by a succession of triangular light patches (their apices forwards). Outside these are three to four pairs of light spots (composed of light hairs) on the basal corners of the triangular light patches. Ventrally, often covered with small dark dots, especially in males. STERNUM : Reddish-brown, with a faint light streak from mid point of anterior margin to centre, and with a darker spot opposite each coxa. CHELICERÆ : Red-brown, with a dark parallel-sided stripe from mid point of basal to outer side of apical end. (This is characteristic and the stripes sometimes appear as a continuation of the carapace stripes, running right across the facies and clypeus down the cheliceræ.) LEGS : ♀ : Femora mottled with red-brown on yellow-brown ground ; tibiæ and metatarsi dark brown (especially IV) ; tarsi light brown. ♂ : Mottling on femora obscure, other segments lighter. EPIGYNE : Text-fig. 131, F. MALE PALP : Text-figs. 131, B, C. A male taken in June (1947) was very dark, the carapace stripes being scarcely visible. The colouring must vary considerably, judging by the descriptions of different authors, but the spider is not likely to be mistaken for any other.

OCCURRENCE : Wicken and Chippenham Fens (Cambridgeshire), Sherwood Forest (Nottinghamshire), Lincolnshire, Thetford (Norfolk). Often abundant locally.

2. Genus **XEROLYCOSA** F. Dahl 1908.

CHARACTERS OF GENUS. Very like *Lycosa* in general appearance. CARAPACE : Wider in front than in *Lycosa;* head, as seen from in front, not so elevated nor so straight sided. EYES : Anteriors small and sub-equal, the row nearly straight and not reaching outside edges of posterior medians. CLYPEUS : About 1·5 times wider than diameter of anterior medians, 1·5–2 times diameter of a lateral. CHELICERÆ : Two teeth in inner row (all others have three, except *Tarentula* and some species of *Trochosa*). LEGS : Tarsi I with trichobothria as in Text-fig. 122, H (cf. *Tarentula*).

Xerolycosa nemoralis (Westring).
(Text-fig. 132, A, B)

Lycosa nemoralis N. Westring, 1861, p. 472. *Tarentula nemoralis* C. Chyzer and L. Kulczynski, 1891–7, I, p. 68 ; F. P. Smith, 1907 (2), p. 185. *Tarentula meridiana* O. P.-Cambridge, 1909, p. 112. *Xerolycosa nemoralis* F. Dahl, 1908, p. 188, and 1927, p. 27 ; A. Holm, 1947, p. 23. *Lycosa nemoralis* E. Simon, 1937, p. 1106.

DESCRIPTION. LENGTH : ♀ : 4·5–7·5 mm. ♂ : 4·5–6 mm. CARAPACE : Deep brown or black ; median light stripe broad, very clear and almost parallel-sided, sometimes with a slight constriction near the middle ; covered with white hairs extending to front of head. Lateral bands formed of white hairs (not pigment). ABDOMEN : ♀ : Usually like *Tarentula barbipes* (see p. 275) at least as regards pattern, but variable in depth of colour especially round the lanceolate median stripe. Pattern in some specimens obscured by dense covering of hairs. ♂ : Darker ; pattern largely covered with a wide band of light hairs (which may become inconspicuous on long preservation). STERNUM : Dark brown to black, sometimes with light punctuations. CHELICERÆ : Dark brown, rather deeper in apical half. LEGS : ♀ : Brown with darker blotches, sometimes amounting to annulations,

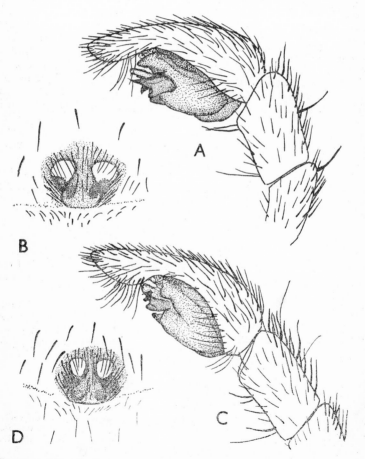

TEXT-FIG. 132.—*Xerolycosa nemoralis:* A, male palp ; B, epigyne. *X. miniata:* C, male palp ; D, epigyne.

except tibiæ and metatarsi III and IV which are not so dark, even light yellow, and tarsi which are all light yellow. ♂ : Rather darker, especially femora. EPIGYNE : Text-fig. 132, B. MALE PALP : Text-fig. 132, A. The spider has a characteristic reddish tinge in nature, but A. R. Jackson, 1932, p. 205, has noted a variety, called by him var. *cretata*, with hoary greyish pubescence. The males when alive are not unlike *Lycosa lugubris* at first sight.

OCCURRENCE : Very local in southern counties, but large numbers may then be found together. On the edges of woods and in clearings and on chalk. Adult towards the end of May and in June.

Xerolycosa miniata (C. L. Koch).
(Text-fig. 132, C, D)

Lycosa miniata C. L. Koch, 1834 (3), Hft., p. 123. *Tarentula miniata* O. P Cambridge, 1879–81, p. 548, and 1904, p. 112 ; C. Chyzer and L. Kulczynski, 1891–7, I, p. 69 ; F. P. Smith, 1907 (2), p. 184. *Xerolycosa miniata* F. Dahl, 1908, p. 190, and 1927, p. 28 ; A. Holm, 1947, p. 24 ; *Lycosa miniata*, E. Simon, 1937, p. 1108.

DESCRIPTION. LENGTH : ♀ : 5·5–6·5 mm. ♂ : 4·5–5·5 mm· This species differs from *X. nemoralis* in the following respects : CARAPACE : Median light band not quite so distinct in outline, with a small distinct constriction half-way from posterior end to front of head. Lateral light bands usually distinct, for their posterior half at least, and due to difference of pigmentation rather than to hairs. ABDOMEN : Ground colour somewhat lighter ; pattern usually less distinct. LEGS : Femora dark, otherwise lighter with the blotches less distinct. The spider has a spotted, sandy appearance (with no reddish tinge), quite distinct from that of *X. nemoralis*. EPIGYNE : Text-fig. 132, D. MALE PALP : Text-fig. 132, C.

OCCURRENCE : More widespread than the last species (it extends into Scotland). On sandhills round the coast. Very local.

3. Genus TARENTULA C. J. Sundevall 1833.

CHARACTERS OF GENUS. The spiders of this genus bear a certain resemblance to the larger species of *Lycosa*, from which they are distinguished by the following characters : CARAPACE : Wider in front than in *Lycosa;* head less elevated and with sloping sides. EYES : Anteriors small, equal in size or medians larger than laterals. Row straight or slightly procurved, not reaching outside edges of posterior medians. Clypeus little, if at all, wider than diameter of an anterior eye. CHELICERÆ : Two teeth in inner row. LEGS : Shorter, relatively, and rather stouter than in *Lycosa*. Tarsi with a long trichobothrium as in Text-fig. 122, F, G (cf. *Xerolycosa*). The covering of long hairs, whose colour determines the appearance of these spiders in the field, is characteristic. Four species are found in Britain : *Tarentula pulverulenta*, *T. cuneata*, *T. barbipes* and *T. fabrilis*.

Tarentula pulverulenta (Clerck).
(= *T. carinata* (Olivier))
(Text-fig. 133, A, E)

Araneus pulverulentus C. Clerck, 1757, p. 94.   *A. carinata* A. G. Olivier, 1789, p. 218.
Tarentula carinata W. S. Bristowe, 1939–41, p. 42.   *Lycosa rapax* J. Blackwall, 1841,
p. 609, and 1861–4, p. 21.   *Tarentula pulverulenta* O. P.-Cambridge, 1879–81, p. 364 ;
C. Chyzer and L. Kulczynski, 1891–7, I, p. 71 ;   F. Dahl, 1908, p. 354, and 1927, p. 24 ;
A. Holm, 1947, p. 18.   *Lycosa pulverulenta* E. Simon, 1937, pp. 1100, 1108.

DESCRIPTION.   LENGTH :   ♀ :   6·5–10 mm (the largest being found
on mountains).   ♂ : 5–8 mm.   CARAPACE :   Dark brown, covered
thickly with hairs.   A broad median lighter band, on which are white
hairs (very conspicuous in the living male) extends from head (which is
black) and tapers slightly from the region of the fovea backwards.   A
series of spine-like hairs runs from posterior median eyes to fovea,
giving appearance of a dark line.   Lateral light bands usually ill
defined or even absent (cf. *T. cuneata*) ;   although there are white
hairs here and there on the coxæ.   ABDOMEN :   Dark reddish-brown
(as seen in spirit) ;   the lighter median lanceolate stripe edged with
black marks, outside which is a clear lighter area, which extends,
tapering, to the spinners.   This area may contain, in its posterior part,
a pattern similar to that typical of *Lycosa*, especially in the male, where
the whole region tends to be darker.   The sides are mottled with black.
(In the living spider the variation is considerable, the pattern being
sometimes light and very distinct, sometimes almost absent ;
occasionally it approaches that of *T. barbipes*.)   STERNUM :   Dark
brown with lighter region in middle.   CHELICERÆ :   Dark brown
(deeper in the male) and darker at apices, sometimes with longitudinal
streaks, especially in the male.   LEGS :   ♀ :   Femora and tibiæ usually
dark brown, femora with dark blotches (sometimes amounting to
annulations on III and IV).   Metatarsi and tarsi yellow-brown (metatarsi I and II darkened in apical half).   ♂ :   Femora and bases, or
whole, of tibiæ I and II deep brown to black ;   metatarsi and tarsi
yellow (no especially thick or dark hairs on tibiæ and metatarsi I, as in
T. barbipes).   EPIGYNE :   Text-fig. 133, E.   MALE PALP :   Text-fig.
133, A ;   the whole limb dark.

OCCURRENCE :   A common and widespread species, occurring on
open ground, heaths and pastures and even urban gardens.   Specimens
from high altitudes (above 2,000 ft.) are often darker and larger than
usual.   Adult from April onwards.

Tarentula cuneata (Clerck).
(= *T. cuneata* (Sundevall))
(Text-figs. 122, G ;   133, B, E)

Araneus cuneatus C. Clerck, 1757, p. 99.   *Lycosa cuneata* C. J. Sundevall, 1832, p. 187.
Tarentula cuneata O. P.-Cambridge, 1879–81, p. 366 ;   C. Chyzer and L. Kulczynski,
1891–7, I, p. 71 ;   F. Dahl, 1908, p. 178, and 1927, p. 23 ;   A. Holm, 1947, p. 18 ;   W. S.
Bristowe, 1947, pl. 17.   *Lycosa cuneata* E. Simon, 1937, pp. 1099, 1103.

DESCRIPTION. LENGTH : ♀: 6–8 mm. ♂: 6–7·5 mm. The female of this species resembles that of *T. pulverulenta* closely and, as ordinarily seen, the epigynes are not distinguishable with any certainty. The following characters will usually serve to separate the present species. CARAPACE : Lateral light bands clearly defined. ABDOMEN : Dorsal light band (within which is the lanceolate stripe and its darker border) very clearly defined. (The living spider is almost always recognisable by this.) Mottlings on sides less distinct than in *T. pulverulenta*, or absent. LEGS : Yellow-brown, rarely so deeply pigmented on femora or tibiæ, but annulations may occur on III and IV. The male is recognisable, even in the field, by the swollen tibiæ I (Text-fig. 122, G). MALE PALP : Text-fig. 133, B.

OCCURRENCE : In the south, and west as far north as Cumberland. On heaths and open ground where the herbage is not too long. Not very common, but may be abundant locally, especially on chalk. Both sexes adult in April ; females continue into the summer.

Tarentula barbipes (Sundevall).
(Text-figs. 122, F ; 133, C, F)

Lycosa barbipes and *L. cruciata* C. J. Sundevall, 1832, p. 184. *Lycosa andrenivora* J. Blackwall, 1861–4, p. 20. *Tarentula andrenivora* O.P.-Cambridge, 1879–81, p. 366. *Tarentula accentuata* C. Chyzer and L. Kulczynski, 1891–7, I, p. 70 ; W. S. Bristowe, 1939–41, p. 41 ; A. Holm, 1947, p. 18. *T. barbipes* F. Dahl, 1908, p. 171, and 1927, p. 16. *Lycosa accentuata* E. Simon, 1937, pp. 1100, 1103.

DESCRIPTION. LENGTH : ♀: 8–12 mm. ♂: 7·5–9 mm. CARAPACE : Very like *T. pulverulenta;* median light band variable, sometimes very distinct, sometimes not (especially in preserved specimens) ; tapering more than in *T. pulverulenta;* in males covered with white hairs. ABDOMEN : General pattern as in *T. pulverulenta*, the chief differences being as follows : On either side of the mid point of the lanceolate stripe is a pair of narrow black bars pointing outwards and backwards (some specimens of *T. pulverulenta* possess these bars, visible particularly in living spiders) and a second pair usually occurs where the stripe ends ; further pairs of diminishing size may occur on the posterior half of the abdomen and outside them are rows of alternate dark and light spots. These markings are very characteristic and are usually visible in the field. They are usually obscured by white hairs in males. STERNUM : Uniform dark brown. LEGS : ♀: Yellow-brown to dark brown, with darker blotches amounting almost to annulations on all segments except tarsi. ♂ : Ventral sides of tibiæ and metatarsi I with dense black hairs (Text-fig. 122, F), which are displayed to the female when these legs are raised during courtship. Markings on other legs less distinct than in female. EPIGYNE : Text-fig. 133, F. MALE PALP : Text-fig. 133, C.

OCCURRENCE : Widespread over England, Scotland and Wales, but rather local. On open heaths and sometimes on chalk. Males adult in April and May ; females throughout the spring and summer.

Tarentula fabrilis (Clerck).
(= *T. fabrilis* (Walckenaer))
(Text-fig. 133, D, G)

Araneus fabrilis C. Clerck, 1757, p. 86. *Lycosa fabrilis* C. A. Walckenaer, 1805, p. 13. *Tarentula fabrilis* O. P.-Cambridge, 1879–81, p. 368 ; F. Dahl, 1908, p. 163, and 1927, p. 21 ; A. Holm, 1947, p. 16. *Lycosa fabrilis* E. Simon, 1937, p. 1099. *Tarentula solitaria* C. Chyzer and L. Kulczynski, 1891–7, I, p. 71.

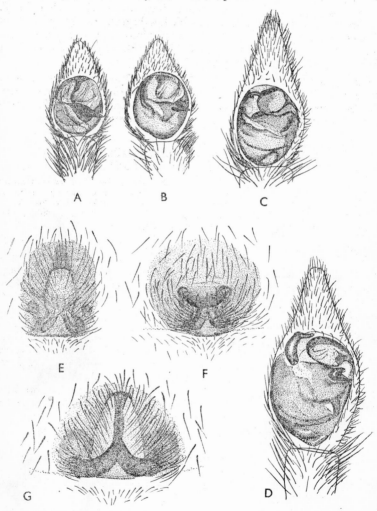

TEXT-FIG. 133.—Male palps (below) : A, *Tarentula pulverulenta;* B, *T. cuneata;* C, *T. barbipes;* D, *T. fabrilis.*
Epigynes : E, *Tarentula pulverulenta* and *cuneata;* F. *T. barbipes;* G, *T. fabrilis.*

DESCRIPTION. LENGTH: ♀: 13–16 mm. ♂: 10–12 mm. This very fine species is marked like *T. barbipes*, but is generally darker, especially on the ventral side of the abdomen. There are no dense, dark hairs on the first legs of the male. EPIGYNE: Text-fig. 133, G. MALE PALP: Text-fig. 133, D.

OCCURRENCE: Bloxworth Heath (Dorset).

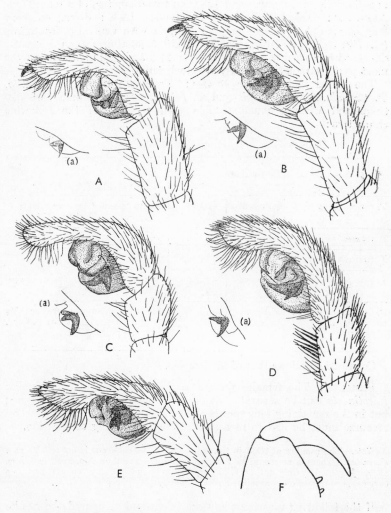

TEXT-FIG. 134.—Male palps: A, *Trochosa ruricola;* B, *T. robusta;* C, *T. terricola;* D, *T. spinipalpis;* E, *T. fulvolineata.* (*a* = median apophyses seen from side and a little above.) F, fang of *T. ruricola* ♂.

4. Genus **TROCHOSA** C. L. Koch 1846.

CHARACTERS OF GENUS. Large spiders (8–15 mm.) General colouration brown (never black). CARAPACE : Broad in front and characteristically marked (Text-fig. 122, D, p. 249). Covered with fine pubescence. EYES : Anteriors rather large ; medians larger than laterals (Text-fig. 122, C, p. 249). Anterior row reaching beyond outside edges of posterior medians. CLYPEUS : Narrow ; width about one diameter of a median and less than two diameters of a lateral eye. ABDOMEN : Covered with fine pubescence. LEGS : Stout, not very long compared to body size. ♀ : Tibia I with ventral *apical* spines (cf. *Pirata*). ♂ : Tibiæ, metatarsi and (sometimes) tarsi I usually darkened and used in courtship. EPIGYNE and MALE PALP : For the most part characteristic and very much alike.

The genus includes five species : *Trochosa ruricola, T. robusta, T. terricola, T. spinipalpis* and *T. fulvolineata*. The males are distinguished without much trouble with the aid of the following characters :

TROCHOSA (males)

	Palpal claw	Tarsus I	Other peculiar characters
T. ruricola . .	Present	Dark	An excrescence on the outside of the fang. (Text-fig. 134, F.)
T. robusta . .	Present	Dark	—
T. terricola . .	Absent	Light	—
T. spinipalpis . .	Absent	Light	Spines on ventral side of palpal tibia. (Text-fig. 134, D.)
T. fulvolineata . .	Absent	Light	The palpal organs are notably different from those of T. terricola

Colouration follows that of the females.

FEMALES : The females present considerable difficulty. *Trochosa fulvolineata* can be separated at once by the very different epigyne ; but in the remaining four species the epigynes can be very similar and recourse must be had to measurement and to noting colouration.

(*Note.*—The number of teeth in the inner row of the cheliceræ is *not* reliable as a character. There is no record of *T. terricola* having more than two, but the others, although quoted by some authors as having three, often possess only two and sometimes only one, or even different numbers on each chelicera.)

If the following measurements are taken and compared the results will provide a separation which has proved reliable on all specimens examined hitherto. *a, b, x, y* and *z* are lengths as indicated in Text-fig.

135. St. is the breadth of the sternum as measured between the coxæ II. It will be obvious that although overlap of the figures is frequent, if a measurement does not fall within such an overlap, it will be of use.

TROCHOSA (females)

	Colouration	Ratio b/St.	Ratio b/a	Ratio x/z of pigmented epigynal area	Ratio: diam. post. med. to diam. ant. med. eyes*
T. ruricola	Olive brown; dorsal abdominal stripe yellowish, lighter than surroundings.	0.18–0.22	3.1–3.9	0.72–1.1 (rather irregular)	1.6–2.1
T. robusta	Similar	0.23–0.30	3.8–4.9	0.85–0.95	2.0–2.3
T. terricola	Reddish brown; dorsal abdominal stripe not yellowish and about same depth of colour as surroundings.	0.30–0.33	4.5–5.7	1.05–1.12	2.1–2.5
T. spinipalpis	Similar but abdomen a deeper brown.	0.24–0.29	3.7–5.4	0.80–0.95	2.1–2.5

Ratio: y/z for T. robusta $=0.27$–0.35 ⎫ This gives a separation in addition to
    ,, ,, T. spinipalpis $=0.44$–0.47 ⎭   colour.

* In the posterior median eyes the clear part of the lens is surrounded by a darker ring. Measurements were made from the outside of this ring.

Trochosa ruricola (Degeer).
(Text-figs. 134, A, F; 136, A)

Aranea ruricola C. Degeer, 1778, p. 282. Lycosa campestris J. Blackwall, 1861–4, p. 18. Trochosa ruricola O. P.-Cambridge, 1879–81, p. 361; C. Chyzer and L, Kulczynski, 1891–7, I, p. 73; F. Dahl, 1908, p. 103, and 1927, p. 54; A. Holm, 1947. p. 13. Lycosa ruricola E. Simon, 1937, pp. 1109, 1112.

DESCRIPTION. LENGTH: ♀: 10–14 mm. ♂: 7·5–9 mm. CARAPACE: Area between lighter median and lateral stripes, dark olive-brown. Lateral bands rather narrow, their edges even. ABDOMEN: Olive-brown; median lanceolate stripe lightish yellow and usually well defined, often edged with darker colour. It is followed by faint lighter patches of diminishing size, sometimes joined, and flanked by darker bars or spots, which may form a continuous band, often alternating with little light streaks. Sides mottled. (In living spiders the pattern, apart from the lanceolate stripe, is obscure. Five to six pairs of light spots, each with a dark spot near it, run the length of the posterior half.) STERNUM: Light brown. CHELICERÆ: Usually with three teeth in inner row, but sometimes only two, or the third

U

(apical) one smaller, or even present one side and absent on the other. ♂: Fang with a small excrescence on the outside (Text-fig. 134, F), a character peculiar to the species. LEGS: Yellow-brown. ♀: Metatarsi, tarsi (and sometimes tibiæ) darker in preserved specimens. ♂: Femora with very faint annulations, which disappear on preservation. Tibiæ, metatarsi and tarsi I much darker and used in courtship. EPIGYNE: Text-fig. 136, A. MALE PALP: Text-fig. 134, A. The tarsus bears a claw; the tibia is rather long.

OCCURRENCE: Common throughout the British Isles. Found under stones, logs, etc.; nocturnal in habits. Adult throughout the year, especially in autumn and spring.

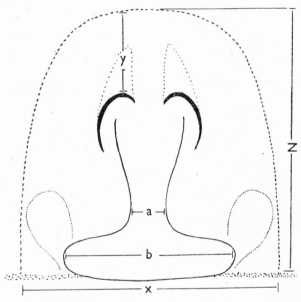

TEXT-FIG. 135.—Epigyne of *Trochosa* (see text).

Trochosa robusta (Simon).
(Text-figs. 134, B; 136, B)

Lycosa robusta E. Simon, 1876, II, p. 286, and 1937, p. 1110. *Trochosa robusta* C. Chyzer and L. Kulczynski, 1891—7, I, p. 73; F. O. P.-Cambridge, 1895, p. 30. *T. lapidicola* F. Dahl, 1908, p. 104, and 1927, p. 57.

DESCRIPTION. LENGTH: ♀: 11–18 mm. ♂: 9–18 mm. This species resembles *T. ruricola* very closely and, after preservation, *T. spinipalpis*. The most reliable characters for separating the species are given on pp. 278, 279. It is usually (but not always) larger than the other of the genus. EPIGYNE: Text-fig. 136, B. MALE PALP: Text-fig. 134, B.

OCCURRENCE: Widespread in England, but rare. In situations similar to *T. ruricola*. Adult in autumn, spring and early summer.

Trochosa terricola Thorell.
(Text-figs. 134, C; 136, C)

Trochosa terricola T. Thorell, 1856, p. 62. *Lycosa agretyca* J. Blackwall, 1861–4, p. 17. *Trochosa terricola* O. P.-Cambridge, 1879–81, p. 362; C. Chyzer and L. Kulczynski, 1891–7, p. 73; F. Dahl, 1908, p. 97, and 1927, p. 56; A. Holm, 1947, p. 14. *Lycosa terricola* E. Simon, 1937, p. 1109.

DESCRIPTION. LENGTH: ♀: 7·5–14 mm. ♂: 7–9 mm. CARA-PACE: Lateral light bands generally a little wider than in *T. ruricola* and with more jagged edges. ABDOMEN: Usually of a characteristic

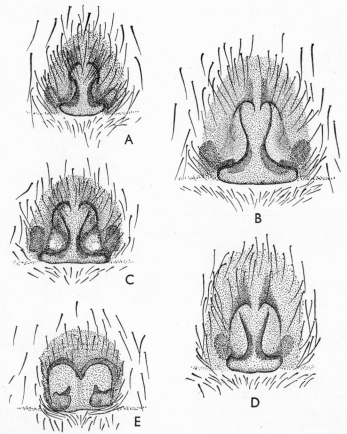

TEXT-FIG. 136.—Epigynes: A, *Trochosa ruricola;* B, *T. robusta;* C, *T. terricola;* D, *T. spinipalpis;* E, *T. fulvolineata.*

reddish-brown, but variable. Pattern similar to that of *T. ruricola,* but lanceolate stripe less well defined, not yellow but reddish-brown, similar to general ground colour. STERNUM: Reddish-brown. CHELICERÆ: With two teeth in the inner row. ♂: Fang with no excrescence (cf. *T. ruricola*). LEGS : Femora with faint dusky annulations (which fade on keeping). ♂ : Tibiæ and metatarsi I (but not tarsi) darkened. EPIGYNE : Text-fig. 136, C. This is characteristically broad. MALE PALP : Text-fig. 134, C. There is no claw on the tarsus ; the tibia is rather short.

OCCURRENCE : Widespread and common throughout the British Isles. It replaces *T. ruricola* locally, especially in dry, heathery places. Adult throughout the year, especially autumn and spring.

Trochosa spinipalpis (F. O. P.-Cambridge).
(Text-figs. 134, D ; 136, D)

Lycosa spinipalpis F. O. P.-Cambridge, 1895, p. 28 ; F. Dahl, 1908, p. 106, and 1927, p. 55 ; A. Holm, 1947, p. 14. *Lycosa spinipalpis* E. Simon, 1937, p. 1110.

DESCRIPTION. LENGTH : ♀ : 9·5 11 mm. ♂ : about 9 mm. This species resembles the last two closely. The distinguishing characters are set out on pp. 278,279. The female can be distinguished further from *T. terricola* if the specimen has three teeth in the inner row of the cheliceræ (as is usually the case). The umber brown colour of the abdomen, especially on the ventral side, is deeper, in adults, than in the other species and tends to persist after quite long preservation. EPIGYNE : Text-fig. 136, D. MALE PALP : Text-fig. 134, D. The ventral spines on the tibia are a distinctive character.

OCCURRENCE : Rare. Found as far north as Durham. Adult throughout the year, especially in May and June.

Trochosa fulvolineata (Lucas).
(Text-figs. 134, E ; 136, E)

Lycosa fulvolineata H. Lucas, 1846, p. 114 ; E. Simon, 1937, p. 1120. *Trochosa fulvolineata* A. R. Jackson, 1937, p. 279.

DESCRIPTION. LENGTH : ♀ : 10·5–12 mm. ♂ : 7·5–8·5 mm. The species bears a strong superficial resemblance to the others of the genus. The following characters will help to distinguish it. CARAPACE : Dark islands on median light band extremely faint, broken or absent. Lateral light bands broken or almost invisible. A series of rather dark bars radiate from fovea. ABDOMEN : Bright yellow lanceolate stripe very clear ; subsequent pattern ill-defined, most of the surface being covered with sooty black mottlings. Ventrally, a narrow tapering darker wedge runs from behind epigyne to spinners. CHELICERÆ : Inner row with two large teeth, with sometimes a third, smaller, apical tooth. LEGS : Brown (as carapace), with very faint annulations on femora. ♂ : No darkening of tibiæ and metatarsi visible. EPIGYNE : Text-fig. 136, E. MALE PALP : Text-fig. 134, E. This has no claw.

OCCURRENCE : Very rare. Hemley and Blythburgh (Suffolk) and in Dorset ; also Lymington and Beaulieu (Hampshire).

5. Genus **ARCTOSA** C. L. Koch 1848.

CHARACTERS OF GENUS. The spiders of this genus differ from those of the last in the following respects. The general colouration is often composed in part of black or grey instead of brown. CARAPACE: With no properly defined longitudinal light band. EYES: Anteriors smaller relatively to the posterior medians (not so obvious in *A. cinerea*). Anterior row rarely reaches beyond outside edges of posterior medians

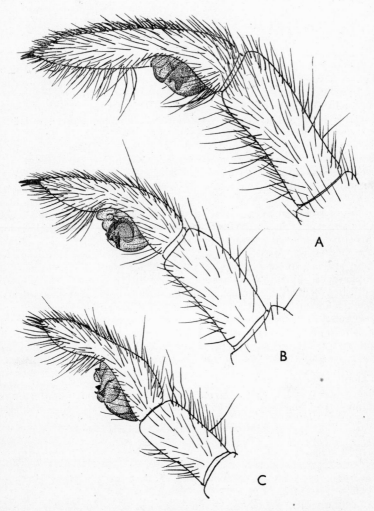

TEXT-FIG. 137.—Male palps : A, *Arctosa cinerea;* B, *A. perita;* C, *A. leopardus.*

(and only slightly so in *A. cinerea*). LEGS : More slender ; clearly annulated in the first two species. EPIGYNE and MALE PALP : Are notably different from *Trochosa*.

There are four British species : *Arctosa perita*, *A. leopardus*, *A. cinerea* and *A. alpigena*.

Arctosa perita (Latreille).
(Text-figs. 137, B ; 138, B)

Aranea perita P. A. Latreille, 1799, p. 170. *Lycosa picta* J. Blackwall, 1861–4, p. 25. *Trochosa picta* O. P.-Cambridge, 1879–81, p. 358. *T. perita* C. Chyzer and L. Kulczynski, 1891–7, I, p. 74. *Arctosa perita* F. Dahl, 1908, p. 144, and 1927, p. 69 ; A. Holm, 1947, p. 20. *Lycosa perita* E. Simon, 1937, p. 1115.

DESCRIPTION. LENGTH : ♀ : 6·5–8 mm. ♂ : about 8.5 mm. The colouring, black mixed with yellow or cream and red-brown, is similar in both sexes but variable. It is so disposed as to break up the surface and, with the annulated legs, the camouflage of the living spider, especially on sand, is very striking. CARAPACE : Ground colour variable from red-brown to grey with a sooty-black marginal band and another within it ; light space between irregular and often broken into isolated patches when the dark bands merge. Dark striæ radiate from fovea. There is a wide clear light patch immediately behind the eyes, on which are two transverse bars, sometimes reduced to spots, sometimes extending from the inner dark margin to the posterior lateral eyes. (Pattern somewhat obscured by pubescence in living spiders.) EYES : Anterior medians a little larger than anterior laterals. ABDOMEN : Typical Lycosid pattern discernible ; ground colour varies from black to a light greyish-brown. Dorsally : two pairs of large light spots, each followed by a pair of smaller spots, and between these are large, black spots or larger black areas. The colour and emphasis of the markings varies considerably, the paler parts are often reddish. Ventrally : almost uniform, black to light grey. STERNUM : Black. CHELICERÆ : Dark brown, a little darker at apices. LEGS : Very clearly annulated. Tibia I with two pairs of ventral spines (apart from the apical pair). Tibia II with two single spines, with sometimes a third (apart from the apical pair) (cf. *A. leopardus*). EPIGYNE : Text-fig. 138, B. MALE PALP : Text-fig. 137, B.

OCCURRENCE : Widespread. Frequent on dry heaths and sandy places, where, although it forms a burrow, it is often found running about in the sunshine. Adult in autumn, spring and early summer.

Arctosa leopardus (Sundevall).
(Text-figs. 137, C ; 138, C)

Lycosa leopardus C. J. Sundevall, 1833, p. 189. *L. cambrica* J. Blackwall, 1861–4, p. 32. *Trochosa leopardus* O. P.-Cambridge, 1879–81, p. 357 ; C. Chyzer and L. Kulczynski, 1891–7, I, p. 74. *Arctosa leopardus* F. Dahl, 1908, p. 147, and 1927, p. 71 ; A. Holm, 1947, p. 21. *Lycosa leopardus* E. Simon, 1937, p. 1116.

DESCRIPTION. LENGTH : ♀ : 8·5–9·5 mm. ♂ : 6·5–7 mm. CARAPACE : Sooty grey to almost black, with darker striations, radiating from fovea, marked out in lighter pubescence. Small lighter patches behind head (reminiscent of those in *A. perita*) sometimes present, and usually faint very irregular lighter lateral bands. Dark regions of the sides, clear of pubescence, pass round sides of head and include the clypeus. EYES : Anterior medians larger than laterals. ABDOMEN : Ground colour olive-brown to deep brown ; median lanceolate stripe distinct in preserved, but not living, specimens, followed by four to five pairs of light spots (consisting of silvery hairs), which are striking in the living spider but difficult to make out in preserved specimens. Two pairs of rather large dark spots occur on the posterior half. Ventrally : a darker grey region a little constricted in the middle, on a light ground. STERNUM : Dark, sometimes with light patches opposite coxæ. CHELICERÆ : Black, dark brown or grey, similar to head. LEGS : Distinctly annulated. Tibia I with one pair of ventral spines (apart from the apical pair), tibia II with a single ventral spine (apart from the apical pair) (cf. *A. perita*). EPIGYNE : Text-fig. 138, C. MALE PALP : Text-fig. 137, C. Each claw is reduced to little more than a stout spine.

OCCURRENCE : Widespread but not common. Amongst moss and detritus in wet or marshy places. It seems not to form a regular burrow, but constructs a cell among rubbish or leaves. Found occasionally running in sunshine, but not often. Adult in late spring and summer.

Arctosa cinerea (Fabricius).
(Text-figs. 137, A ; 138, D)

Aranea cinerea J. C. Fabricius, 1777, p. 249. *Lycosa allodroma* J. Blackwall, 1861–4, p. 23. *Trochosa cinerea* O. P.-Cambridge, 1879–81, p. 545 ; C. Chyzer and L. Kulczynski, 1891–97, I, p. 73. *Arctosa cinerea* F. Dahl, 1908, p. 138, and 1927, p. 70 ; A. Holm, 1947, p. 20. *Lycosa cinerea* E. Simon, 1937, p. 1113.

DESCRIPTION. LENGTH : ♀ : 12–17 mm. ♂ : about 14 mm. This is one of our largest spiders and cannot very well be taken for any other species. CARAPACE : Dark brown or grey, almost uniform but for radiating striæ. ABDOMEN : Dark. Lanceolate stripe dilated at about its mid point, edged with black and flanked by two black spots on its front half. From its posterior half three to four dark bars proceed outwards and backwards. Dark transverse marks and light patches occur on posterior half of abdomen. STERNUM and CHELICERÆ : Dark brown or black. LEGS : Annulated, obscurely on ventral sides, especially femora. Tibia I with two pairs of ventral spines (excepting the apical ones). EPIGYNE : Text-fig. 138, D. MALE PALP : Text-fig. 137, A.

OCCURRENCE : A northern species, possibly on account of its habitat. It is found among stones in river beds and by lakes, where it constructs a silken tube, usually opening under a stone. It appears to stay in its tube even when the river rises and covers the stones during the winter months. Adult in autumn, spring and early summer and, possibly, throughout the year.

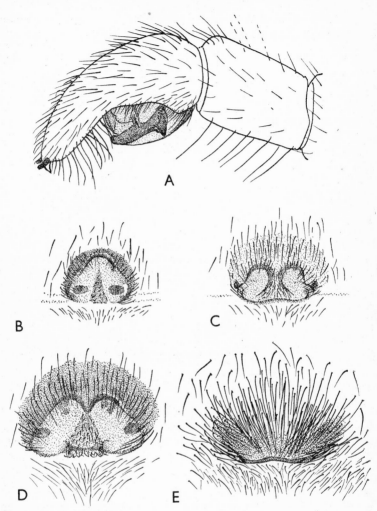

TEXT-FIG. 138.—A, male palp, *Arctosa alpigena.*
Epigynes : B, *A. perita;* C, *A. leopardus;* D, *A. cinerea;* E, *A. alpigena.*

Arctosa alpigena (Doleschal).
(Text-fig. 138, A, E)

Lycosa alpigena L. Doleschal, 1852, p. 643. *L. biunguiculata* O. P.-Cambridge, 1873 (2), p. 526, and 1879–81, p. 544. *Arctosa biunguiculata* W. S. Bristowe, 1939–41, p. 43 (corrected to *A. alpigena,* 1941, p. xi). *Arctosa alpigena* F. Dahl, 1908, p. 149, and 1927, p. 67 ; J. Braendegaard, 1939, p. 5 ; A. Holm, 1947, p. 22. *Lycosa alpigena* E. Simon, 1937, p. 1112.

DESCRIPTION. LENGTH : ♀: ca. 10 mm. ♂: ca. 8 mm. CARAPACE:
Red-brown, with darker, almost black, radiating markings, especially
two oblique dark bars at juncture of cephalic and thoracic regions.
Covered thickly on the head with grey-brown hairs, whose colour
predominates in living specimens. ABDOMEN : Brown, with black bars
along the front margin. Lanceolate stripe, which is striking in the
living spider, nearly white with a black border, obtuse at its posterior
end, followed by transverse bars, which are considerably broken up.
(It would seem that the British specimens are less clearly marked than
those from Greenland, in which clearly-defined cross lines follow the
lanceolate stripe. Braendegaard, 1939.) Abdomen in the living
spider covered with brown hairs. The lanceolate stripe cream and
conspicuous, flanked in its posterior half by a pair of dark patches.
The transverse bars picked out along their posterior edges with whitish
hairs. LEGS : Coloured as carapace ; no markings except for dusky
patches on femora. Tibiae I and II with two pairs of ventral spines
(excepting the apical pair). EPIGYNE : Text-fig. 138, E. MALE PALP :
Text-fig. 138, A. The tarsus is curved down at the tip like a hawk's
beak, and on either side is a short, stumpy projection (as opposed to the
longer claws found in the other species of the genus).
OCCURRENCE : Very rare. On mountains above 3,000 ft. The
Cairngorms. Adult in June and July and, possibly, later.

6. Genus **PIRATA** C. J. Sundevall 1833.

CHARACTERS OF GENUS. At first sight these spiders resemble those
of the genus *Lycosa;* the general colouration varies from light brown to
almost black with, often, conspicuous white hairs along the sides of the
carapace and in little tufts on the abdomen. CARAPACE : Marked with
a more or less distinct " V " just in front of fovea and pointing backwards (not very clear in *P. piscatorius*) ; arms of V may extend to
between posterior median eyes (Text-fig. 122, E). EYES : Anterior
medians equal to, or little larger than, laterals. Row reaches outside
edge of posterior medians, exceeding it slightly in *P. piscatorius*.
CLYPEUS : About equal to diameter of anterior median eye (cf. *Lycosa*).
LEGS : Tibia I with no ventral *apical* spines (cf. *Trochosa*).
The four British species, *Pirata piraticus*, *P. hygrophilus*, *P.
latitans* and *P. piscatorius*, inhabit marshes and damp places. They
sometimes build silk tubes opening on the surface of water, on which
they can run easily. The egg-cocoon is spherical and white.

Pirata piraticus (Clerck).
(= *P. piraticus* (Olivier))
(Text-fig. 139, B, F)

Araneus piraticus C. Clerck, 1757, p. 102. *Aranea piratica* A. G. Olivier, 1789,
p. 218. *Lycosa piratica* J. Blackwall, 1861–4, p. 34. *Pirata piraticus* O. P.-Cambridge,
1879–81, p. 353 ; C. Chyzer and L. Kulczynski, 1891–7, I, p. 76 ; F. Dahl, 1908,
p. 113, and 1927, p. 64 ; A. Holm, 1947, p. 10 ; B. J. Kaston, 1948, p. 309. *Lycosa
piratica* E. Simon, 1937, p. 1118.

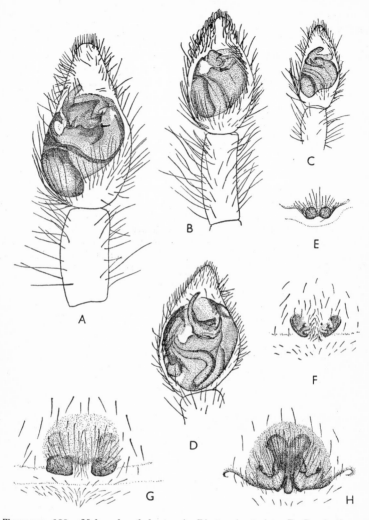

TEXT-FIG. 139.—Male palps (below): A, *Pirata piscatorius;* B, *P. piraticus;* C, *P. latitans;* D, *P. hygrophilus.*
Epigynes: E, *Pirata latitans;* F, *P. piraticus;* G, *P. piscatorius;* H, *P. hygrophilus.*

DESCRIPTION. LENGTH: ♀: 4·5–9 mm. ♂: 4–6·5 mm. CARAPACE: Brown; median light band widely dilated in front of fovea. Within this dilation is a pair of brown streaks, with a narrow light streak between them, forming a point at fovea and extending forwards to head, where they converge again. Ocular area with a narrow light margin. Lateral light bands somewhat variable and usually stopping just anterior to fovea. There is a broken dark marginal line, sometimes doubled, and white hairs along margin, visible especially in living spiders. EYES : Anterior medians larger than laterals ; anterior row as long as distance between outsides of posterior medians. ABDOMEN : Reddish to yellow-brown. Lanceolate median mark distinct, with no dark margin, but flanked by two pairs of dark patches and followed by four to five obscure dark transverse bars. On ends of these bars are groups of white hairs forming spots, which are thus disposed in two longitudinal rows. (They are conspicuous in the living spider, and often appear blue, but are difficult to see in most preserved specimens.) The sides mottled with white, due to groups of hairs, not pigment. STERNUM : Light brown, usually with dark patches opposite first three pairs of coxæ (characteristic of this species). CHELICERÆ : Yellow to light brown. LEGS : Brown, as carapace. Very faint annulations sometimes on femora of dark specimens. EPIGYNE : Text-fig. 139, F. MALE PALP : Text-fig. 139, B.

OCCURRENCE : Frequent in damp situations and marshes throughout the country. Males adult in April, May and June ; females probably throughout the year.

Pirata hygrophilus Thorell.
(Text-fig. 139, D, H)

Pirata hygrophilus T. Thorell, 1872, p. 343. *Lycosa piscatoria* J. Blackwall, 1861–4' p. 36. *Pirata hygrophilus* O. P.-Cambridge, 1879–81, p. 352 ; C. Chyzer and L. Kulczynski, 1891–7, I, p. 76 ; F. Dahl, 1908, p, 120 and 1927, p. 59 ; A. Holm, 1947, p. 9. *Lycosa hygrophilus* E. Simon, 1937, p. 1116.

DESCRIPTION. LENGTH : ♀ : 5–6·5 mm. ♂ : 4·5–5·5 mm. This species differs from the foregoing in the following respects : CARAPACE : A dark band between margin and lateral light band. Light margin round ocular area very faint or, more usually, absent. EYES : Anterior row very slightly shorter than distance between outsides of posterior medians. ABDOMEN : Lanceolate stripe less distinct, with dark border, followed by a series of triangular light markings (their apices forwards) with white spots, formed of white hairs, on ends of their bases. STERNUM : Darker (especially in the male) with a lighter central area in most specimens. No dark spots opposite coxæ. LEGS : Annulations on femora usually visible. EPIGYNE : Text-fig. 139, H. MALE PALP : Text-fig. 139, D. The general colouring is usually darker than in the last species and the spider often appears almost black when running.

OCCURRENCE : All over the British Isles ; in marshy places, often very common. Males adult April to July ; females probably at all seasons.

Pirata latitans (Blackwall).
(Text-fig. 139, C, E)

Lycosa latitans J. Blackwall, 1841, p. 612, and 1861–4, p. 33. *Pirata latitans* O.P. Cambridge, 1879–81, p. 355 ; C. Chyzer and L. Kulczynski, 1891–7, I, p. 76 ; F. Dahl, 1908, p. 298, and 1927, p. 61. *Lycosa latitans* E. Simon, 1937, p. 1117.

DESCRIPTION. LENGTH : ♀: 4–5 mm. ♂: 2·5–4·5 mm. CARA-
PACE : Median light band absent or very narrow and obscure. Immediately in front of fovea is a dark wedge-shaped mark (sometimes with
a faint light margin) pointing backwards, not divided as in last two
species and more obtuse, reaching rather less than half-way to head.
No lateral light bands, but a number of white hairs in that region,
difficult to make out in preserved specimens, and a very narrow dark
line along the margin. Radiating dark brown veinings usually well
defined. EYES : Anterior row not wider (usually a little narrower)
than distance between outsides of posterior medians. ABDOMEN :
Rather dark reddish-brown ; lanceolate stripe not well defined, sometimes surrounded by a broken ill-defined dark border. Subsequent
bars and light spaces sometimes well marked but usually very obscure
or absent. White spots occur as in other species. There are also
white hairs on fore part and sides, difficult to see in preserved specimens.
STERNUM : Dark brown, sometimes with lighter area in centre. LEGS :
Faint traces of annulations. Colour darker in male as a rule.
EPIGYNE : Text-fig. 139, E. MALE PALP : Text-fig. 139, C.

OCCURRENCE : Widespread, but rare or very local. Marshes.
Adult from April to July and possibly at other seasons.

Pirata piscatorius (Clerck).
(= P. umbraticola (C. L. Koch))
(Text-fig. 139, A, G)

Araneus piscatorius C. Clerck, 1757, p. 203. *Trochosa umbraticola* C. L. Koch, 1848
(1), XIV, p. 137. *Pirata umbraticola* W. S. Bristowe, 1939–41, p. 45, and 1947, pl. 18.
P. piscatorius O. P.-Cambridge, 1879–81, p. 351 ; C. Chyzer and L. Kulczynski, 1891–7,
I, p. 76 ; F. Dahl, 1908, p. 118, and 1927, p. 63 ; A. Holm, 1947, p. 10. *Lycosa
piscatoria* E. Simon, 1937, p. 1118.

DESCRIPTION. LENGTH : ♀: 5–10 mm. ♂: 4·5–8·5 mm. CARA-
PACE : Deep red-brown with no clear central or lateral bands, but with
white hairs along the sides. A very slightly lighter region behind head
contains the wedge-shaped marking, consisting of two, often very
obscure bars converging nearly to a point at fovea. EYES : Anterior
row slightly longer than distance between outside edges of posterior
medians. ABDOMEN : Usually deep brown ; pattern obscure but for
lanceolate stripe. The white spots (groups of hairs) are on dark blotches
between which are light transverse spaces, but these latter may be
obscure or absent. STERNUM : Deep red-brown with, sometimes, a
lighter central streak. LEGS : Red-brown with faint streaks on femora.
EPIGYNE : Text-fig. 139, G. MALE PALP : Text-fig. 139, A.

OCCURRENCE : Widespread. A rather rare species of marshes.
Adult in May and June ; females probably at all seasons.

7. Genus **AULONIA** C. L. Koch 1848.

CHARACTERS OF GENUS. General appearance like *Lycosa*. CARA-
PACE : Attenuated in front, head long. No light central or lateral
bands. EYES : Anterior row strongly procurved, as seen from in front,

not reaching outside edges of posterior medians. ABDOMEN : Posterior
SPINNERS the longest, with basal segment wider apically than at base
(Text-fig. 122, A, p. 249). CHELICERÆ : With apices somewhat
attenuated. PALP : Patella light yellow or white (in both sexes), the
rest darkened.

There is but one British species, *Aulonia albimana*.

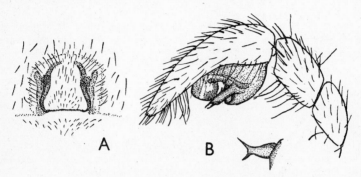

TEXT-FIG. 140.—*Aulonia albimana:* A, epigyne ; B, male palp.

Aulonia albimana (Walckenaer).
(Text-figs. 122, A ; 140, A, B)

Lycosa albimana C. A. Walckenaer, 1805, p. 14. *Aulonia albimana* C. Chyzer and
L. Kulczynski, 1891–7, I, p. 50 ; F. Dahl, 1908, p. 128, and 1927, p. 73 ; E. Simon,
1937, p. 1087 ; W. S. Bristowe, 1939, p. 44 ; A. Holm, 1947, p. 22.

DESCRIPTION. LENGTH : ♀ : 3·5–4·5 mm. ♂ : about 3·5 mm.
CARAPACE : Dark brown with deeper mottlings and striæ, head dark.
No lateral bands but a border of white hairs. ABDOMEN : Dark
brown with fine lighter mottlings. No distinct pattern, but lanceolate
stripe just visible. Colour darker, almost black in male. STERNUM :
Medium brown, sometimes with indistinct darker bars converging to
middle. CHELICERÆ : Little lighter than carapace, with very faint
streaks and slight darkening apically. LEGS : Femora I black, the
rest uniform yellow-brown. PALP : Patella light yellow or white, in
both sexes (a character very noticeable, even in the field). EPIGYNE :
Text-fig. 140, A. MALE PALP : Text-fig. 140, B.

OCCURRENCE : In a gravel pit near Dunster, Somerset. Adult in
May and June ; females probably later.

17. Family PISAURIDÆ.

The spiders of this family are intermediate in structure between the LYCOSIDÆ and the AGELENIDÆ. They are distinguished from the former family by four obvious characters. EYES: The second row is much shorter than the third row; the distance between the posterior eyes being more than double the distance of each eye from the corresponding eye in the second row (Text-fig. 10, C, D, p. 35). FOOT CLAWS: Larger than in LYCOSIDÆ, the paired ones bearing many teeth. ABDOMEN: More tapering behind. MALE PALPAL TIBIA: With an apophysis (Text-fig. 142, A, C). The females carry their egg-cocoons in their chelicerae and not attched to the spinners, as do the LYCOSIDÆ.

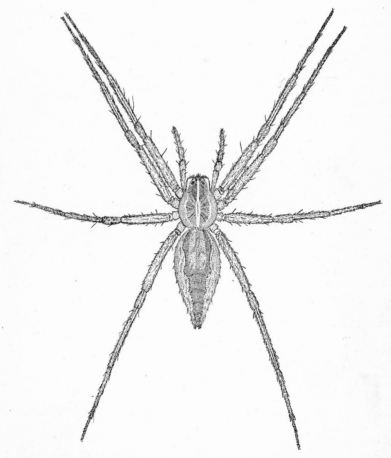

TEXT-FIG. 141.—*Pisaura mirabilis* ♀ (PISAURIDÆ).

The two British representatives, *Pisaura mirabilis* (Clerck) and *Dolomedes fimbriatus* (Clerck), are very distinct species and are easy to recognise.

1. Genus **PISAURA** E. Simon 1885.

Pisaura mirabilis (Clerck).

(= *P. listeri* (Scopoli))
(Text-figs. 141 ; 142, A, B)

Araneus mirabilis C. Clerck, 1757, p. 108. *Aranea listeri* J. A. Scopoli, 1763, p. 397.
Dolomedes mirabilis J. Blackwall, 1861–4, p. 37. *Ocyale mirabilis* O. P.-Cambridge,
1879–81, p. 346. *Pisaura mirabilis* C. Chyzer and L. Kulczynski, 1891–7, I, p. 78.
P. listeri F. Dahl, 1908, p. 84, and 1927, p. 7 ; A. Holm, 1947, p. 40. *P. mirabilis*
E. Simon, 1937, p. 1048.

DESCRIPTION. LENGTH : ♀ : 12-15 mm. ♂ : about 12 mm. Text-fig. 141 shows the female in an attitude often adopted when at rest. The colouration is somewhat variable but generally as in the following description. CARAPACE : Red-brown, with a narrow longitudinal yellowish stripe reaching to front of head. Striæ radiating from fovea form a distinct pattern. Between central stripe and margins run two fainter light stripes. (The white and yellow hairs present on the carapace become much obscured in spirit.) ABDOMEN : Pattern generally as in Text-fig. 141, but varies considerably according to depth of colouring ; general colouration brown, lighter regions being yellowish or even white. The whole abdomen covered with a dense pubescence, with central region often darker in males. LEGS : Nearly uniform brown. ♂ resembles ♀ but with markings usually more distinct. EPIGYNE : Text-fig. 142, B. MALE PALP : Text-fig. 142, A

OCCURRENCE : Common almost everywhere, in long grass, heather and in open woods. Adult in May ; females persist into July. The female carries her egg-cocoon in her cheliceræ, and when the eggs are about to hatch she constructs a covering like a tent, in which the young remain until they are dispersed. The mother guards them, but often runs away if disturbed.

2. Genus **DOLOMEDES** Latreille 1804.

Dolomedes fimbriatus (Clerck).

(= *D. fimbriatus* (Linnaeus))
(Text-fig. 142, C, D)

Araneus fimbriatus C. Clerck, 1757, p. 166. *A. fimbriatus+virescens+palustris*
C. Linnaeus, 1758, p. 621. *Dolomedes fimbriatus+ornatus* J. Blackwall, 1861–4, p. 40.
D. fimbriatus O. P. Cambridge, 1879–81, p. 348. *D. fimbriatus+limbatus+plantarius*
C. Chyzer and L. Kulczynski, 1891–7, I, p. 76. *D. fimbriatus* F. Dahl, 1908, p. 78, and
1927, p. 8 ; E. Simon, 1937, p. 1050 ; A. Holm, 1947, p. 40.

DESCRIPTION. LENGTH : ♀ : 13-20 mm. (and possibly larger). ♂ : 9-13 mm. CARAPACE : Deep brown, with two broad longitudinal pale yellow (or white) bands not far from each margin. ABDOMEN : Deep brown, with two lateral longitudinal light yellow-white bands which appear as a continuation of those on the carapace, but with rather less clearly-cut edges.   A median lanceolate mark is present, but not so striking as the other bands.   Between the two, small white spots occur in some specimens. LEGS : Uniform brown. EPIGYNE : Text-fig. 142, D.   MALE PALP : Text-fig. 142, C.

This very fine spider, with light longitudinal bands on a deep brown background, is very striking and could not be mistaken for another

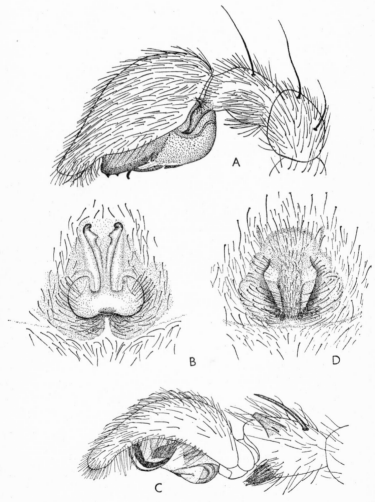

TEXT-FIG. 142.—*Pisaura mirabilis:* A, male palp ; B, epigyne. *Dolomedes fimbriatus:* C, male palp ; D, epigyne.

British species. (The markings owe their appearance partly to colours of the hairs and are consequently less striking after preservation.)

OCCURRENCE : Widespread over the British Isles but very local, being found only in swamps or pools or streams which do not dry up. Many may be found together. They will climb down the stems of plants to beneath the surface of water if alarmed. Adult in spring or early summer.

X

VII. BIBLIOGRAPHY

AUDOUIN, V., 1827. Explication sommaire des planches d'Arachnides de l'Égypte et de la Syrie. (*In*) Savigny, Descr. de l'Egypte, 2nd edit., **22**, pp. 169–434.

BERLAND, J., 1916. Note préliminaire sur le cribellum et le calamistrum des araignées cribellates et sur les moeurs de ces araignées. *Arch. Zool. Exp. Gén. Paris*, **55**, Notes et Revue (4), pp. 53–66 ; 8 figs.

BERLAND, L., 1911. Sur deux araignées recueillies à la Sorbonne ; *Physocyclus simoni* n. sp. et *Macrargus dentichelis* E. Simon. *Arch. Zool. Exp. Gén.* (5), **6**, Notes et Revue, pp. cx–cxv.

BERTKAU, P., 1878. Versuch einer natürlich Anordnung der Spinnen, nebst Bemerkungen zu einzelnen Gattungen. *Arch. Naturgesch. Berlin*, **44** (1), pp. 351–410, pl. xii.

BLACKWALL, J., 1833. Characters of some undescribed genera and species of Araneidæ. *Phil. Mag.* (3), **3**, pp. 104–112, 187–197, 344–352, 436–443.

———— 1834. Researches in Zoology, London.

———— 1836. Characters of some undescribed species of Araneidæ. *Phil. Mag.* (3), **8**, pp. 481–491.

———— 1841. The difference in the number of eyes with which spiders are provided. *Trans. Linn. Soc. London*, **18**, pp. 601–670.

———— 1845. A Catalogue of Spiders not previously recorded, etc. *Trans. Linn. Soc. London*, **19**, pp. 113–130.

———— 1846. Descriptions of some newly discovered species of Araneida. *Ann. Mag. Nat. Hist.* (1), **18**, pp. 297–303.

———— 1851. A Catalogue of British Spiders. *Ann. Mag. Nat. Hist.* (2), **7**, pp. 256–262, 396–402, 446–452, **8**, pp. 37–44, 95–102, 332–339, 442–450.

———— 1853. Descriptions of some newly discovered species of Araneidea. *Ann. Mag. Nat. Hist.* (2), **11**, pp. 14–25.

———— 1854. Descriptions of some newly discovered species of Araneidea. *Ann. Mag. Nat. Hist.* (2), **13**, pp. 173–180.

———— 1855. Descriptions of two newly discovered species of Araneidea. *Ann. Mag. Nat. Hist.* (2), **16**, pp. 120–122.

———— 1857. Description of the male of *Lycosa tarentuloides Maderiana* Walck., and of three newly discovered species of the genus *Lycosa*. *Ann. Mag. Nat. Hist.* (2), **20**, pp. 282–287.

———— 1859. Descriptions of six recently discovered species, and characters of a new genus of Araneida. *Ann. Mag. Nat. Hist.* (3), **3**, pp. 91–98.

———— 1861. Descriptions of several recently discovered spiders. *Ann. Mag. Nat. Hist.* (3), **8**, pp. 441–446.

———— 1861-4. A history of the spiders of Great Britain and Ireland, **1**, 1861, pp. 1–174, pls. i–xii ; **2**, 1864, pp. 175–384, pls. xiii–xxix. *Ray Society, London*.

BOSENBERG, W., 1901–3. Die Spinnen Deutschlands. *Zoologica, Stuttgart*, **14**, Heft 35 (1), pp. 1–96, pls. i–viii (1901) ; (2, 3, 4), pp. 97–384, pls. ix–xxxvi (1902) ; (5, 6), pp. 385–465, pls. xxxvii–xliii (1903).

BRAENDEGAARD, J., 1932. Fortegnelse over Danmarks Edderkopper. (I) E. Nielsen, De Danske Edderkoppers Biologi, Copenhagen, **1932**, pp. 679–712.

———— 1939. *Arctosa alpigena* Doleschall, 1852 and *Arctosa insignata* Thorell, 1872. *Medd. Grønland*, **108** (7), pp. 5–11, five figs.

———— 1940. Spiders from North East Greenland. *Medd. Grønland*, **125** (8), pp. 12–30.

———— 1946. Spiders of East Greenland. *Medd. Grønland*, **121** (15), pp. 1–128, 49 figs.

BRISTOWE, W. S., 1922. Spiders found in the neighbourhood of Oxshott. *Proc. S. Lond. Ent. Nat. Hist. Soc.*, 1922–3, pp. 1–11, two pls.

—— 1930. Notes on the biology of spiders, III. *Ann. Mag. Nat. Hist.* (10), **6,** pp. 347–353.

—— 1933 (1). Notes on the biology of spiders, IX. The British species of *Atypus. Ann. Mag. Nat. Hist.* (10), **11,** pp. 289–302, eight figs.

—— 1933 (2). Notes on the biology of spiders, X. *Ann. Mag. Nat. Hist.* (10), **11,** pp. 509–514, two figs.

—— 1938. The classification of spiders. *Proc. Zool. Soc. London,* Ser. B., **108,** pp. 285–322, 13 figs.

—— 1939–41. The Comity of Spiders. *Ray Society, London,* **1,** 1939, pp. 1–228, 15 figs., pls. i–xix, **2,** 1941, pp. 229-560, 80 figs., pls. xx–xxii.,

—— 1945. Spider miscellany. *Journ. Queckett Micr. Club* (ser. 4), **2,** pp. 63–67.

—— 1947. Spiders. *Penguin Books,* London, pp. 1–33, pls. i–xxiv. (The plates were drawn by A. T. Hollick in 1867–70 for a supplement, planned by O. Pickard-Cambridge, to J. Blackwall's " Spiders of Great Britain and Ireland " (1861–4).)

—— 1948. Notes on the structure and systematic position of Oonopid spiders. *Proc. Zool. Soc. London,* **118,** pt. iii, pp. 88–891, 26 figs.

CAMBRIDGE, F. O. PICKARD-, 1895. Notes on British spiders, with descriptions of new species. *Ann. Mag. Nat. Hist.* (6), **15,** pp. 25–40, two pls.

—— 1901. A review of the genera of the Araneæ or spiders with reference to their type species. *Ann. Mag. Nat. Hist.* (7), **7,** pp. 51–65.

—— 1902. A revision of the genera of the Araneæ or spiders, with reference to their type species. *Ann. Mag. Nat. Hist.* (7), **9,** pp. 5–20.

—— 1903. A revision of the genera of Araneæ or spiders with reference to their type species. *Ann. Mag. Nat. Hist.* (7), **11,** pp. 32–51.

*CAMBRIDGE, O. PICKARD-, 1861. Descriptions of ten new species of spiders lately discovered in England. *Ann. Mag. Nat. Hist.* (3), **8,** pp. 428–441, one pl.

—— 1862. Descriptions of ten new species of British spiders. *Zoologist,* **20,** pp. 7951–7969.

—— 1863. Descriptions of twenty-four new species of spiders. *Zoologist,* **21,** pp. 8561–8599.

—— 1871. Descriptions of some British spiders new to science. *Trans. Linn. Soc. London,* **27,** pp. 393–464, four pls.

—— 1873 (1). On British spiders. *Trans. Linn. Soc. London,* **28,** pp. 433–458, three pls.

—— 1873 (2). On new and rare British spiders. *Trans. Linn. Soc. London,* **28,** pp. 523–555, one pl.

—— 1873 (3). On some new species of European spiders. *Jour. Linn. Soc. London,* **11,** pp. 530–547, two pls.

—— 1874. On some new species of Drassides. *Proc. Zool. Soc. London,* **1874,** pp. 370–419, two pls.

—— 1875. Notes and descriptions of some new and rare British spiders. *Ann. Mag. Nat. Hist.* (4), **16,** pp. 317–322, one pl.

—— 1878. Notes on British spiders with descriptions of new species. *Ann. Mag. Nat. Hist.* (5), **1,** pp. 105–128, one pl.

—— 1879–81. The Spiders of Dorset. Sherborne, Pt. 1 (1879), pp. 1–235 ; Pt. 2 (1881), pp. 236–625, six pls.

—— 1879. On some new and rare British spiders, with characters of a new genus. *Ann. Mag. Nat. Hist.* (5), **4,** pp. 190–215, one pl.

—— 1882. Notes on British spiders, with descriptions of three new species and characters of a new genus. *Ann. Mag. Nat. Hist.* (5), **9,** pp. 1–13, one pl.

—— 1885 (1). On new and rare British spiders, with some remarks on the formation of new species. *Proc. Dorset Nat. Hist. Field Club,* **6,** pp. 1–17, one pl.

*In his earlier works the author designated himself " The Rev. O. P. Cambridge " and in most of the literature references to his work are found under the name " Cambridge." Later he wrote " The Rev. O. Pickard-Cambridge ", which is the family name. We have thought it best, however, to list the references to his work under the name " Cambridge ", as this will be found most convenient when consulting other literature. The works rf his nephew, F. O. Pickard-Cambridge, may be found also under either heading.

—— 1885 (2). Descriptions of two new species of Araneida. *Ann. Mag. Nat. Hist.* (5), **16**, pp. 237–238, one pl.

—— 1886. On some new and rare British spiders. *Proc. Dorset Nat. Hist. Field Club*, **7**, pp. 70–78 (sep. 1–9), one pl.

—— 1889. On new and rare British spiders. *Proc. Dorset Nat. Hist. Field Club*, **10**, pp. 107–138, one pl.

—— 1893. On new and rare British spiders. *Proc. Dorset Nat. Hist. Field Club*, **14**, pp. 142–164, one pl

—— 1894 (1). On new and rare British spiders found in 1893, with rectifications of synonyms. *Proc. Dorset Nat. Hist. Field Club*, **15**, pp. 103–116, one pl.

—— 1894 (2). Description of a new spider from East Lothian. *Proc. Roy. Phys. Soc. Edin.*, **12**, pp. 589–590, one pl.

—— 1895. On new and rare British spiders. *Proc. Dorset Nat. Hist. Field Club*, **16**, pp. 92–128, two pls.

—— 1896. On new and rare British spiders observed in 1895. *Proc. Dorset Nat. Hist. Field Club*, **17**, pp. 54–63, one pl.

—— 1899. Notes on British spiders observed in 1898. *Proc. Dorset Nat. Hist. Field Club*, **20**, pp. 1–22, one pl.

—— 1902 On new and rare British Arachnida. *Proc. Dorset Nat. Hist. Field Club*, **23**, pp. 16–40, one pl.

—— 1903. On new and rare British spiders. *Proc. Dorset Nat. Hist. Field Club*, **24**, pp. 149–171, one pl.

—— 1905. On new and rare British Arachnida. *Proc. Dorset Nat. Hist. Field Club*, **26**, pp. 40–74, one pl.

—— 1908. On new and rare British Arachnida, noted and observed in 1907. *Proc. Dorset Nat. Hist. Field Club*, **29**, pp. 161–194, one pl.

—— 1909 (1). On British Arachnida noted and observed in 1908. *Proc. Dorset Nat. Hist. Field Club*, **30**, pp. 97–115, one pl.

—— 1909 (2). Arachnida in : Additions to the wild Fauna and Flora of the Royal Botanic Gardens, Kew. IX. *Bull. Misc. Inform.*, **1909**, pp. 246–250, one pl.

—— 1910. On British Arachnida noted and observed in 1909. *Proc. Dorset Nat. Hist. Field Club*, **31**, pp. 47–70, one pl.

—— 1912. On new and rare British Arachnida noted and observed in 1911. *Proc. Dorset Nat. Hist. Field Club*, **33**, pp. 70–95, one pl.

—— 1913. On new and rare British Arachnida noted and observed in 1912. *Proc. Dorset Nat. Hist. Field Club*, **34**, pp. 107–136, one pl.

—— 1914. On new and rare British Arachnida noted and observed in 1913. *Proc. Dorset Nat. Hist. Field Club*, **35**, pp. 119–142, one pl.

CARPENTER, G. H., 1898. A list of the spiders of Ireland. *Proc. Roy. Irish Acad.* (iii), **5**, pp. 128–210, nine text-figs.

CHYZER, C., and KULCZYNSKI, L., 1891–97. Araneæ Hungariæ, Budapest, three vols., I, pp. 1–168, six pls. II (1), pp. 1–151, five pls., II (2), pp. 147–366, five pls.

CLERCK, C., 1757. Svenska Spindlar (Aranei Suecici), Stockholmiae, pp. 1–154, six pls.

DAHL, F., 1908. Die Lycosiden oder Wolfspinnen Deutschlands. Halle. Abh. der Kaiserl. Leop.-Carol. *Deutsch. Akad. Naturf.*, **88** (3), pp. 175–678. (Internal numbering. pp. 1–504, Refs. are to these.) 86 text-figs.

—— 1926. Spinnentiere oder Arachnoidea, I. Springspinnen (Salticidæ). *Tierw. Deutsch. Jena.* (3rd pt.), pp. 1–55, 159 figs.

—— F. and M., 1927. Spinnentiere oder Arachnoidea, II. Lycosidæ *s. lat.* (Wolfspinnen im weiteren Sinne.) *Tierw. Deutsch. Jena.* (5th pt.), pp. 1–80, 192 figs.

DALMAS, R. de., 1916. Revision du genre *Orchestina* E. S., etc. *Ann. Soc. Ent. France*, **85**, pp. 203–258, 36 figs.

DEGEER, C., 1778. Mémoires pour servir à l'histoire des insectes. Stockholm, 1752–1778. Seven vols. (Spiders : Tome **7**, pp. 1–950, 11 pls.)

DOLESCHALL, L., 1852. Systematisches Verzeichnis der im Kaiserthum Österreich vorkommenden Spinnen. *Sitz. ber. Akad. Wiss. Wien*, **9**, pp. 622–651.

EICHWALD, E., 1830. Zoologica specialis, etc. Vilna, 1830–31, Pars. alt. pp. 63–7.

FABRICIUS, J. C., 1775. Systema Entomologiæ, etc. Flensburgi et Lipsiæ, pp. 1–832 (Araneæ, pp. 431–439).

—— 1777. Genera Insectorum, etc. Cilonii, 1777, pp. 1–310 (Araneæ, pp. 152, 249–250).

FALCONER, W., 1912. The spiders of Wicken Fen. *Naturalist, London,* **1912,** pp. 310–324, one pl.

FUESSLIN, J. C., 1775. Verzeichnis der ihm bekannten schweizerischen Insekten. Zürich und Winterthur, pp. 1–62, one pl.

GEER, C. de, *see* Degeer, C.

GISTEL, J., 1848. Naturgeschichte des Thierreichs für höhere Schulen. Stuttgart, pp. i–xvi and 1–220, 32 pls

HAHN, C. W., 1826. Monographie der Spinnen, 4 Heft., Nürnberg, pp. 1–2, four pls·
—— 1831–34. Die Arachniden, Nürnberg, 1831–48, 16 Bande. (The first two, Abt. I and II (1831 and 1834), were by Hahn, the rest by C. L. Koch, *q.v.*)

HOLM, A., 1947. Svensk Spindelfauna (3) Stockholm. Fam. 8–10, Oxyopidæ, Lycosidæ, Pisauridæ, pp. 1–48, ten pls.

JACKSON, A. R., 1908. On some rare arachnids captured during 1907. *Trans. Nat. Hist. Soc. Northumb.* (N.S.), **3** (1), pp. 49–78, one pl.
—— 1909. On some rare arachnids captured during 1908. *Trans. Nat. Hist. Soc. Northumb.* (N.S.), **3** (2), pp. 418–439, one pl.
—— 1910. On some arthropods observed in 1909. *Lancs. Nat.* (N.S.), **3,** pp. 17–51.
—— 1911. Notes on arachnids observed during 1910, I. On three additions to the British Fauna. *Lancs. Nat.* (N.S.), **3** (36), pp. 385–392, one pl.
—— and PACK-BERESFORD, D. R., 1913 (1). *Clubiona juvenis* Simon. A spider new to the British Isles recently found in Ireland. *Irish Nat.,* **22,** pp. 205–207, one pl.
—— 1913 (2). On some new and obscure British spiders. *Trans. Notting. Nat. Soc.,* **60,** pp. 20–49, two pls.
—— 1914. A contribution to the spider fauna of Scotland. *Proc. Roy. Phys. Soc. Edinb.,* **19,** pp. 108–128, two pls.
—— 1915. A second contribution to the spider fauna of Scotland : with descriptions of a new spider of the genus *Clubiona. Proc. Roy. Phys. Soc. Edinb.,* **19,** pp. 17–190, one pl.
—— 1916. On some arthropods observed in 1915. I. Arachnida. *Lancs. Nat.* **1916,** pp. 355–364.
—— 1924. On new and rare British Spiders. *Proc. Dorset Nat. Hist. Field Club,* **45,** pp. 101–120.
—— 1930. Results of the Oxford University Expedition to Greenland, 1928. *Ann. Mag. Nat. Hist.* (10), **6,** pp. 639–656, one pl.
—— 1932. On new and rare British spiders. *Proc. Dorset Nat. Hist. Field Club,* **53,** pp. 200–214.
—— 1934. Notes on Arctic spiders obtained in 1933. *Ann. Mag. Nat. Hist.* (10), **14,** pp. 611–620, one pl.
—— 1937 (with Morley, C.). *Trans. Suffolk Nat. Soc.,* **3** (iii), p. 279.

KASTON, B. J., 1948. Spiders of Connecticut. *State Geol. and Nat. Hist. Survey,* Hartford, **70,** pp. 1–874, 144 pls.

KOCH, C. L. (1), 1836–48. Die Arachniden, Nürnberg. (The first two were by C. W. Hahn, 1831, 1834.) 1836, Abt. III, 119 pp. ; 1838, IV, 144 pp. ; 1839, V, 158 pp. ; 1839, VI, 156 pp. ; 1839, VII, 130 pp. ; 1841, VIII, 131 pp. ; 1842, IX, 108 pp. ; 1843, X, 142 pp. ; 1845, XI, 174 pp. ; 1845, XII, 166 pp. ; 1846, XIII, 234 pp. ; 1848, XIV, 210 pp. ; 1848, XV, 136 pp. ; 1848, XVI, 80 pp., 562 pls in all.

—— (2), 1837–50. Übersicht des Arachnidensystems, Nürnberg, Hefte 1–5. 1837, I, 39 pp. ; 1839, II, 38 pp. ; 1842, III, 131 pp. ; 1847, IV, 136 pp. ; 1850, V, 104 pp., 30 pls. in all.

———— (3), 1833–1837. Arachniden. (In) Panzer, Faunæ Insectorum Germaniæ initia. Fortgesetz von Herrich-Schaffer, Regensburg, Hefte 111–190. Spiders : 1833, Hft. 119–121 ; 1834, Hft. 122–127 ; 1835, Hft. 128–131 ; 1836, Hft. 134, 137, 138, 139 ; 1837, Hft. 141.

KOCH, L., 1866–7. Die Arachniden-Familie der Drassiden, Nürnberg, Hefte 1–6 (1866), pp. 1–304 ; Heft 7 (1867), pp. 305–352.

———— 1870. Beiträge zur Kentnis der Arachnidenfauna Galiziens. Jahrb. k. k. Gelehr. Ges. Krakau, 41, pp. 1–56.

———— 1872. Beitrag zur Kentnis der Arachnidenfauna Tirols, Zweite Abhandlung. Zeits. Ferd. Tirol Voral. (3), 17, pp. 239–328.

———— 1875. Beschreibungen einiger von Herrn Dr. Zimmermann bei Niesky in der Oberlausitz und im Riesengebirge entdeckter neuer Spinnenarten. Abh. naturf. Ges. Görlitz, 15, pp. 1–21, one pl.

———— 1876. Verzeichnis der in Tirol bis jetz beobachteten Arachniden nebst Beschreibungen einiger neuen oder weniger bekannten Arten. Zeits. Ferd. Tirol Voral. (3), 19, pp. 221–354.

———— 1877. Verzeichnis der bei Nürnberg bis jetz beobachteten Arachniden etc. Abh. Naturg. Ges. Nürnberg, 6, pp. 113–198.

KULCZYNSKI, L., 1882. Spinnen aus der Tatra und den westlichen Beskiden. Krakan pp. 1–34.

———— 1891–7 (see CHYZER, C.)

———— 1898. Symbola ad faunam araneorum Austriæ inferioris cognoscendam. Rozpr. Wydz. Mat.-Przyrod. Akad. Umiej., 36, pp. 1–114, two pls. Also sep : Cracoviæ, 1898, pp. 1–114, two pls. Also resumé : Bull. Akad. Cracovie, 1898, pp. 87–88.

———— 1899. Arachnoidea opera Rev. E. Schmitz collecta in insulis Maderianis, etc. Rozpr. Wydz. Mat.-Przyrod. Akad. Umiej., 36, pp. 319–461. Also resumé : Bull. Akad. Cracovie, 1899, pp. 136–137.

LATREILLE, P. A., 1799. Déscription d'une nouvelle espèce d'araignée. Bull. Sci. Soc. Phil., 2 (20), p. 170.

———— 1804 (1). Tableau méthodique des insectes. Nouv. Dict. Hist. Nat., 24, pp. 131–135.

———— 1804 (2). Histoire naturelle générale et particulière des Crustacés et des insectes. Paris, 14 vols., Arachnides, 7, pp. 144–305, three pls.

———— 1806. Genera Crustaceorum et Insectorum, Paris, 1806–9, four vols. Aranéides, 1 (1806), pp. 82–127.

LESSERT, R. DE. Notes arachnologiques. Rev. Suisse Zool., 15, pp. 93–128.

———— 1910. Catalogue des invertebrés de la Suisse, Fasc. 3, Araignées. Mus. Hist. Nat. Genève, pp. 1–635, 250 figs.

LINNAEUS, C., 1758. Systema Naturæ, Ed. X, Helmiae, 1, pp. 1–821.

LUCAS, H., 1836. (Description of Attus venator), Mag. Zool. Guérin, 6, Cl. viii, pp. 1–4, one pl.

———— 1846. Histoire naturelle des animaux articulés. (In) Exploration scientifique d'Algérie, Zoologie, Paris, Tome I (1846), Aranéides, pp. 89–271 (17 pls. in Tome IV).

MACLEAY, W. S., 1839. On some new forms of Arachnida. Ann. Mag. Nat. Hist. (1), 2, pp. 1–14, two pls.

MARPLES, M. J. and B. J., 1937. Notes on the spiders Hyptiotes paradoxus and Çyclosa conica. Proc. Zool. Soc. London (A), 107, Cl. 3, pp. 213–221, two figs., two pls.

MENGE, A., 1866–78. Preussische Spinnen. Schr. Naturf. Ges. Danzig, N.F., 11 Abteilungen, pp. 1–560, 91 pls. ; 1866, Abt. I, pp. 1–152 ; 1868, II, pp. 153–218 ; 1869, III, pp. 219–264 ; 1871, IV, pp. 265–296 ; 1872, V, pp. 297–326 ; 1873, VI, pp. 327–374 ; 1874, VII, pp. 375–422 ; 1875, VIII, pp. 423–454 ; 1876, IX, pp. 455–494 ; 1877, X, pp. 495–542 ; 1878, XI, pp. 543—560.

MORLEY, C. (see JACKSON, A. R., 1937).

NIELSEN, E., 1932. The Biology of Spiders, Copenhagen, 1 (in English), pp. 1–248, ten figs., 32 pls., 2 (in Danish), pp. 1–725, 426 figs., five pls.

OHLERT, E., 1865. Arachnologische Studien. Off. Prüf. Schül. Höh. Progra mm pp. 1-·12.

OLIVIER, A. G., 1789. Article : Araignée. (In) Encycl. Méth. Hist. Nat. Ins., Paris, 4, pp. 173–240.

PALLAS, P. S., 1772. Spicilegia zoologica, Berolini, Tom. I. 10 fasc., 1767–1774. Aranea, IX, pp. 44–50, two pls.

PANZER, G. W. F., 1797. Faunæ insectorum Germaniæ initia, Regensburg. Heft 40. Aranea : fol. 21, 22.

—— 1801. Faunæ insectorum Germaniæ initia, Regensburg. Aranea : 74, fol. 19, 20 ; 78, fol. 21 ; 83, fol. 21.

PAVESI, P., 1873. Catalogo sistematico dei Regni del cantone ticino, etc. Ann. Mus. Civ. Stor. Nat. Genova, 4, pp. 5–215.

PECKHAM, G. W. and E. G., 1885. On some new genera and species of Attidæ. Proc. Nat. Hist. Soc. Wisc., pp. 25–42, one pl. ; 62–85, two pls. Trans. Wisc. Acad. Sci. Arts Lett., 6, pp. 255–342, four tab.

PETAGNA, V., 1787. Specimen insectorum ulterioris Calabriæ, Napoli, pp. 1–46.

PETERS, H., 1938. Über das Netz der Dreieckspinne, Hyptiotes paradoxus. Zool. Anz., 121, pp. 49–59, five figs.

PICKARD-CAMBRIDGE, O. See " Cambridge, O. Pickard- ".

REIMOSER, E., 1937. Spinnentiere oder Arachnoidea, VIII. 17 Familie : Anyphænidæ oder Zartspinnen, pp. 42–44, one fig. ; 18 Familie: Clubionidæ oder Röhren-spinnen, pp. 45–99, 103 figs. (In) Die Tierwelt Deutschlands, Jena.

ROEWER, C. F., 1928. Araneæ, Echte oder Webespinnen. (In) Die Tierwelt Mittel-europas, Leipzig, pp. 1–144, 1,583 figs.

ROSSI, P., 1790. Aranea. (In) Fauna Etrusca, etc., Liburni, 2, pp. 126–138, three pls.

SCHRANK, F. VON P., 1803. Fauna Boica, Landshut, 3 (1) (1803), pp. 229–244.

SCOPOLI, J. A., 1763. Entomologia Carniolica, Vindobonæ, pp. 1–420.

SIMON, E., 1864. Histoire naturelle des araignées, Paris (1st ed.), pp. 1–540, 207 figs.

—— 1868. Monographie des éspèces européennes de la famille des Attides. Ann. Soc. Ent. France (4), 8, pp. 11–72, 529–726, three pls.

—— 1870. Aranéides nouvaux ou peu connus du midi de l'Europe. Mém. Soc. Roy. Sci. Liège (2), 3, pp. 271–358 (sep. pp. 1–90).

—— 1871. Revision des Attidae Européens. Ann. Soc. Ent. France (5), 1, pp. 125–230, 329–360.

—— 1873. Études arachnologiques. Note sur trois éspèces françaises du genre Atypus Latr. Ann. Soc. Ent. France (5), 3, pp. 109–116, one pl.

—— 1874–84. Les arachnides de France Paris five Tomes. 1874, 1, pp. 1–269 ; 1875, 2, pp. 1–350 ; 1876, 3, pp. 1–364 ; 1878, 4, pp. 1–330 ; 1881, 5, pt. 1, pp. 1–180 ; 1884, 5, pt. 2, pp. 181–420 ; 5, pt. 3, pp. 421–885.

(The pages of vol. 6 (of which parts 2–5 were published by L. Berland and L. Fage, after Simon's death in 1924), are numbered continuously throughout, and are referred to by their dates in the text. See E. Simon, 1914, 1926, 1929, 1932, 1937.)

—— 1884. Études arachnologiques, 16ᵐ Mémoire xxiii. Matériaux pour servir à la faune des arachnides de la Grèce. Ann. Soc. Ent. France (6), 4, pp. 305–356.

—— 1885. Études arachnologiques, 18ᵐᵉ Mémoire xxvi. Matériaux pour servir à la faune des arachnides de Sénégal. Ann. Soc. Ent. France (6), 5, pp. 345–396.

—— 1889. Arachnidæ transcaspicæ ab ill. Dr. G. Radde, Dr. A. Walter et A. Conchin inventæ (annis 1886–1887). Verh. Zool. Bot. Ges. Wien, 39, pp. 373–386.

—— 1891. On the spiders of the Island of St. Vincent. Part I. Proc. Zool. Soc. London, 1891, pp. 549–575, one pl.

—— 1892–1903. Histoire naturelle des araignées, Paris (2nd ed.). Two vols. 1, pt. 1, 1892, pp. 1–256 ; pt. 2, 1893, pp. 257–488 ; pt. 3, 1894, pp. 489–760 ; pt. 4, 1895, pp. 761–1084. 2, pt. 1, 1897, pp. 1–192 ; pt. 2, 1898, pp. 193–380 ; pt. 3, 1901, pp. 381–668 ; pt. 4, 1903, 669–1080.

—— 1902. Études arachnologiques. 32me Mém. li. Descriptions d'éspèces nouvelles de la famille des Salticidæ (suite). *Ann. Soc. Ent. France*, **71**, pp. 389–421.

—— 1914. Arachnides de France, **6**, pt. 1, pp. 1–308, 537 figs.

—— 1926. Arachnides de France, **6**, pt. 2, pp. 309–532, 274 figs.

—— 1929. Arachnides de France, **6**, pt. 3, pp. 533—772, 300 figs.

—— 1932. Arachnides de France, **6**, pt. 4, pp. 773–978, 389 figs.

—— 1937. Arachnides de France, **6**, pt. 5, pp. 979–1298, 527 figs.

SMITH, F. P., 1902. The spiders of Epping Forest. *Essex Nat.*, **12**, pp. 181–201, three pls.

—— 1904. The spiders of Epping Forest. *Essex Nat.*, **13** (5), pp. 209–218, two pls.

—— 1907 (1). The British spiders of the Genus *Lycosa*. *Journ. Queckett Micr. Club* (2), **10**, pp. 9–30, four pls.

—— 1907 (2). Some British spiders taken in 1907. *Journ. Queckett Micr. Club* (2), **10**, pp. 177–190, one pl.

STRAND, E., 1900. Zur Kenntnis der Arachniden Norwegens. *Kong. Norsk. Vid. Selsk. Skr*, 1900 (**2**), pp. 1–46.

STROEM, H., 1768. Beskrivelse over Norske Insekter, andet Stekke. *Tronndh. Selsk. Skr.*, **4**, pp. 313–371.

SUNDEVALL, C. J., 1831. Svenska Spindlarnes beskrifning. *Nova Acta Soc. Sci. Upsal.*, 1831, pp. 108–148. Also *Kongl. Svenska Vet. Akad. Handl.*, 1831, pp. 108–148.

—— 1832. Svenska Spindlarnes beskrifning. *Nova Acta Soc. Sci. Upsal.*, 1832, pp. 171–272. Also *Kongl. Svenska Vet. Akad. Handl.*, 1832, pp. 171–272.

—— 1833. Conspectus arachnidum. Londini Gothorum, pp. 1–39.

TEMPLETON, R., 1835. On the spiders of the Genus *Dysdera* Latr. with the description of a new allied genus. *Zool. Jour.*, **5**, pp. 400–408, one pl.

THORELL, T., 1856. Recensio critica Aranearum Suecicarum, quas descripserit Clerckius, Linnaeus, de Geerus. *Nova Acta Soc. Sci. Upsal.* (3), **2**, (1), pp. 61–176.

—— 1869–70. On European spiders. *Nova Acta Soc. Sci. Upsal.* (3), **7**, pp. 1–108 (1869) ; pp. 109–242 (1870).

—— 1870–73. Remarks on synonyms of European spiders. Upsala, pt. I, 1870, pp. 1–96 ; pt. II, 1871, pp. 97–228 ; pt. III, 1872, pp. 229–374 ; pt. IV, 1873, pp. 375–644.

—— 1875 (1). Descriptions of several European and North African spiders. *Kongl. Svenska Vet. Akad. Handl.* (N. F.), **13**, pp. 3–203.

—— 1875 (2). Diagnoses Aranearum Europaearum aliquot novarum. *Tijdschr. Ent.*, **18**, pp. 81–108.

—— 1875 (3). Verzeichniss südrüssicher Spinnen. *Horæ Soc. Ent. Ross.*, **11** pp. 39–122.

TULLGREN, A., 1944. Svensk Spindelfauna, 3. Stockholm, Fam. 1–4. Salticidæ, Thomisidæ, Philodromidæ, Eusparassidæ, pp. 1–138, 18 pls.

—— 1946. Fam. 5–7. Clubionidæ, Zoridæ, Gnaphosidæ. (In) Svensk Spindelfauna, 3. Stockholm. pp. 1–141, 21 pls.

WALCKENAER, C. A., 1802. Faune parisienne. Insectes, Paris. Tome II, pp. 187–250.

—— 1805. Tableau des aranéides. Paris, 1805, pp. i–xii, 1–88, nine pls.

—— 1806. Histoire naturelle des aranéides. Paris-Strasbourg, 1806 (four series of ten plates, with explanatory pages not numbered).

—— 1825. Aranéides. (In) Faune française, etc., Paris, 1825–30, 240 pp.

—— 1833. Mémoire sur une nouvelle classification des aranéides. *Ann. Soc. Ent. France*, **2**, pp. 414–446.

WARBURTON, C., 1892. Spiders from Madeira. *Ann. Mag. Nat. Hist.* (6), **10**, pp. 216–228, one pl.

WESTRING, N., 1851. Förteckning öfver de till närvarande tid Kande, i Sverige förekommande Spindlarten, utgörande ett antal af 253, deraf 132 äro nya för svenska Faunan. *Göteb. Kongl. Vet. Handl.*, **2**, pp. 25–62.

—— 1861.   Araneæ Svecicæ.   *Göteb. Kongl. Vet. Handl.*, **7**, pp. 1–615.   (Also Sep. Gothoburgi, 1861, pp. 1-615.)

WIDER, 1834.   Bescreibung der Arachniden.   (In) Reuss, A.   Zoologischen Miscellen . *Mus. Senck.*, **1**, pp. 195–282, five pls.

WIEHLE, H., 1927.   Beiträge zur Kenntnis des Radnetzbaues der Epeiriden, Tetragnathiden und Uloboriden.   *Zeits. Morph. Okol. Tiere.*, **8** (3–4), pp. 468–537, 27 figs, 7 pls.

VOLUME I

INDEX TO FAMILIES, GENERA AND SPECIES